Electrical Systems Analysis and Design for Industrial Plants

Electrical Systems Analysis and Design for Industrial Plants

Irwin Lazar

McGraw-Hill Book Company

New York   St. Louis   San Francisco   Auckland
Bogotá   Singapore   Johannesburg   London
Madrid   Mexico   Montreal   New Delhi
Panama   São Paulo   Hamburg
Sydney   Tokyo   Paris
Toronto

Library of Congress Cataloging in Publication Data

Lazar, Irwin.
    Electrical systems analysis and design for industrial
plants.

    Includes index.
    1. Factories—Electric Equipment. 2. Factories—
Power supply. 3. Electric engineering. I. Title.
TK4035.F3L39   621.319'24   80-11069
ISBN 0-07-036789-2

1234567890   HDHD   89876543210

The editors for this book were Tyler G. Hicks and Carolyn Nagy,
the designer was Naomi Auerbach, and the production supervisor
was Sally Fliess. Printed and bound by Halliday Lithograph.

To my wife Susanne,
without whose patience, help, and understanding
this book would not have been written.

Contents

Customer Values for
US Filter - SYNETIX Proj.

$I_{sc_{sys}} = 159\,MVA$

$SWGR = 250\,MVA$

$SWGR\ CB\ rating = 400A$

Preface

The increasing use of more complex electrical equipment, as well as the growing demand for more safety, reliability, and energy savings in industrial plants has created the need for up-to-date Power System study and equipment application information.

This book responds to numerous information requests from engineers responsible for the study, analysis, and application of modern electrical Power Systems and equipment.

The material covered in the book is what the author has extensively used in his work for over 20 years as an analytical engineer in charge with Power System Analysis.

The text is especially valuable to industrial plant engineers, consulting engineers, electrical designers, and others who do planning, design, and studies of electrical facilities for industrial plants and commercial buildings.

References are made to applicable ANSI and NEMA standards as well as to the National Electrical Code. The latest editions of these standards together with the Electrical Power System Analysis and examples covered in this volume can serve as the basis for sound engineering application.

I would like to thank all equipment manufacturers for their technical information. Much of the information in this book has been published previously by me in various engineering magazines. I wish to express my appreciation especially to the editors of *Specifying Engineer* and *Power* magazines, with special gratitude to R. Oliverson of *Specifying Engineer*. And, finally, I want to thank Messrs. B. Goodman, T. Rafferti, and R. Ptaszek along with the rest of the management of The Heyward-Robinson Company, Inc. for their help and encouragement in publishing this book.

Introduction

Electrical systems analysis for industrial plants consists primarily of the techniques employed to predict or improve the performance of a proposed or an existing power system.

The main types of industrial system analysis include: short-circuit studies and calculations, selective coordination of protective devices, system grounding, voltage drop at motor starting, power factor improvement, uninterruptible power systems, proper selection of transformers, electrical energy savings, and combinations of the above-mentioned items.

The application of these techniques to industrial power systems has somehow lagged behind utility practice. With the increasing size and complexity of industrial power systems, the gap has recently substantially decreased. Industrial as well as commercial power systems are more and more subjected to power systems analysis as the rewards of these studies are increasingly known.

The main objective of power systems analysis is to provide design engineers with the information they need to be able to achieve: safety, reliability, high power quality, continuity of service, easy operation and maintenance, easy expansion possibilities, minimum initial and operating costs, and energy savings.

This book shows the most commonly used techniques of power system analysis and calculations, and how these techniques can help make power systems meet their specific objectives. Great emphasis has been given in this book to practical short-circuit studies and calculation as well as selective coordination of protective devices.

Protective relays and fuses are devices providing adequate protection and isolating troubles, provided they are selected and set to operate at correct current values and through proper coordination with each other. A system study is necessary to determine these values and coordination requirements.

Unfortunately it sometimes takes an electrical accident, fire, or a serious shutdown in the electrical system to alert plant management that the system protection needs study, updating, or maintenance.

A properly protected system includes all the protective devices ranging from the main circuit breakers or fuses in the plant's incoming substation down to the various circuit breakers, fuses, and relays on the medium- and low-voltage distribution system throughout the plant.

Protective devices in electrical distribution systems might have been properly sized and coordinated when the systems were originally designed and built, but there is no guarantee that they have retained their coordination. Quite often system alterations and additions can change the protection requirements. Some of the protective devices may be unable to interrupt the available short circuits of the expanded system. Changes in incoming power, plant load, and protective devices could mean that the protection once present is no longer there. Furthermore, hypersensitive protection (when minor overloads cause unnecessary tripping) or overprotection (when a complete system instead of just a single affected branch can drop out) may develop in an expanded system. For these reasons, many plants are operating under some serious if not dangerous misconceptions.

Periodic studies of protective device settings are just as important in preventing power outages as is periodic maintenance of the distribution system. These periodic studies are especially vital in industrial plants which rely more and more on continuous electric power service. In most industrial processes, even a momentary loss of power can cause serious loss of material and production. Only through a system coordination analysis and study and proper application can the relay, breaker, and fuse setting be selected that will provide maximum protection of the equipment and also trip selectively during fault conditions.

It is the purpose of this book to give step-by-step indications, as well as practical numerical examples for following up these system studies and to show how to apply them to the particular conditions of the electrical power system requirements.

IRWIN LAZAR

Electrical Systems Analysis and Design for Industrial Plants

1

Short-Circuit Calculations

1.1 Fundamental Considerations of Fault Calculation

The proper selection of protective devices and their selective trip settings is based on short-circuit calculation. A short-circuit protective device can be defined as an electrical device inserted in a circuit to protect it against damage from an overload or short circuit. This is achieved by automatically interrupting any excessive current in accordance with the device's short-circuit capability.

The chief short-circuit protective devices are, of course, circuit breakers and fuses. Circuit breakers automatically protect the circuit by means of relays (separate or built-in) that sense abnormal currents and command the breaker to trip. Fuses both sense the abnormal current and interrupt it with an element which melts and opens the circuit.

Inadequate short-circuit protection often is the source of disastrous failures that result in unnecessary damage, power interruption, injury of personnel and expensive production shutdowns. Conversely, arbitrary oversized or overrated protective devices constitute a waste in unnecessary extra-cost equipment. It follows that an exact determination of short-circuit conditions on an electric-power system is of paramount importance. Interrupting capacity represents the maximum short-circuit current that a power system causes to flow through a breaker or a fuse when a fault occurs in the circuit. Even more important, non-interrupting devices such as cables, bus-ducts, disconnect switches, must withstand thermal and mechanical stresses of high short-circuit currents.

For suitable application of breakers and fuses, selection must be made on the basis of proper and safe opera-

tion. The normal continuous current they carry must be considered. The possible short-circuit faults may be phase-to-phase in ungrounded systems, and phase-to-phase as well as phase-to-ground in grounded systems.

The magnitude of the power-system supplying the load dictates the amount of short-circuit current. Under normal operation, the load draws a current proportional to the voltage applied and the load impedance. If a short-circuit occurs, the voltage is applied across a low impedance of only the conductors and transformer from the source of voltage to the point of the short circuit; it is no longer opposed by the normal-load impedance

Breakers which are selected on the basis of the continuous current they carry must also be capable of withstanding and interrupting the high short-circuit currents that occur. The load current is determined by the normal load that the breaker carries and has no relationship to the size of the system supplying the load. The magnitude of the short-circuit current, however, is dependent on the size of the supplying system and independent of the normal load.

The order of magnitude, the effect of short-circuits, and the factors on which they depend are best illustrated by a simple example of fault current calculation. Let's consider a source of infinite capacity and a single-phase 50-kVA transformer feeding a 10-hp motor as shown in Fig. 1. The transformer has a secondary voltage of 240 V and an impedance of $Z_T=1.4\%$. For simplicity, let's neglect the line impedance between a fault at point A and the transformer.

Under normal conditions the motor

draws 50 A—the current perceived by the protective breaker. Let's assume that a bolted short-circuit fault occurs at point A. The maximum short-circuit current, considering the transformer impedance, is easily calculated by the simplest formula: $I_{SCmax} = (100\%/Z_T) I_{FLsec}$, where I_{SCmax} is the maximum short-circuit current, I_{FLsec} is the secondary full-load current of the transformer, and $\%Z_T$ is the percent impedance of the transformer.

The secondary full-load current of transformer = 50 kVA (1000)/240 V = 208A is calculated by substituting in the short-circuit formula, $I_{SCmax} = (100/1.4) \times 208 = 14,857$ A. The breaker protecting the feeder and the motor, then, must not only be capable of carrying the normal load of 50 A but must withstand the maximum short-circuit possible, namely 14,857 A.

At present, we have neglected the assymetrical nature of these short-circuit currents. In reality, these currents are higher in value depending on the ratio of the resistance to the reactance of the circuit considered. We will consider this point in the next section. Assume now that instead of the selected 50-kVA transformer, we have a 500-kVA transformer with an impedance $\%Z_T=2.2$ supplying the same 50-hp motor as shown in Fig. 2. The secondary full-load current of the transformer is: 500 kVA (1000)/240 V=2080 A.

If the same fault occurs at point "A" the short-circuit current will be: $I_{SCmax}=(100/2.2) \times 2080=94,545$ A. The normal load of the breaker protecting the feeder and the motor is the same as in Fig. 1, but the breaker must now be selected to withstand 94,545 A short-circuit symmetrical instead of 14,857 A symmetrical.

This numerical example proves that the magnitude of the short-circuit is

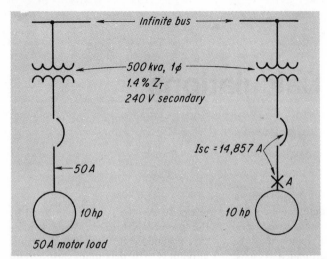

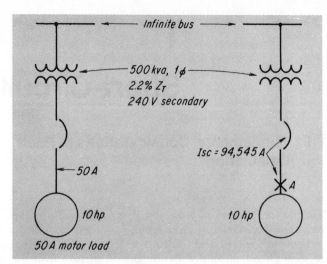

1—Under normal conditions the circuit breaker sees the 50-A motor current, but it must be able to interrupt 14,857 A

2—With a larger transformer serving the same load, breaker now has to be selected to withstand 94,545-A short circuit

dependent mainly on the size of the supplying power system. It also proves that the short-circuit availability in a system is of great importance in choosing the right size breakers or fuses. Those selected must safely withstand and interrupt the maximum short-circuit current delivered by the system into the bolted short without destroying the interrupting devices.

An analogy is possible by comparing a "short-circuit proof" interrupting device with an explosion-proof device intended for hazardous areas. The device must perform a certain function independent of an explosion that might occur within. The device has to be built so as to confine that explosion within; it must be able to withstand the thermal and mechanical stresses accompanying the explosion. Besides its normal operation, the device has to be explosion proof in the same way as an interrupting device. It also must be short-circuit proof to avoid destruction of the device and the possible spread of thermal and mechanical effects.

The comparison of normal loads and short-circuit currents with the water flow in hydroelectric generating plants illustrates another well-known classical analogy. The normal load of the turbine determines the flow of water for normal conditions of operation and has no bearing on the magnitude of the reservoir behind the dam. If the dam breaks the quantity of water that flows will depend on the magnitude of the reservoir; it bears no relationship to the normal

load of the turbines. The normal flow of water is comparable to the normal flow of electrical current. If the dam breaks, this flow of water is comparable to the flow of short-circuit currents which produce unwanted effects. The interrupting devices prevent such mishaps by possessing corresponding short-circuit capability.

Coordinated selective protection in modern power systems assures effective isolation of faulted sections of the systems, allowing the rest of the system to operate normally. Clearing of faults by the breakers nearest to the faults is achieved by the following: careful short-circuit calculation; a detailed study of the time-current characteristics of the protective devices; proper selection for short-circuit withstandability.

The consequences of improper selection of interrupting and protective devices can be disastrous. When short-circuit protective equipment is not carefully selected, or when it is chosen with the intent to save in installation cost, the result is inadequate protection. I would compare it with the ostrich policy. If the devices fail to operate successfully just once during their lifespan, then all the investment in these devices is wasted. Publicity concerning the disastrous accidents that occur during fault currents due to inadequate selection of protective equipment, is not great enough. The state of California and the Edison Electric Institute reveal in their reports cases of fire, completely destroyed switchhouses, losses of pro-

duction, casualties in death of personnel—all due to inadequate selection of protective devices.

To insure adequacy of short-circuit protection, and to prevent accidents:

(1) Available short-circuit current must be accurately determined. Only then can short-circuit protection devices be carefully selected.

(2) The load growth of the plant and the knowledge that interrupting devices in their short-circuit capability depend on the magnitude of the power system must be kept in mind. Their selection should be made with an eye to future growth; otherwise, these interrupting devices will have to be replaced when the plant expands.

(3) All circuit stresses in bus-bars, etc, have to be checked. These stresses are proportional to the square of the short-circuit current.

(4) Check cable size for its ability to withstand short-circuit heating, besides normal load current.

(5) Check all of the power system, from the supply side down to the last motor, for short-circuit safety.

(6) Approach the problem of short-circuit determination on an engineering basis rather than on the basis of "good luck." "Hoping" that failures will not occur is a bad policy. This is proved by countless recorded mishaps caused by improper interrupting devices.

In the next section we will examine the nature and shape of the short-circuit currents more closely—factors on which their magnitude depends and sources that generate them.

1.2 Short-Circuit Currents Behavior

Sources of short-circuit currents and circuit components which limit them; nature and shape of short-circuit current waves; and behavior and magnitude of short-circuit currents

The importance of an exact knowledge of short-circuit current magnitude was discussed in section 1.1. The magnitude of the currents depends on the different sources that generate them, on their reactances, and on the system reactances up to the fault location. Sources of short-circuit current are: utility systems, generators, synchronous motors and induction motors (Fig. 1).

The utility system usually supplies power through step-down transformers at the customer's desired voltage level. Although transformers are sometimes considered a source of short-circuit current, strictly speaking this is not correct. Transformers change voltage and current magnitudes, but do not generate them.

The short-circuit current delivered through a transformer depends on its secondary voltage rating and its percent reactance. It also depends on the reactance of generators and system down to the terminals of the transformer, as well as on the reactance of the circuit between transformer and fault. The percent reactance of a transformer is the percent of rated primary voltage applied to the transformer to produce the full-rated load current in the short-circuited secondary. Percent reactance is a percent voltage measure, not an impedance.

The utility company usually provides information about their available short-circuit current. Since the utility system is much larger than the plant system, little if any decrease in symmetrical short-circuit current will

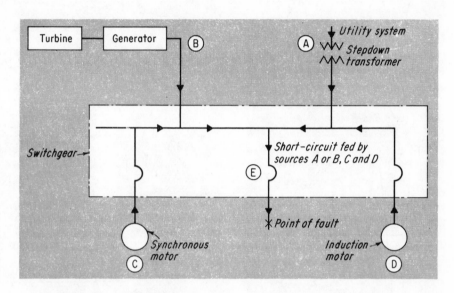

1—Short-circuit current flowing into the point of fault is contributed by **several** possible sources including the utility system, plant generators and motors

be noticed during a fault (see A, Fig. 2).

When speaking about a short-circuit current, we are concerned with the measurements of the root-mean-square (rms) or effective value of its sinusoidal wave. These current waves may be classified into two groups:

A *symmetrical* sinusoidal current wave is an alternating current balanced around the zero line, in this case, the axis of the wave (Fig. 3).

An *asymmetrical* sinusoidal current wave is an alternating current not balanced around the zero line, which in this case does not coincide with the axis of the wave (Fig. 4).

Generators in the customer's system can be a source of short-circuit current. They are driven by prime

movers such as steam or gas turbines, diesel engines and water wheels. When a short-circuit occurs, the generator continues to be driven by its prime mover and to produce voltage, since field excitation is maintained by the generator rotating at normal speed.

The voltage generated produces a short-circuit of large current magnitude which flows to the fault. This flow is limited only by the reactance of the generator and the circuit between the generator and the point of fault. Reactance of a generator changes with time after the inception of a fault. The reactance is formed by the following values:

X''_d = *Subtransient reactance,* which determines short-circuit current immediately after fault inception. This value lasts for the first few cycles after the fault occurs and in about 0.1

3

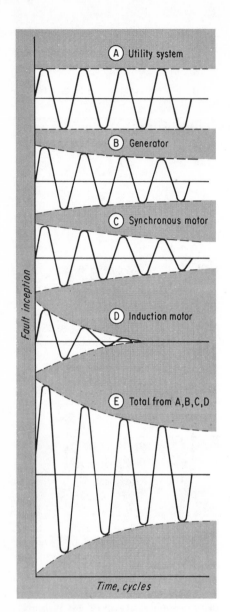

Fault inception

A — Utility system

B — Generator

C — Synchronous motor

D — Induction motor

E — Total from A, B, C, D

Time, cycles

2—The total symmetrical short-circuit current is a summation of the fault currents contributed by several sources, each source behaving in a characteristic way

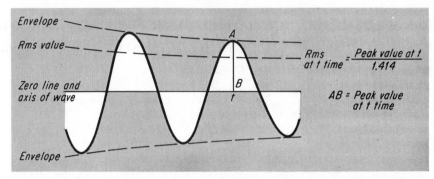

Envelope

Rms value

Zero line and axis of wave

Envelope

A

B

t

$$\frac{\text{Rms}}{\text{at } t \text{ time}} = \frac{\text{Peak value at } t}{1.414}$$

AB = Peak value at t time

3—A symmetrical sinusoidal wave has its axis coinciding with the zero line established under normal conditions. The sinusoid may decrease in magnitude

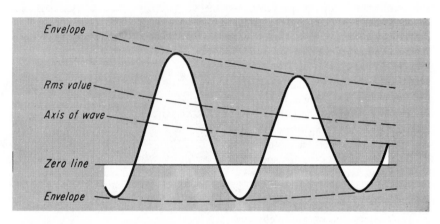

Envelope

Rms value

Axis of wave

Zero line

Envelope

4—An asymmetrical sinusoidal wave has an axis not coincident with the normal zero line. The envelope defines the peak values of the wave about its own axis

seconds increases to the next value.

X'_d = *Transient reactance,* which lasts for about two seconds while increasing to the final value.

X_d = *Synchronous reactance,* which determines the current flow after a steady-state condition is reached. It is not effective until several seconds after the short circuit occurs.

A generator has a variable reactance which increases in magnitude with time. Consequently, short-circuit current decreases exponentially in time from an initially high value to a lower steady-state level as shown at B in Fig. 2. The rate of decay depends upon the generator constants. The values of X''_d and X'_d given by the machine manufacturer are the lowest values; their use results in maximum short-circuit current available.

Synchronous motors behave sim-

ilarly to synchronous generators. When a fault occurs and the voltage of the system is reduced to a very low value, the synchronous motor stops taking power from the system to rotate its load, and starts slowing down. But the inertia of the load tends to prevent the motor from slowing down quickly. The inertia acts as a prime mover and, with excitation maintained, the motor acts as a generator supplying short-circuit current for several cycles after the short circuit occurs, shown at C, Fig. 2.

The same designations are used for the variable reactances of a synchronous motor as for a generator. However, values of X''_d, X'_d and X_d will be different for synchronous motors. The magnitude of the short-circuit current due to synchronous motors also depends upon horsepow-

er, voltage rating and reactance of synchronous motor, as well as reactance of the system to point of fault.

Induction motors contribute short-circuit current because of generator action produced by the inertia of the load and rotor driving the motor after the fault occurs. But there is a major difference between the short-circuit current contribution of induction motors and synchronous motors. The field flux of the induction motor is produced by induction from the stator and not from a dc field winding. Since this flux decays rapidly after a fault, the induction motor contribution drops off quickly and dies out completely after a few cycles. There is no steady-state fault-current contribution. Consequently, induction motors are assigned only a subtransient value of reactance, X''_d.

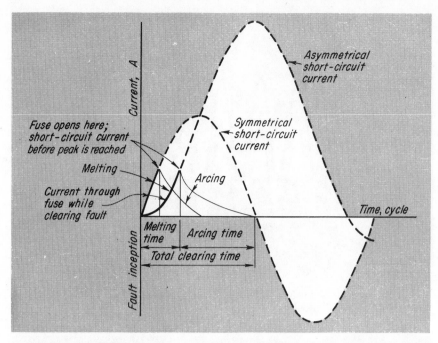

5—Current-limiting fuses clear the fault in ¼ cycle of both symmetrical and asymmetrical short-circuit currents. Fuse element melts before peak is reached

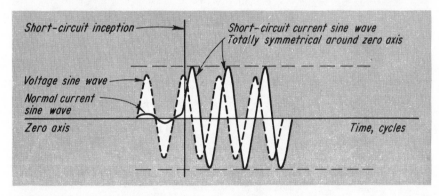

6—When short circuit occurs at the instant of a voltage peak, and the short circuit is totally reactive, short-circuit wave is symmetrical about zero axis

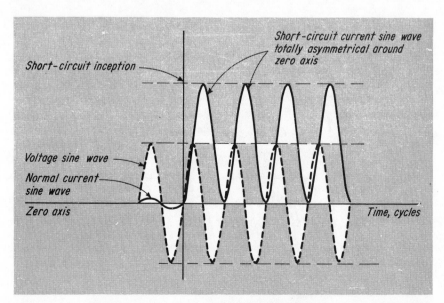

7—When short circuit occurs at a voltage zero, and the short circuit is totally reactive, the short-circuit wave has no symmetry with respect to zero axis

The value of X''_a is nearly equal to the locked-rotor reactance. It follows that the initial symmetrical value of short-circuit current is almost equal to the full-voltage starting current of the motor, which is about 600-900% of the normal load current (see D in Fig. 2). The magnitude of the short-circuit current contributed by the induction motor depends on the horsepower, voltage rating, reactance of the motor, and reactance of the system to the point of fault.

The total symmetrical short-circuit current is a combination of all the sources of short-circuit current we have described. Utility supply, generators, synchronous and induction motors all contribute short-circuit current into a fault. The flux in the machines decays with time after the inception of the fault, hence their fault-current contribution also decays with time. Consequently, the resulting total short-circuit current decays with time as shown at E in Fig. 2. The current magnitude is highest during the first half-cycle and decreases in value after a few cycles. After one or two cycles, the induction-motor contribution disappears.

So far, we have considered only the symmetrical component of short-circuit current contribution. But bear in mind, the magnitude of short-circuit current is further increased during the first few cycles by the so-called dc component, as we shall see later. The dc component causes the short-circuit current wave to be asymmetrical, and decays with time, resulting in a still greater difference in magnitude between the first cycle—after fault inception—and several cycles later.

Because short-circuit current magnitude varies with time, any procedure for short-circuit calculation must determine the current magnitude at various times after the fault occurs.

Components limiting current during short circuits are transformer impedances, reactors, cables, buses, current-limiting fuses and any other circuit impedances. Transformers, due to their reactance, reduce the magnitude of short-circuit currents produced by sources to which they are connected.

Reactors are used to limit short-circuit current by deliberately introducing a reactance into the circuit. Reactors have some pronounced disadvantages, however. They produce a voltage drop which can be the cause of system voltage dips when faults occur, or when starting large motors. They might adversely affect voltage regulation, and may cause tripping of undervoltage devices. They are also energy consumers. These shortcomings have to be considered when deciding between reactors, greater interruption capacity circuit breakers, or current-limiting fuses.

Cables and busways are part of the link between sources of short-circuit current and the point of fault. Their natural impedance limits the short-circuit current, and the amount of limitation depends on size, nature and length of the cable. Some busway designs may be used to introduce impedance deliberately. Values of resistance, reactance and impedance for busways and cables can be found in their manufacturers' catalogs.

Current-limiting fuses open the circuit before the short-circuit current has risen to its peak value, Fig. 5. Interruption usually takes place in the first ¼ cycle. As shown in Fig. 5, total clearing time consists of a melting time as heat builds up in the fuse element, and an arcing time after the element melts and gaseous arc products are cooled by the filler components of the fuse. The arc introduces impedance which limits the current, reducing it finally to zero. The current-limiting fuse has a low impedance until a very high current starts to flow through it. It is both a current-limiting device and a short-circuit current-interrupting device, while typical fuses and circuit breakers are interrupting devices only.

A short circuit has three major classes of components: (1) sources having time-variable reactances and *producing* short-circuit currents; (2) circuit components with fixed reactances, which *limit* short-circuit current magnitude; (3) breakers and fuses *interrupting* short-circuit currents. Determination of their reactances for a specific fault is the first step in short-circuit calculation. Short-circuit current in the first half-cycle is determined by subtransient reactances, X''_d. These determine the momentary duty of breakers and fuses, which is the highest stress that they must withstand.

Short-circuit current waves in industrial power systems are mainly of sine-wave shape, Figs. 3 and 4. The resistance of typical power circuits is

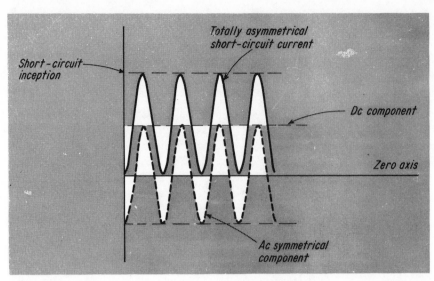

8—The asymmetrical short-circuit current can be visualized as a summation of a symmetrical alternating current with a dc component superimposed upon it

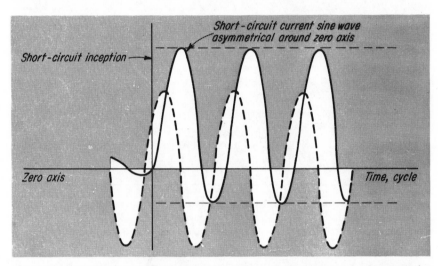

9—In a real circuit, the short circuit most often occurs at some point between the peak and zero values of the voltage wave. Circuit shown is totally reactive

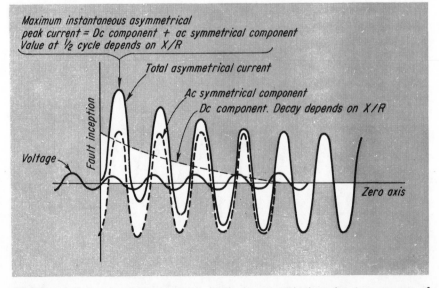

10—The dc component in an actual circuit decays with time due to presence of some resistance. Initial asymmetrical current changes into symmetrical current

negligible compared with their reactance. Besides, when a short-circuit occurs, much of the resistance is shorted out and the remainder is a highly reactive circuit.

If a fault occurs in such a circuit at *the instant of voltage-wave peak*, the short-circuit current would start at almost zero and its sine wave, which must be 90-degrees out of phase with the voltage, would be totally symmetrical about the zero axis, Fig. 6.

If the short-circuit occurs at *the voltage-wave zero-point*, the current—also starting at zero—cannot increase with the voltage and remain in phase with it. The current wave must lag the voltage by 90 degrees; therefore, it is displaced from the zero axis. As the voltage reaches its peak, the current wave continues to increase until the voltage becomes zero, producing a totally asymmetrical short-circuit current, Fig. 7.

We can visualize the total asymmetrical current as a symmetrical current having a direct-current component superimposed upon it, Fig. 8. The dc component represents displacement of the sine wave from the zero axis. An actual short-circuit is likely to occur anywhere between zero and peak voltage. The offset of the short-circuit current wave will be somewhere between the two extremes, depending on the point of the voltage wave at which the short circuit occurs, Fig. 9.

Any real circuit has resistance, and this causes the dc component to decay to zero several cycles after the fault inception. The effect is a change from

an initial asymmetrical current to a symmetrical one. The dc component is assumed to be generated in the ac system and not by any external source. Consequently, its energy will be dissipated as an I^2R loss in the resistance of the circuit, Fig. 10.

X/R factor is the reactance-to-resistance ratio of the circuit considered. The decay (or decrement) of the dc component depends on the X/R ratio; X and R being formed by the reactance and resistance of all the circuit components between the source and fault. *If R = O*, the ratio is infinity and the dc component will never decay, Fig. 8. *If X = O*, the ratio is zero and the dc component decays instantly. For ratios in between, the dc component decays in time to zero, the time depending on the particular X/R ratio, Fig. 10: the greater the reactance in relation to the resistance, the longer it will take for the dc component to decay.

Exact calculation of rms asymmetrical current at different times after fault inception is very involved. Accurate factors of rate of change in apparent generator reactances and decrement factors for dc components would have to be known. Simplified methods account for the dc components with an accepted multiplier. These multipliers convert calculated symmetrical rms amperes into asymmetrical rms amperes (including the dc component).

For the application of short-circuit protective devices, only maximum dc components will be considered for the

momentary duty of breakers and fuses. Thus, we make sure that the applied protective device will withstand the maximum short circuit that can possibly occur in the system.

For the momentary duty all the subtransient reactances of the sources must be considered at the first half-cycle of the symmetrical short-circuit current, before the multiplier is applied. In practical calculations, a multiplier of 1.5-1.6 is generally used for medium- and high-voltage circuits, and approximately 1.25 for low-voltage circuits. Table below is abbreviated list of multipliers published by the National Electrical Manufacturers Association (NEMA). Fig. 11 shows multipliers for different X/R values, 0-7 cycles after fault inception.

The interrupting duty is based on the magnitude of short-circuit current at the moment when the circuit breaker contacts seperate or that the fuse blows. A circuit breaker interrupts after three, five or eight cycles, eight-cycle breakers being used generally in industrial plants. After eight cycles, the induction motor contribution has vanished and the synchronous motor reactance has changed from a subtransient to a transient one. That is why, for the interrupting duty of breakers above 600 volts, we have to use the generator subtransient reactance and the synchronous motor transient reactance, neglecting the induction motors. The dc component after eight cycles has almost disappeared. Consequently, for these breakers a multiplier of 1.0 is used.

Asymmetrical short-circuit current can be found by applying multipliers to symmetrical current

| Short-circuit power factor, % | Short-circuit X/R ratio | Ratio to rms symmetrical amperes | | |
		Max 1-ø instantaneous peak A	Max 1-ø rms A at ½ cycle	Average 3-ø rms A at ½ cycle
5	19.974	2.625	1.568	1.301
10	9.9301	2.455	1.436	1.229
15	6.5912	2.309	1.330	1.171
20	4.8990	2.183	1.247	1.127
25	3.8730	2.074	1.181	1.093
30	3.1798	1.978	1.130	1.066
35	2.6764	1.894	1.091	1.046
40	2.2913	1.819	1.062	1.031
45	1.9845	1.753	1.041	1.020
50	1.7321	1.694	1.026	1.013
55	1.5185	1.641	1.015	1.008
60	1.3333	1.594	1.009	1.004
65	1.1691	1.553	1.004	1.002
70	1.0202	1.517	1.002	1.001

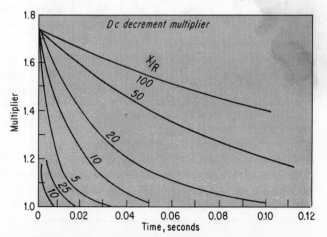

11—Multipliers at various X/R ratios and various times after fault inception give the asymmetrical current of the fault

1.3 Per-Unit Method Applied to Short-Circuit Current Calculations

Basis for rating ac circuit breakers and fuses, per-unit method applied to short-circuit calculations, and conversion of per-unit values to total equivalent reactance

Selective protection of electric power systems starts with short-circuit studies. The purpose of such calculations is proper selection of protective devices—circuit breakers and fuses.

The rating of power circuit breakers (above 600 V) is complicated by the few cycles it takes for the breaker to open after start of a short circuit. This time is a summation of the times necessary for the protective relay to close contacts, for the breaker trip coil to release its operating mechanism, for the breaker's contacts to part, and for the arc to be interrupted in the arc chamber. The highest mechanical stresses are produced during the first half cycle because of the dc component and the current contributions of motors and generators.

From the inception of a short circuit until breaker contacts part, the current decreases because of dc component decay and change in motor reactance values. Consequently, the current the breaker must interrupt at four, five or eight cycles after the fault occurs is less than the maximum value during the first half cycle. Because current magnitude changes with time, two bases of short-circuit current ratings must be considered for power circuit breakers:

The momentary rating, accounting for breaker's ability to close against and to withstand the mechanical and thermal stresses of the maximum short-circuit current of the first half cycle of the fault.

The interrupting rating, accounting

for the breaker's ability to interrupt the flow of short-circuit current within its interrupting element after four, five or eight cycles, according to the breaker type.

Power-circuit-breaker ratings are specified by ANSI and NEMA standards and IEEE recommendations. They are classified according to the type of breaker, voltage, current, interrupting capacity, etc. Table 1, power-circuit-breaker characteristics, has 13 columns, each having a specific rating for a selected breaker.

There are four limits which should never be exceeded in the selection of a power circuit breaker: operating voltage (column 3, Table 1); momentary current (column 8); interrupting MVA (column 10); maximum interrupting rating amperes (column 12). For a power circuit breaker, commonly referred to as a 4160-V, 250-MVA

Table 1—Air power circuit breaker characteristics

Column 1	2	3	4	5	6	7	8	9	10	11	12	13
	Voltage ratings			Insulation level withstand test		Current ratings, amperes			60-Hz interrupting rating			Rated interrupting time in cycles (60-Hz basis)
Type of breaker	Rated kV	Maximum design kV	Minimum operating kV at rated MVA	Low frequency rms kV	Impulse crest kV	Continuous at 60 Hz	Short time		3-phase rated MVA	Rms amperes At rated voltage	Total Maximum rating	
							Momentary	Four second				
4.16-75	4.16	4.76	3.5	19	60	1200	20,000	12,500	75	10,500	12,500	8
4.16-250	4.16	4.76	3.85	19	60	1200, 2000	60,000	37,500	250	35,000	37,500	8
4.16-250B	4.16	4.76	3.85	19	60	1200, 2000	80,000	37,500	250	35,000	37,500	8
4.16-350	4.16	4.76	4.0	19	60	1200, 3000	80,000	50,000	350	48,600	50,000	8
7.2-500	7.2	8.25	6.6	36	95	1200, 2000	70,000	44,000	500	40,000	44,000	8
13.8-500	13.8	15.0	11.5	36	95	1200, 2000	40,000	25,000	500	21,000	25,000	8
13.8-500B	13.8	15.0	11.5	36	95	1200, 2000	60,000	25,000	500	21,000	25,000	8
13.8-750	13.8	15.0	11.5	36	95	1200, 2000	60,000	37,500	750	31,500	37,500	8
13.8-750B	13.8	15.0	11.5	36	95	1200, 2000	80,000	37,500	750	31,500	37,500	8
13.8-1000	13.8	15.0	11.5	36	95	1200, 3000	80,000	50,000	1000	42,000	50,000	8

breaker, the four pertinent ratings are:

Operating voltage, listed as maximum design kV, is 4.76 kV; it is the highest rms voltage at rated frequency for which the breaker is designed.

Momentary current is 60,000 A; it is the maximum rms asymmetrical current the breaker will withstand including short-circuit currents from all sources and the dc component. It accounts for the maximum current during the first half cycle after fault inception. It defines the breaker's ability to close against and withstand the mechanical stresses produced by the largest offset of the short-circuit current. It is important because mechanical stresses vary with the square of the current. Power circuit breakers are so proportioned that their momentary rating is about 1.6 or more times the maximum interrupting rating in amperes.

Interrupting MVA, listed as three-phase rated MVA, is 250 MVA (the rated interrupted MVA at the specified voltage). This value is the product of the kV at which the breaker operates, the rated short-circuit current in kiloamperes to be interrupted, the square root of three, that is, 4.16 x 32 x $\sqrt{3}$.

Maximum interrupting rating amperes is 37,500 A, the highest rms current that the circuit breaker will interrupt regardless of how low the voltage may be.

Where there is no short-circuit contribution from motors, only an interrupting duty (MVA) check is necessary. If this value does not exceed the column-10 value, then the maximum short-circuit current—including the dc component—will be within the momentary rating of the breaker. When there is a substantial motor load contributing to the short circuit, then both momentary and interrupting duty should be checked.

The maximum momentary duty of the power circuit breaker is found by determining the current at the first half cycle. The short-circuit current during this time includes all sources of short-circuit current contributed by generators, synchronous and induction motors and the utility supply connection. Subtransient reactances of generators, synchronous and induction motors all have to be accounted for in the total reactance diagram. The dc component, which is maximum in the first half cycle, also has to be accounted for by a multiplier in the general case; as shown in Table 3, the multiplier is 1.6. In the special case, where the calculated symmetrical duty exceeds 500 MVA and the circuit is fed directly from generators or entirely through current-limiting reactors, the multiplier is 1.5.

Interrupting duty of a power circuit breaker is checked by determining the short-circuit current at the moment the circuit breaker's contacts part. The fewer the cycles required for the contacts to part, the greater will be the current to be interrupted.

Accordingly, power circuit breakers are grouped into classes corresponding to the breaker's operating speed. There are eight-cycle, five-cycle and three-cycle breakers. Instead of accounting for the time at which the short-circuit current has to be calculated, a multiplier (Table 3) is used to account for the generator and motor reactances at the time.

5-8-cycle breakers are generally used in industrial and power plants. Normally, the induction motor contribution has disappeared; the reactances of synchronous motors have changed from subtransient to transient values even before the contacts part. Consequently, in calculating the interrupting duty, the generator subtransient reactances and the synchronous motor reactances are to be used and the induction motors neglected. At the time the breaker contacts part (after eight cycles), almost all the dc component has died out—which explains why a multiplier of 1.0 is used.

In large power systems, where the symmetrical interrupting duty is 500 MVA or greater and the circuit is fed mainly from generators or entirely through current-limiting reactors, the special-case multipliers in Table 3 should be used. In this special case, there may be some dc component left when the breaker contacts part.

High-voltage fuses are of two types: current-limiting, which open the current before the first current peak, and noncurrent-limiting, which open the

Table 2—Standard ratings of low-voltage air circuit breakers

Breaker type	Voltage		Interrupting rating*, amperes		30-cycle short-time rating**, amperes		Frame size, continuous current rating, amperes
	Ac	Dc	Asymmetrical	Symmetrical	Asymmetrical	Symmetrical	
15	600-481	250 & below	15,000	14,000	15,000	14,000	225
15	480-241	—	25,000	22,000	15,000	14,000	225
15	240 & below	—	30,000	25,000	15,000	14,000	225
25	600-481	250 & below	25,000	22,000	25,000	22,000	600
25	480-241	—	35,000	30,000	25,000	22,000	600
25	240 & below	—	50,000	42,000	25,000	22,000	600
50	600-481	250 & below	50,000	42,000	50,000	42,000	1600
50	480-241	—	60,000	50,000	50,000	42,000	1600
50	240 & below	—	75,000	65,000	50,000	42,000	1600
75	600-481	250 & below	75,000	65,000	75,000	65,000	3000
75	480-241	—	75,000	65,000	75,000	65,000	3000
75	240 & below	—	100,000	85,000	75,000	65,000	3000
100	600-481	250 & below	100,000	85,000	100,000	85,000	4000
100	480-241	—	100,000	85,000	100,000	85,000	4000
100	240 & below	—	150,000	130,000	100,000	85,000	4000

*Current measured at instant ½-cycle after fault. **Excluding series trip device.

Table 3—Machine reactances and multipliers used in simplified calculations

Kind of equipment Interrupting duty	Machine reactances to use			Multipliers	
	Synchronous generators	Synchronous motors	Induction Motors	General case	Special case
Power circuit breakers with interrupting times of:					
8 cycles	Subtransient	Transient	Neglect	1.0	1.1a
5 cycles	Subtransient	Transient	Neglect	1.1	1.2a
3 cycles	Subtransient	Transient	Neglect	1.2	1.3a
2 cycles	Subtransient	Transient	Neglect	1.4	1.5a
L-V power circuit breakers	Subtransient	Subtransient	Subtransient	1.0b	—
Molded-case circuit breakers	Subtransient	Subtransient	Subtransient	1.0	—
Fuses and fused cutouts (above 1500 V)	Subtransient	Subtransient	Subtransient	1.6	1.2c
L-V fuses (600 V and below)	Subtransient	Subtransient	Subtransient	1.0d	—
L-V motor controllers (incorporating fuses or m-c breakers)	Subtransient	Subtransient	Subtransient	1.25	—
Momentary duty					
Power circuit breakers	Subtransient	Subtransient	Subtransient	1.6	1.5e

(a) Use only if calculated symmetrical value exceeds 500 MVA and circuit is mainly fed directly from generators or entirely through current-limiting reactors. (b) Factor based on test at X/R equals or is less than 6.6; for X/R values above this but less than or equal to 12, use 1.25. (c) Use only if 15 kV or less, fuses are not current limiting and X/R is less than 4. (d) Includes NEMA standard current-limiting fuses. (e) Use only if 5 kV or less and circuit is not mainly fed directly from generators or entirely through current-limiting reactors.

circuit in one or two cycles after inception of the fault. Fuses are rated on the basis of maximum rms current flowing in the first cycle after the short circuit occurs. Fuses are rated in terms of available short-circuit current, which is determined using the subtransient reactances of all generators, induction motors, synchronous motors and utility sources, and allowing for the maximum dc component with a 1.6 multiplier. In the special case, where the operating voltage is 15 kV or below, the fuses are not current limiting and the supply circuit X/R ratio is less than four, the multiplier to use is 1.2. Thus, the *interrupting* rating of power fuses, in amperes, is calculated in the same way as the momentary rating of power circuit breakers.

Low-voltage circuit breakers (up to 600 V) are different than high-voltage breakers because they are almost instantaneous in operation at currents close to their interrupting rating. The breaker's contacts part during the first cycle of short-circuit current. Because of this fast operation, the low-voltage breaker's momentary and interrupting duties are considered to be the same.

The short-circuit current to be determined is the current at the first half cycle. Subtransient reactances of generators, induction motors and synchronous motors should be used and the dc component accounted for. The multiplier is lower than with high-voltage circuit breakers due to the lower X/R ratio in low-voltage circuits. The lower X/R ratio results in a faster decay of dc component compared with higher-voltage circuits.

In the past, low-voltage circuit-breaker interrupting ratings were based on the total asymmetrical rms current of the first half cycle as an average of all three phases. NEMA standards and IEEE have recognized a multiplier of 1.25 based on an X/R ratio of 11.72. The multiplier was applied to the symmetrical short-circuit current of the first half cycle.

For several years, NEMA standards have been established on a symmetrical current interrupting basis. The breakers are tested under maximum asymmetrical conditions with a test circuit X/R no less than 6.6, which corresponds to an average multiplier of 1.17. This multiplier accounts for most low-voltage systems supplied by oil-filled transformers. For dry-type transformers, the X/R ratio can be more than 6.6, and in these cases the breakers must be selected on the basis of their asymmetrical ratings.

Table 2 lists symmetrical as well as asymmetrical interrupting ratings in amperes at half-cycle for low-voltage breakers. If data is not available to calculate the actual X/R ratio, and there is indication that this ratio is more than 6.6, it is advisable to use the 1.25 multiplier corresponding to the 11.72 ratio. When it is known that X/R does not exceed 6.6, use the multiplier 1.0.

The per-unit method is extensively used in short-circuit calculations. Since short-circuit currents are dependent on the values of reactances, X, from and including the sources up to the point of fault, the main problem in calculation is to find the total reactance. To get the total reactance we must first determine the reactance of each source and element in the circuit and then combine them in series and parallel.

After the total reactance has been obtained, the fault current is calculated by applying Ohm's law, $I = E/Z$, where I is the symmetrical short-circuit current, E the system voltage and Z the total impedance. The voltage E is the line-to-neutral voltage—the line-to-line voltage divided by $\sqrt{3}$.

The impedance Z is expressed by the formula $Z = \sqrt{R^2 + X^2}$. However, the resistance is usually neglected in fault calculation above 600 V, with the resulting error of a few percent being on the safe side. In systems above 600 V, the cable resistance is relatively small and is usually neglected. In systems of 600 V and below, the resistance of feeders and buses should be considered if their value is more than one quarter of the reactance between the source and the point of fault.

There are three main systems for expressing the element reactances of a circuit. The reactances can be expressed in *ohms*, in *percent* and in *per-unit on a chosen kVA base value*. Reactances expressed in per-unit values can easily be combined using more than one voltage level—no conversion is necessary going from one level to another. The per-unit method is used in IEEE publications.

A per-unit system is a convenient means of expressing different numbers which makes comparison easy. The per-unit value is a ratio:

$$\text{Per-unit} = \frac{\text{a number}}{\text{a chosen base number}}.$$

The base number is called *unit value*.

The per-unit method applied to short-circuit calculations converts all the different reactances of a circuit to a ratio on a conveniently chosen base number. The base number is a kVA value, frequently the largest transformer in the circuit, and is usually a round number such as 1000 or 10,000 kVA.

The following formulas are required to convert reactance data to per-unit values and to combine per-unit into a total per-unit reactance on a chosen base. In the formulas, *ohms* is the line-to-neutral, single-conductor value; *kVA* is the chosen three-phase kVA base; *kV* is the line-to-line voltage.

Formula 1. is used to convert reactances given in ohms for cables, buses, etc to per-unit values:

$$\text{Per-unit reactance} = \frac{\text{ohms} \times \text{kVA}}{1000 \times \text{kV}^2}.$$

Formula 2 is used to convert percent reactance to per-unit reactance:

$$\text{Per-unit reactance} = \frac{\text{percent reactance}}{100}.$$

Formula 3 is used to get percent reactance if required:

Percent reactance =
$$\text{per-unit reactance} \times 100.$$

Formula 4 is used to convert per-unit reactance on an equipment-rating base to per-unit reactance on the chosen kVA base. Reactance of motors, generators and transformers are usually given in percent of their own kVA rating, which may be converted to per-unit using formula 2, then formula 4.

Per-unit reactance =
$$\frac{\text{p-u reactance (on kVA rating)} \times \text{kVA}}{\text{kVA rating}}$$

For example, assume a 1000-kVA transformer having a 5.75% reactance. What is its per-unit reactance on a 10,000-kVA base? Applying formula 2, the per-unit reactance on the kVA rating = 5.75/100 = 0.0575; applying formula 4, the per-unit reactance on the chosen kVA base = 0.0575 x 10,000/1000 = 0.575.

Formula 5 is used to convert the available short-circuit kVA at the utility service to per-unit reactance:

$$\text{Per-unit reactance} = \frac{\text{kVA}}{\text{available s-c kVA}}$$

In low-voltage systems, the utility company may express the available short-circuit current in amperes. It must be determined whether this value is symmetrical or asymmetrical, and the value of X/R at the service entrance must be learned. If the short-circuit current is in asymmetrical amperes, you should find the multiplier appropriate for the given X/R value from the tables.

Formula 6 converts asymmetrical amperes to symmetrical amperes:

$$A_{sym} = \frac{A_{asym}}{\text{multiplier}}$$

Formula 7 converts symmetrical rms amperes to per-unit reactance:

$$\text{Per-unit reactance} = \frac{\text{kVA}}{A_{sym} \times \text{kV} \times \sqrt{3}}$$

After all the reactances have been converted to per-unit values on the chosen kVA base, they must be combined in series and parallel combinations to arrive at the total equivalent per-unit reactance. This is done using formulas 8 through 12, shown below.

Formula 13 is used to obtain the symmetrical short-circuit kVA from the total per-unit reactance:

$$\text{Sym s-c kVA} = \frac{\text{kVA}}{\text{total per-unit reactance}}$$

Formula 14 is used if symmetrical rms amperes are required:

Sym s-c A =
$$\frac{\text{kVA}}{\text{total per-unit reactance} \times \text{kV} \times \sqrt{3}}$$

The interrupting and momentary duty are obtained by applying the correct multipliers from Table 3 to the calculated symmetrical values.

Formula 8 - Combining series branches

$$X = X_1 + X_2$$

Formula 9 - Combining two parallel branches

$$X = \frac{X_1 X_2}{X_1 + X_2}$$

Formula 10 - Combining several parallel branches

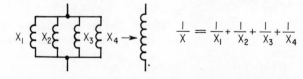

$$\frac{1}{X} = \frac{1}{X_1} + \frac{1}{X_2} + \frac{1}{X_3} + \frac{1}{X_4}$$

Formula 11 - Transforming wye to delta

$$X_A = \frac{X_b X_c}{X_a} + X_b + X_c$$

$$X_B = \frac{X_a X_c}{X_b} + X_a + X_c$$

$$X_C = \frac{X_a X_b}{X_c} + X_a + X_c$$

Formula 12 - Transforming delta to wye

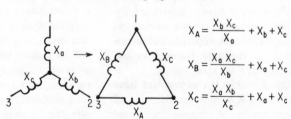

$$X_a = \frac{X_B X_C}{X_A + X_B + X_C}$$

$$X_b = \frac{X_A X_C}{X_A + X_B + X_C}$$

$$X_c = \frac{X_A X_B}{X_A + X_B + X_C}$$

1.4 Industrial Short-Circuit Current Calculation

Data necessary for a simplified fault-current calculation and an example determining the initial value of rms symmetrical current

The basic principles of fault calculation and protective device application were investigated. We are now ready to apply a simplified method of calculation which may be used as a reliable basis for selection of interrupting devices. This method may be used in place of complicated methods involving decrement curves, which often are unnecessary.

There are seven steps to follow in a short-circuit study: (1) Prepare a one-line diagram of the system, (2) select a convenient base kVA, (3) get proper reactance values for all equipment from manufacturers' data, (4) convert the one-line diagram into a reactance diagram based on per-unit values, (5) combine the reactances into a single equivalent reactance, (6) determine the symmetrical short-circuit current and kVA, and (7) determine the asymmetrical short-circuit current and kVA (section 1.3).

Step 1—Prepare a one-line diagram showing all short-circuit current sources and all impedance elements, Fig. 1. The one-line diagram should include utility supplies, generators, induction and synchronous motors as well as significant impedance elements such as transformers, reactors, cables, buses, circuit breakers, etc.

Step 2—Select a convenient base kVA which is a common base for all voltage levels. A convenient round number such as 1000, 10,000 or 100,-000 may be used. Separate base voltages are selected for each nominal voltage level. Usually transformer voltages are selected as base values.

Step 3—Get proper reactance values, preferably from manufacturers' data. Tables 1, 2, 3 and 4 give typical reactance data. With ac rotating machine sources the reactance varies within a short time period after the fault inception from the subtransient (X''d) to the transient (X'd) and to the synchronous (Xd) reactances. Induction motors have only a subtransient reactance (X''d) assigned; they are considered only in calculating momentary circuit-breaker and fuse ratings. They are not considered in calculating interrupting duty of circuit breakers above 600 V, and are removed from the reactance diagram.

The selection of subtransient and transient reactances for rotating equipment contributing short-circuit current has been covered in section 1.2 and section 1.3. Table 3 from section 1.3 is a guide for correct selection of reactance values. The selected reactance values are introduced into the reactance diagram (step 4) after being converted by the per-unit method on chosen base kVA (section 1.3.)

Step 4—Make a reactance diagram by converting the one-line diagram to per-unit values on a chosen base. This diagram should include all significant reactances and resistances. Reactances will be mainly used, for if impedances were to be used instead, vector calculation would be necessary to combine resistances with reactances. Usually the resistance of most parts of the system is a small percentage of the corresponding reactance, and a negligible error on the safe side is made by ignoring resistance. This is the rule above 600 V; at 600 V and below, the resistance of feeders and branch circuits may become significant.

A typical reactance diagram is shown in Fig. 2. It is obtained by drawing a zero-reactance bus (source bus) and connecting all short-circuit current sources to this bus. Then, adding all significant reactances, a complete reactance diagram is obtained which reflects all reactances to the fault point.

Step 5—Combine reactances into a single equivalent reactance including all reactances between the zero-reactance bus and the fault point, using formulas No. 8 through No. 12. The resulting total equivalent reactance in per-unit on a chosen base is used to determine the short-circuit current and kVA at the fault point.

Step 6—Determine symmetrical value of the short-circuit current or kVA. The symmetrical short-circuit current is found by formula 14:

$$\text{Sym s-c A} = \frac{\text{Base kVA}}{\text{total reactance} \times \text{kV} \times \sqrt{3}}$$

For symmetrical kVA use formula 13:

$$\text{Sym s-c kVA} = \frac{\text{Base kVA}}{\text{total per-unit reactance}}$$

Step 7—Find the asymmetrical value of the short-circuit current or kVA by applying appropriate offset multipliers. Table 3 (section 1.3) gives the proper multipliers for various applications. Fig. 2 (section 1.2) provides the multipliers for the rms asymmetrical current required for a given short time after fault inception and for various X/R ratios.

A numerical example of short-circuit calculation for a medium- and low-voltage industrial power system may now be calculated.

Step 1. The one-line diagram of an industrial power system is shown in

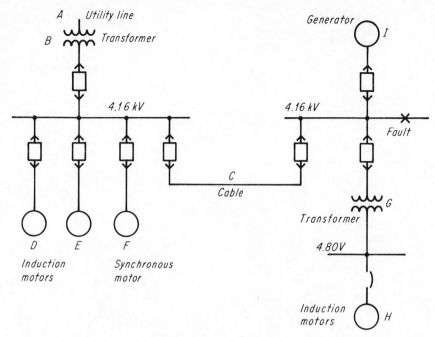

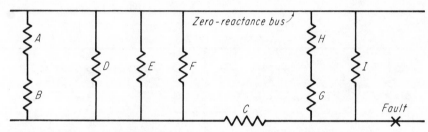

1—The one-line diagram shows all short-circuit sources and impedance elements

2—A typical reactance diagram is derived from the one-line diagram

Reactance conversion calculations

Circuit element	Reactance on element's own rating base		Per unit reactance on chosen base	
Utility line	500 MVA available		$\dfrac{10,000}{500,000} = 0.02$	(5)
Utility transformer	6.5% = 0.065 pu	(2)	$0.065 \times \dfrac{10,000}{3000} = 0.216$	(4)
3125-kVA generator	8% = 0.08 pu	(2)	$0.08 \times \dfrac{10,000}{3125} = 0.356$	(4)
1000-kVA substation	8% = 0.08 pu	(2)	$0.08 \times \dfrac{10,000}{1000} = 0.8$	(4)
4000-V induct motor	16.7% = 0.167 pu	(2)	$0.167 \times \dfrac{10,000}{600} = 2.78$	(4)
4000-V synch motor	X″d = 16% = 0.16 pu	(2)	$0.16 \times \dfrac{10,000}{500} \times \left(\dfrac{4000}{4160}\right)^2$ $= 3.0$	(4)
	X'd = 27% = 0.27 pu	(2)	$0.27 \times \dfrac{10,000}{500} \times \left(\dfrac{4000}{4160}\right)^2$ $= 4.8$	(4)
480-V induct. motor	X″d = 25% = 0.25 pu	(2)	$0.25 \times \dfrac{10,000}{1000} = 2.5$	(4)
Cables to 4-kV motors	$\dfrac{600 \text{ ft}}{1000} \times (0.0377 \text{ X}) \text{ ohms}$		$\dfrac{\text{ohms} \times 10,000}{1000 \times 4.16^2} = 0.0131 \times$	(1)
Cables to 1000-kVA transformer	$\dfrac{400 \text{ ft}}{1000} \times (0.0381 \text{ X}) \text{ ohms}$		$\dfrac{\text{ohms} \times 10,000}{1000 \times 4.16^2} = 0.0088 \times$	(1)

Numbers in parentheses refer to formulas given in preceding section 1.3.

Fig. 3 where a utility line and a local generator may supply the plant at the same time. The substation, 4.16 kV to 480 V, has a 1000-kVA transformer with an impedance of 8%. The induction motors fed by this substation are assumed equal to the substation kVA with 25% subtransient reactance (X'd) on the substation rating base. Cables are three-conductor, interlocked steel armor type. The ratings and reactances of the rest of equipment is shown in the one-line diagram, Fig. 3.

Step 2. Select the base kVA; in this system 10,000 kVA is a convenient number. The medium-voltage base is 4.16 kV and the low-voltage base is 480 V.

Step 3. Convert the various reactance values in the one-line diagram to per-unit values on the chosen kVA base. The following formulas, discussed in the August article, are repeated for convenience:

Formula 1.

$$\text{Per-unit reactance} = \frac{\text{ohms} \times \text{kVA}}{1000 \times \text{kV}^2}$$

Formula 2.

$$\text{Per-unit reactance} = \frac{\text{percent reactance}}{100}$$

Formula 4.

$$\text{Per-unit reactance} = \frac{\text{p-u reactance (on kVA rating)} \times \text{kVA}}{\text{kVA rating}}.$$

$$\text{Per-unit reactance} = \frac{\text{kVA}}{\text{available s-c kVA}}$$

(In these formulas kVA alone means chosen base kVA.)

The calculated per-unit reactance values are listed in the table below.

Step 4. Convert the one-line diagram into a reactance diagram.

Steps 5, 6, 7. Combine the reactances into a single equivalent value.

A. Calculate momentary duty at fault (1) on the 4.16-kV bus using sub-transient reactances for all rotating equipment. The resulting reactance diagram and the combined total per-unit reactance is shown in Fig. 4.

Symmetrical momentary s-c A =

$$\frac{10,000}{0.105 \times 4.16 \times \sqrt{3}} = 13,200 \text{ A} \quad (14)$$

Asymmetrical momentary s-c A =

$$1.6 \times 13,200 = 21,100 \text{ A}$$

Symmetrical momentary kVA =

$$\frac{10,000}{0.105} = 95,000 \text{ kVA} \quad (13)$$

Asymmetrical momentary kVA =
$$1.6 \times 95,000 = 152,000 \text{ kVA}$$

B. Calculate the interrupting duty at the 4.16-kV bus fault (1). For interrupting duty the contribution of induction motors is neglected, and is not shown on the reactance diagram. The synchronous motor is accounted for with a transient (X′d) value. This eliminates the substation branch and changes the reactance value of the synchronous motor. The utility and generator branches remain the same. The reactance diagram for interrupting duty, and the combined total per-unit reactance, is shown in Fig. 5.

Interrupting duty s-c amperes =
$$\frac{10,000}{0.12 \times 4.16 \times \sqrt{3}} = 11,600 \text{ A} \quad (14)$$

Interrupting duty s-c kVA =
$$\frac{10,000}{0.12} = 83,500 \text{ kVA} \quad (13)$$

C. Calculate short-circuit current at fault (2) on the 480-V bus. The present design of low-voltage circuit breakers differs from that of medium- and high-voltage power circuit breakers. They are practically instantaneous, their contacts often parting during the first cycle of current. Therefore, the short-circuit current determined should be for the first half cycle, and is done on the same basis as checking the momentary duty for medium- and high-voltage breakers; that is, using subtransient reactances of generators and induction and synchronous motors. On this basis, the reactance diagram, and the combined total per-unit reactance, is shown in Fig. 6.

Symmetrical s-c amperes =
$$\frac{10,000}{0.71 \times 0.48 \times \sqrt{3}} = 17,000 \text{ A} \quad (14)$$

Asymmetrical s-c amperes =
$$1.25 \times 17,000 = 21,200 \text{ A}$$

Selection of circuit breakers can now be made using the tables given in section 1.3. The breakers are to be selected on the basis of their nominal current, voltage and capability to withstand the calculated momentary and interrupting duty.

The next step is to properly coordinate the breaker tripping relays so that they will operate sequentially in a predetermined pattern. The breakers nearest the fault should trip first to isolate the troubled section from the rest of the system. The protective devices toward the power source should serve as backup protection should the ones nearer the fault fail to isolate the fault from the system.

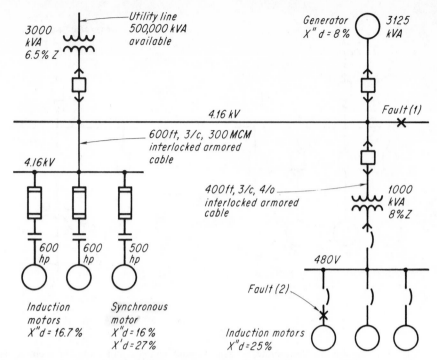

3—Example of an industrial power system has this one-line diagram

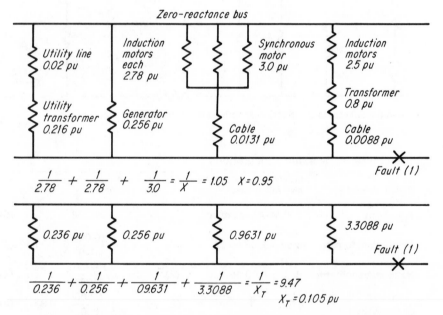

4—Reactance diagram is used for momentary duty of fault (1) on 4.16 kV bus

Table 1—Generator subtransient reactance, approximate p-u X on kVA rating

Salient pole with damper winding	12 poles or less	0.18
	14 poles or more	0.24
Salient pole without damper winding	12 poles or less	0.25
	14 poles or more	0.35
Distributed pole, 625 to 9375 kVA	2 poles	0.09
12,500 kVA and up	2 poles	0.10
12,500 kVA and up	4 poles	0.14

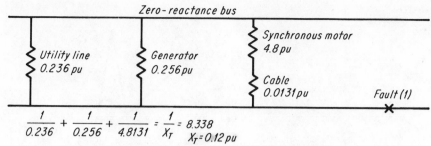

5—Interrupting duty for fault (1) on 4.16-kV bus requires this diagram

The diagram shows: Zero-reactance bus with Utility line 0.236 pu, Generator 0.256 pu, Synchronous motor 4.8 pu, Cable 0.0131 pu, Fault (1)

$$\frac{1}{0.236} + \frac{1}{0.256} + \frac{1}{4.8131} = \frac{1}{X_T} = 8.338 \quad X_T = 0.12\ pu$$

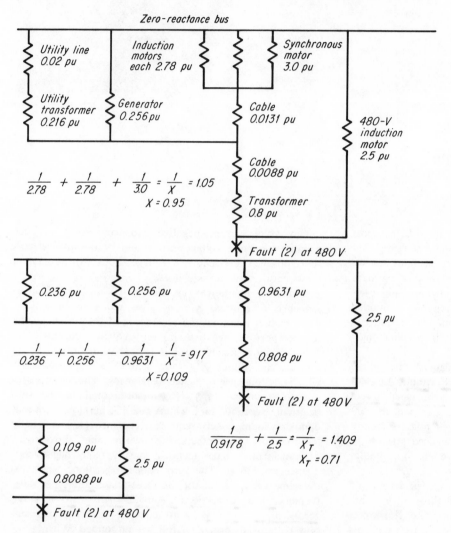

6—This reactance diagram is used for fault (2) where voltage is 480 V

The diagram shows: Zero-reactance bus with Utility line 0.02 pu, Utility transformer 0.216 pu, Induction motors each 2.78 pu, Generator 0.256 pu, Synchronous motor 3.0 pu, Cable 0.0131 pu, Cable 0.0088 pu, Transformer 0.8 pu, 480-V induction motor 2.5 pu, Fault (2) at 480 V

$$\frac{1}{2.78} + \frac{1}{2.78} + \frac{1}{3.0} = \frac{1}{X} = 1.05 \quad X = 0.95$$

Second stage: 0.236 pu, 0.256 pu, 0.9631 pu, 2.5 pu, 0.808 pu, Fault (2) at 480 V

$$\frac{1}{0.236} + \frac{1}{0.256} - \frac{1}{0.9631} \frac{1}{X} = 917 \quad X = 0.109$$

Third stage: 0.109 pu, 0.8088 pu, 2.5 pu, Fault (2) at 480 V

$$\frac{1}{0.9178} + \frac{1}{2.5} = \frac{1}{X_T} = 1.409 \quad X_T = 0.71$$

Table 2—Motor reactances, approximate p-u X on kVA rating

	Subtransient	Transient
Synchronous, individual large motor 6 poles	0.10	0.15
8 to 14 poles	0.15	0.24
Synchronous groups, 600 V or less	0.25	0.33
above 600 V	0.15	0.25
Induction, individual large	0.25	—
Induction groups, 600 V or less	0.25	—
above 600 V	0.20	—

Table 3—Transformer reactances, p-u X on transformer kVA base

Three-phase load centers, primary 13.8 kV or less, low-voltage secondary

300 to 500 kVA	0.050
750 to 2500 kVA	0.055

Single-phase distribution transformers

kVA	5 kV and below	5.1 to 15 kV
3 to 5	0.020	0.023
10 to 15	0.020	0.020
25 to 50	0.025	0.024
75 to 167	0.033	0.037
250 to 500	0.047	0.051

Three-phase power transformers, secondary above 2.4 kV, above 500 kVA

Primary kv	P-u X on kVA base
11-23	0.055
34.5	0.060
46	0.065
69	0.070

Single-phase power transformers, secondary above 2.4 kV, above 500 kVA

Primary kV	P-u X on kVA base
2.2 to 25	0.055
25.1 to 34.5	0.060
34.6 to 46	0.065
46.1 to 69	0.070

Table 4—Cable and busway, ohms per 1000 ft, line to neutral

A	R	X	Z	X/R
Plug-in busway, copper bus bars				
225	0.0836	0.0800	0.1157	
400	0.0437	0.0232	0.0495	
600	0.0350	0.0179	0.0393	
800	0.0218	0.0136	0.0257	
1000	0.0145	0.0135	0.0198	
Plug-in busway, aluminum bus bars				
225	0.1090	0.0720	0.1313	
400	0.0550	0.0222	0.0592	
600	0.0304	0.0121	0.0327	
800	0.0243	0.0154	0.0288	
Low-impedance feeder busway				
800	0.0219	0.0085	0.0235	
1000	0.0190	0.0050	0.0196	
1350	0.0126	0.0044	0.0134	
1600	0.0116	0.0035	0.0121	
2000	0.0075	0.0031	0.0081	
2500	0.0057	0.0025	0.0062	
3000	0.0055	0.0017	0.0058	
4000	0.0037	0.0016	0.0040	
Current-limiting busway				
1000	0.013	0.063	0.064	4.85
1350	0.012	0.061	0.062	5.08
1600	0.009	0.056	0.057	6.22
2000	0.007	0.052	0.052	7.45
2500	0.006	0.049	0.049	8.15
3000	0.005	0.046	0.046	9.20
4000	0.004	0.042	0.042	10.50

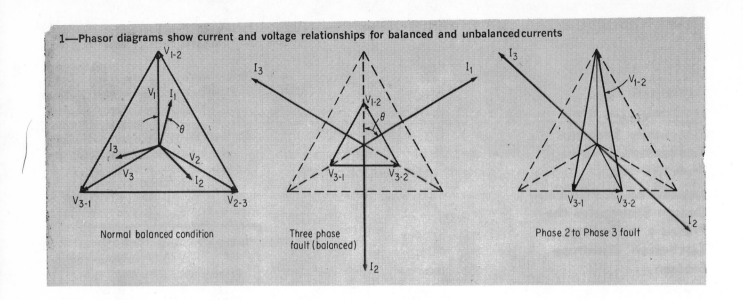

1—Phasor diagrams show current and voltage relationships for balanced and unbalanced currents

Normal balanced condition

Three phase fault (balanced)

Phase 2 to Phase 3 fault

1.5 Symmetrical Components

Three-phase ungrounded faults usually impose the most severe duty on protective devices, and the simplified method of calculation shown in previous sections reflects such balanced faults. However, a three-phase power system also may be subjected to phase-to-ground faults; phase-to-phase ungrounded faults; and phase-to-phase grounded faults. A phase-to-ground fault may sometimes produce a larger current than a three-phase fault if peculiar reactance values exist.

A three-phase short circuit on a balanced three-phase system produces a balanced three-phase fault. Line-to-ground or line-to-line faults produce unbalanced three-phase faults. The method of symmetrical components consists of reducing an unbalanced system of phasors (representing volts or amperes) into three balanced systems of phasors designated as positive, negative and zero-phase-sequence components.

A balanced three-phase system is one in which the three quantities corresponding to the three phases are equal in magnitude and 120 deg apart in phase. If a three-phase fault occurs in such a system, its effect on currents and voltages can be visualized as in Fig. 1, left. When a phase-to-phase or phase-to-ground fault occurs, it produces an unbalanced three-phase system; Fig. 1, right.

Symmetrical component method allows unbalanced three-phase quantities to be expressed as the sum of three components, two of which are balanced, or symmetrical, three-phase systems (Fig. 2). The three quantities of the zero-sequence system are equal and in phase.

In a balanced (symmetrical) power system the voltages generated by rotating machinery are equal in magnitude and 120 deg out of phase. In such a system the impedances in all phases are taken to be equal up to the point of fault. Positive-sequence currents produce only positive-se-

quence voltage drops, negative-sequence currents produce negative-sequence voltage drops and zero-sequence currents produce zero-sequence voltage drops. No interaction exists between phase sequences.

Sequence reactances are designated as X_1 = positive-sequence reactances, X_2 = negative sequence reactances. These values represent the reactances of the system to the flow of positive, negative and zero-sequence currents.

Synchronous machinery has typical values of reactance (X_d = synchronous, X'_d = transient, X''_d = subtransient) which are positive sequence reactances. The negative-sequence reactance (X_2) is generally equal to the subtransient, except for waterwheel generators without damper windings. Zero-sequence reactance (X_0) is usually less than any of the others, as shown in table, above right.

Transformers have identical positive and negative-sequence reactances. The zero-sequence reactance has also the same value except for the three-phase core-type transformers when connections are made such as to block the zero-sequence current. Zero-sequence currents will not flow if the transformer neutral is ungrounded. When zero-sequence cannot flow, then X_0 is considered to be infinite. In most cases where zero-sequence currents can flow, X_0 is the same as the positive-sequence reactance.

In wye-delta connected transformers the zero-sequence current can flow through the neutral connection of the wye if the neutral is grounded. There are no zero-sequence currents flowing in the delta-side connection. In a wye-wye connected transformer the zero-sequence currents flow in both the primary and the secondary, provided there are enough connections from neutral to ground to give current paths. The resistance of transformer windings is usually neglected in short-circuit calculations.

For transmission lines and cables positive and negative-sequence reactances are considered to be the same. In

16

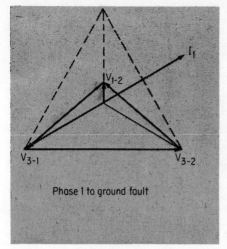

Phase 1 to ground fault

Reactance values of three-phase, 60-Hz rotating equipment

Apparatus	Positive sequence			Negative sequence X_2	Zero sequence X_0
	Synchronous X_d	Transient X_d'	Subtransient X_d''		
2-pole generator (45 psi H_2 inner cooled)	1.22-1.91* 1.65*	0.20-0.35 0.27	0.17-0.25 0.21	0.17-0.25 0.21	0.04-0.14 0.093
2-pole generator (30 psi H_2 cooled)	1.61-1.86 1.72	0.188-0.303 0.23	0.116-0.17 0.14	0.116-0.17 0.14	0.03-0.073 0.042
4-pole generator (30 psi H_2 cooled)	1.36-1.67 1.49	0.265-0.30 0.281	0.169-0.208 0.19	0.169-0.208 0.19	0.041-0.1825 0.106
Salient pole generators and motors with dampers	0.6-1.5 1.25	0.2-0.5 0.3	0.13-0.32 0.2	0.13-0.32 0.2	0.03-0.24 0.18
Salient pole generators without dampers	0.6-1.5 1.25	0.2-0.5 0.3	0.2-0.5 0.3	0.35-0.65 0.48	0.03-0.24 0.19
Synchronous condensers (air cooled)	1.25-2.20 1.85	0.3-0.5 0.4	0.19-0.3 0.27	0.18-0.4 0.26	0.025-0.15 0.12
Synch condensers (H_2 cooled, ½ psig rating)	1.5-2.65 2.2	0.36-0.6 0.48	0.23-0.36 0.32	0.22-0.48 0.31	0.03-0.18 0.14

*Upper values give the range, lower values the average.

transmission lines, the zero-sequence reactance is different because the zero-sequence current returns via the earth or overhead ground wire. The zero-sequence reactance is usually larger than the positive and negative-sequence.

As for cables, the zero-sequence reactance of the three-phase cable is larger than the positive and negative-sequence reactances because the spacing between outgoing and return conductors is larger in the zero-sequence circuit than in the positive or negative ones. The return path through a sheath or a distributed earth conductor may carry all the zero-sequence currents. This introduces a voltage drop three times larger than the one produced if the return path carried the current of only one outgoing conductor. The return path in the zero-sequence circuit is given an impedance three times its actual impedance.

Accurate determination of zero-sequence reactances of cables and transmission lines is involved. For fair estimates, ratios of X_0/X_1 give minimum values. For example, a three-conductor cable with a nonmetallic sheath or conduit and an earth return with distributed, average conductivity will have an X_0/X_1 ratio ranging from 3 to 5.

Sequence diagrams are developed for calculations, Figs. 3,4. Since the three sequence components are independent up to the point of fault, three network diagrams (phase-to-neutral of the power system) are necessary.

The positive-sequence network shows generator voltages, reactances of generators, transformers, and lines.

The negative-sequence network is usually a replica of the positive-sequence network except that: (1) No generator voltages are shown since no synchronous generator operates with reverse phase order. (2) Negative sequence reactance of synchronous machinery may occasionally differ from positive sequence reactance.

The zero-sequence network is usually similar to the negative-sequence network except that: (1) Special consideration is given to transformer connections. Wye-wye grounded transformers allow zero-sequence current to flow from one side of the bank to the other. Wye-delta connected banks allow current to flow in the grounded neutral, but block passage of zero-sequence current from one side of the bank to the other. (2) Resistors and reactors connected between machine or transformer neutrals and ground are shown at three times their nominal value.

Negative or zero-sequence currents cannot flow in balanced systems because synchronous or induction machines generate only positive sequence voltages. When a fault occurs, it acts as a converter which changes positive-sequence voltages into negative and zero-sequence voltages. The negative and zero-sequence components are determined by setting up networks having one single source of voltage at the fault.

Calculation of unbalanced faults is illustrated in Fig. 3. The positive-sequence network includes the generated voltages E_s and E_U as well as the positive-sequence voltage E_{1F} at the point of fault. The negative and zero-sequence networks include the voltages E_{2F} and E_{0F} produced by conversion at the fault. After reducing all the reactances to an equivalent single reactance for the positive (X_1), negative (X_2) and zero (X_0) sequence network values, the following formulas are applied:

$$\text{Single line-to-ground fault} = \frac{3\,E_{\phi-N}}{X_1 + X_2 + X_3} \tag{1}$$

$$\text{Line-to-line fault} = \frac{E_{\phi-N}\sqrt{3}}{X_1 + X_2} \tag{2}$$

$$\text{Double line-to-ground fault} = \frac{3\,E_{\phi-N}\,X_2}{X_1 X_2 + X_0(X_1 + X_2)} \tag{3}$$

$$\text{Three-phase fault} = E_{\phi N}/X_1 \tag{4}$$

If the networks are set up in ohms on a voltage base, the currents will be obtained directly at the voltage base by these formulas. Usually reactances of machines and transformers are expressed in percent or per-unit values on their own kVA rating. Since different units may be involved, it is necessary to reduce all of them to a chosen kVA base. Formulas for converting from one way of expressing reactances to another were given in section 1.3. It is desirable to be conversant with calculations involving reactances expressed in all three methods—per-unit, percent, or ohms.

Numerical example of a short-circuit calculation by the symmetrical component method is shown in Fig. 4. The system consists of a generating station, a transmission line of 120 kV and an infinite generating system. The reactance shown is in ohms referred to 120 kV phase-to-phase chosen as base. All resistances are negligible. The transmission line voltage to neutral is:

$$V_{\phi-N} = 120/\sqrt{3} = 69.3 \text{ kV}$$

Single line-to-ground fault =

$$\frac{3E_{\phi-N}}{X_1+X_2+X_0} = \frac{3 \times 69,300}{125+144+490}$$

$$= \frac{207,900}{759} = 274\text{A} \qquad (1)$$

Line-to-line fault =

$$\frac{E_{\phi-N}\sqrt{3}}{X_1+X_2} = \frac{120,000}{269} = 446\text{A} \qquad (2)$$

Double line-to-ground fault =

$$\frac{3\,E_{\phi-N}\,X_2}{X_1 X_2 + X_0(X_2+X_2)}$$

$$= \frac{29,937,600}{149,810} = 200\text{ A} \qquad (3)$$

Three-phase fault =

$$\frac{E_{\phi-N}}{X_1} = \frac{69,300}{125} = 554\text{A} \qquad (4)$$

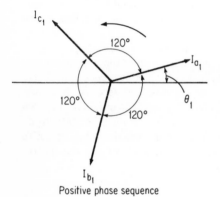

Positive phase sequence

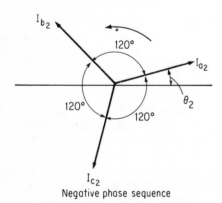

Negative phase sequence

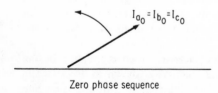

Zero phase sequence

2—Vector relations are shown for positive (subscript 1), negative (sub 2) and zero-sequence (sub 0) currents equivalent to an unbalanced three-phase fault

18

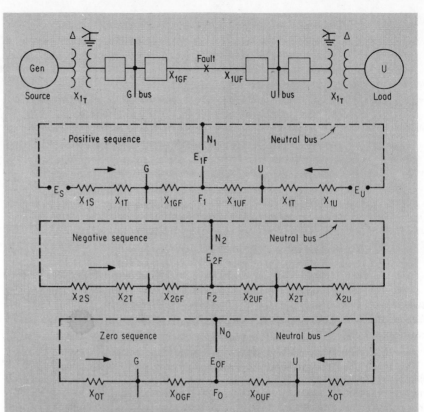

3—One-line diagram illustrates a typical, simple three-phase system with a fault at F. Positive, negative and zero-sequence networks are shown for this system

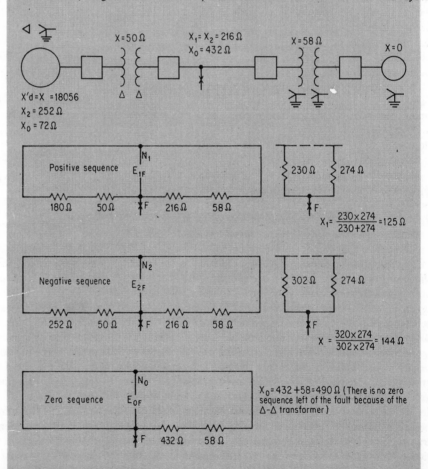

4—Numerical example is based on a 120-kV transmission line, with positive, negative and zero-sequence reactances given in ohms and all resistances negligible

1.6 Voltage Drop at Motor Starting

Short-circuit data can be used to calculate voltage drop produced at critical points in a system when motors are started

To develop sufficient starting torque, general purpose ac motors—both squirrel-cage and synchronous—require a full-voltage starting current from five to ten times their normal full-load running current. Such sudden increases in current drawn from the power system can result in substantial voltage dips. The adverse effects of these voltage dips include: (1) transient shaft torques in operating motors, which may cause excessive stresses in the mechanical systems, (2) excessive voltage drop, which may prevent acceleration of the drive to normal speed, and (3) malfunction of other plant equipment such as relays and contactors, and annoying light flicker.

Supplying large motors from primary feeder power lines is not troublesome, normally, because the motors are generally located in industrial areas with inherently heavy utility lines. Because few residential customers are served from the same line in these areas, wider limits of voltage drops are permitted. Nevertheless, there are cases where motor ratings are too high for the power facilities, especially when the individual process involves a large motor with a number of low-horsepower auxiliary motors. In such cases, voltage drop for the largest motor—or group of motors that may be started simultaneously—should be calculated to determine the extent of the problem.

Starting current is all reactive, it is commonly assumed. Indeed, the starting power factor is usually lagging in the 15 to 30 percent range. To keep motors running and prevent contactors from dropping out, the voltage should not dip below about 70 percent of rated voltage. This assumes that light flicker is not important. Limits on allowed voltage drop may be imposed either by utilities supplying the power or by local industrial plant requirements. Where safety and continuity of operation are paramount, plants restrict voltage drops at motor starting to as little as 10%.

On the other hand, motor loads varying cyclically with each power stroke produce corresponding variations in line current, and these can cause objectionable voltage variations. Typical of such loads are large air compressors and pumps pulsating at six to twelve times per second. The consequences of excessive voltage drops caused by motor starting may become severe when continuous process lines (such as automobile assembly lines or paper mills) are shut down completely. Considerable time may be required to restore the plant to normal operation and a substantial amount of production can be lost—possibly accompanied

by equipment damage. Another possibility is that automatic sequencing equipment associated with modern industrial digital control may lose sequence during inadmissible voltage dips on the system.

Motor contactors can have a dropout voltage as low as 30% or as high as 70% of rated voltage, depending on the type, size and manufacturer. These contactors may drop out in a short time—from 3/4 of a cycle up to 12 cycles.

Most flicker problems arise while the motor is starting. They occur with single-phase fractional-horsepower motors, integral horsepower motors operated from secondary distribution circuits, and large integral horsepower motors operated from primary lines.

Voltage dips can be reduced by improving relay coordination, by installing capacitors, and by reducing the reactance of the supply system to these industrial loads. Better yet, you can minimize dips through proper selection of motor-starting methods.

Plant engineers normally prefer full-voltage starting with a squirrel cage induction motor or a synchronous motor, since this is the least expensive, simplest and most reliable method. When alternative methods are adopted to reduce starting current, hence voltage dips, they also reduce motor torque. Therefore, be sure that load torque requirements are satisfied with the method you select.

Making the calculation

The minimum symmetrical interrupting duty at the supply point of the plant is the first data required in making the calculation. Then, compute the system line impedance or reactance between the supply point and the motor. The impedance of the motor can be calculated from the manufacturer's catalog, which usually gives values for full-voltage and locked-rotor current.

If accelerating performance is also desired over a speed range, design values of motor torque, rpm, starting current and power factor will be needed for different speeds as well as the inertia (WK^2) of the motor and the driven load.

Consider the elements of a typical plant power system, Fig. 1. Between the incoming bus and the motor terminals there are usually several impedances in series or parallel. The procedure for calculating voltage drop at the motor during motor starting involves the use of the maximum available short-circuit current of the primary, the line voltage, the various line, transformer and motor impedances, and motor characteristics.

We make the assumption that all of the voltage drop

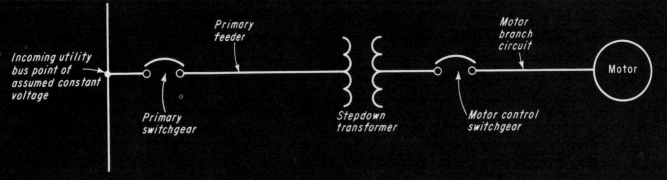

1—Typical circuit arrangement for a medium-voltage motor supplied from a higher-voltage distribution system. Setup uses a stepdown transformer and switchgear for control of the motor

$S = starting$
$B = Base$
$pu = per unit$

$Z_{pu_s} = \dfrac{Z_{\Omega s}}{Z_B}$, $Z_B = \dfrac{V_{M\Omega}}{\sqrt{3}\, I_{FL}}$, $Z_{\Omega_s} = \dfrac{V_m}{\sqrt{3}\, I_{LR}}$, $Z_{\%} = Z_{pu} \times 10^2$ $Z_{pu} = \dfrac{I_{FL}}{I_{LR}}$

occurs in the static circuit elements, such as cables, transformers, reactors and transmission lines, and that the supply voltage is constant.

Formula 15 is used to obtain voltage V_s at the motor when it starts:

$motor$
$Bus\ Volts = $ $$V_s = \frac{Z_m \times V_I}{\sqrt{(R_m + R_s)^2 + (X_m + X_s)^2}}, \qquad (15)$$

where

$\quad V_I =$ initial voltage at starting $= Source\ Voltage = 1\ pu$
$\quad Z_m =$ impedance of the motor being started (ratio of applied voltage to current drawn)
$\quad R_m = Z_m \cos\theta_m$
$\quad X_m = Z_m \sin\theta_m$
$\cos\theta_m =$ power factor of the current drawn by the motor being started
$\quad R_s =$ total resistance of the circuit between the motor and the point in the system where voltage is assumed to remian constant
$\quad X_s =$ total reactance of the circuit between the motor and the point in the system where voltage is assumed to remain constant.

All impedances, resistances and reactances should be expressed in ohms, in percent or per-unit on a conveniently chosen base. The voltage drop can be calculated with little error by neglecting resistances and considering only the reactances of the circuit elements in series with the motor. Formula 16 is a simplified formula for calculating the voltage at the motor when starting: $V_I = 1\ per\ unit = 100\%$

$$V_s = \frac{Z_m}{Z_m + X_s} \times V_I, \qquad (16)$$

It is derived from formula (15) by neglecting resistances and phase angle. When the ratio X_s/R_s of the circuit elements is 2 or greater, formula (16) gives a voltage drop which is within 10% of the correct value given by calculating with formula (15).

Transformers of 100 kVA and larger usually have a X_s/R_s ratio greater than 2. Since voltage drop calculations at start are usually made for motors exceeding 100 hp, the error that results in applying the simplified formula is negligible. The percent voltage drop at starting

$$\% V_s = \frac{\% Z_m}{\% Z_m + \% X_s} \times 100.$$

The motor impedance Z_m in ohms is:

$$Z_m = \frac{V_m}{\sqrt{3} \times I_s}, \quad on\ motor\ base,$$
$convert\ to\ chosen\ base$
$if\ different.$

where
$\quad V_m =$ voltage rating of motor in volts
$\quad I_s =$ starting current in amperes at rated motor voltage.
Formula (17) gives the motor percent impedance:

$$\% Z_m = \frac{100}{I_{LR}/I_{FL}}, \qquad (17)$$

where
$\quad I_{LR} =$ locked-rotor current in amperes
$\quad I_{FL} =$ full-load current in amperes.
The value of I_{LR}/I_{FL} varies from 5 to 10 according to the type and characteristics of the motor.

For voltage-drop calculations, follow the five steps for **short-circuit calculations described in section 1.4, until you obtain a reactance diagram. Then proceed as follows:**

Step 6—Find percent of system voltage at starting, using the formula

$$\% V_s = \frac{\% Z_m}{\% Z_m + \% X_s} \times 100.$$

Step 7—Obtain percent of motor rated voltage at starting by multiplying percent of V_s by the ratio between system voltage and motor voltage.

Step 8—Check for starting torque required, by multiplying the percent full-voltage starting torque by the square of the percent voltage drop at starting. (Torque varies with the square of the voltage.)

If the calculated voltage drop is 30% or above, it is excessive.

Now, follow this example for calculating voltage dip at motor starting for a medium-voltage industrial power distribution system.

Step 1. The single-line diagram for a 3500-hp induction motor supply is shown in Fig. 2. The utility incoming line supplies a main switchyard bus at 12 kV. An overhead 4000-ft line of two 3-1/c-750-MCM, 15-kV, shielded aerial triplexed cable connects the main switchyard bus to a remote 12-kV switchgear. Latter supplies a 3500-hp induction motor via a 1000-ft line of two 1-3/c-500 MCM, 15-kV shielded armored cable, a 10,000-kVA 12-kV/2.4-kV transformer and a .4-kV switchgear.

Since the length of cable connecting the 2.4-kV switchgear to the motor is less than 500 ft, its effect is negligible.

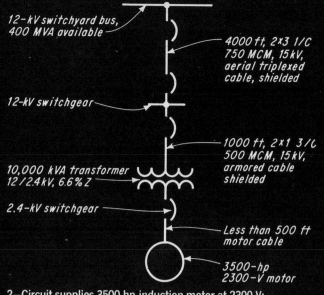

12-kV switchyard bus, 400 MVA available

4000 ft, 2×3 1/C 750 MCM, 15 kV, aerial triplexed cable, shielded

12-kV switchgear

1000 ft, 2×1 3/C 500 MCM, 15 kV, armored cable shielded

10,000 kVA transformer 12/2.4 kV, 6.6% Z

2.4-kV switchgear

Less than 500 ft motor cable

3500-hp 2300-V motor

2—Circuit supplies 3500-hp induction motor at 2300 V; 748 A full load, 5000 A locked rotor; 60% starting torque

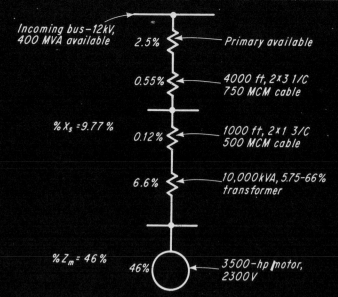

Incoming bus—12kV, 400 MVA available

2.5% — Primary available

0.55% — 4000 ft, 2×3 1/C 750 MCM cable

% X_s = 9.77 %

0.12% — 1000 ft, 2×1 3/C 500 MCM cable

6.6% — 10,000 kVA, 5.75-66% transformer

% Z_m = 46%

46% — 3500-hp motor, 2300V

3—Circuit elements are represented in percent reactance on a 10,000-kVA base (rating of the transformer)

Step 2. The minimum available symmetrical interrupting duty, obtained from the utility supply company, is 400 MVA.

Step 3. A value of 10,000 kVA is selected as base—same rating as the stepdown transformer.

Step 4. Converting the primary available and the impedances of cables, transformer and motor into terms of percent impedance on the chosen base, the following values are obtained:

• Minimum primary available:

$$\frac{10,000 \text{ kVA base}}{400,000 \text{ kVA available}} \times 100 = 2.5\%$$

• Cable percent reactances:

For the 4,000-ft, two 3-1/c, 750-MCM, 15-kV, shielded aerial triplexed cable (from tables), X = 0.0396 ohms/ 1,000 ft L-N. Reactance of 4,000 ft, two cables in parallel:

$$X = \frac{4 \times 0.0396}{2} = 0.0792 \text{ ohm.}$$

Then, applying formula (1),

$$\% \text{ X cables} = \frac{\text{ohms} \times \text{kVA base}}{10 \times (\text{kV})^2}$$

$$= \frac{0.0792 \text{ ohms} \times 10,000 \text{ kVA}}{10 \times (12)^2} = 0.55\%.$$

For the 1,000-ft, two 3-1/c-500-MCM, 15-kV, shielded armored cable, from reactance tables obtain the value X = 0.0351 ohms/1,000 ft L-N. Then, the reactance of 1,000 ft, two cables in parallel, is $X = \dfrac{0.0351}{2} = 0.01755$ ohm.

Applying formula (1):

$$\% \text{ X cables} = \frac{0.01755 \text{ ohms} \times 10,000 \text{ kVA}}{10 \times (12)^2} = 0.12\%.$$

• Motor impedance:

Convert motor horsepower into kVA by using motor data characteristics:

$$\frac{3,500 \text{ hp} \times 0.746}{0.96 \text{ eff.} \times 0.92 \text{ pf}} = 3,000 \text{ kVA}$$

By formula (17), % $Z_m = \dfrac{100}{\dfrac{5,000 \text{ A}}{748 \text{ A}}} = \dfrac{100}{6.7} = 15\%$. ^on motor Base

As the kVA drawn by a motor varies with the square of the voltage, the percent motor impedance is:

$$\% \text{ } Z_m = 15\% \times \left(\frac{2300}{2400}\right)^2 = 15\% \times 0.92 = 13.8\%$$

$$\% \text{ } Z_m \text{ on base} = \frac{10,000 \text{ kVA base}}{3,000 \text{ kVA}} \times 13.8\% = 46\%$$

• Transformer impedance is 6.6% maximum on the chosen base, the same 10,000 kVA as the transformer rating.

Step 5. The reactance diagram reflecting the values of step 5 is shown in Fig. 3.

Step 6. Percentage of system voltage at motor starting is obtained from formula (16):

$$\% \text{ } V_s = \frac{\% \text{ } Z_m}{\% \text{ } Z_m + \% \text{ } X_s} \times 100 = \frac{46\%}{55.77\%} \times 100 = 83\%.$$

The voltage dip at the 2.4-kV bus is 100% − 83% = 17% of 2,400 V.

Step 7. Percent of motor rated voltage at starting is:

$$\% \text{ } V_m = \frac{2,400}{2,300} \times 83\% = 86.5\%.$$

The voltage dip at the motor is:

$$100\% - 86.5\% = 13.5\% \text{ of } 2,300 \text{ V.}$$

Step 8. Since full-voltage starting torque is 60% of full load torque, the available starting torque at the 86.5% reduced voltage is $60\% \times (86.5)^2 = 45\%$. Be sure to verify that this value satisfies the driven load starting torque requirements.

The importance of calculating voltage dips—and trying to reduce them if excessive—becomes greater and greater as automation grows. A survey of problems resulting from outages and voltage dips of short duration has shown that most complaints stem mostly from momentary disturbances on motor undervoltage releases, and consequent loss of production, rather than from damage to equipment.

2—Sectionalizing a substation bus with reactors employs a basic arrangement: A, straight bus; B, ring bus; and C, star bus

1—Current-limiting reactors' usual applications include: 1, feeders; 2 synchronizing bus; 3, bus ties; 4, generators —series; 5, generators; 6, duplex; 7, motor-starting devices

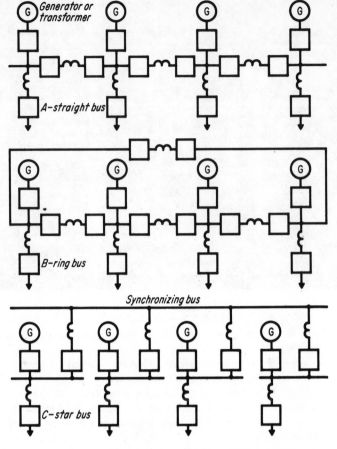

Synchronizing bus

1.7   Reactors Reduce Short-Circuit Currents

Judicious use of current-limiting reactors often can keep fault-current magnitudes within capability of installed equipment

Current-limiting reactors are used primarily to reduce short-circuit current magnitude, with the object of reducing stresses in all components carrying the short-circuit current. This makes it possible to employ circuit breakers of lower interrupting capacity with resulting savings in total equipment cost. However, electric system growth often increases the available short-circuit current beyond the interrupting capacity of existing circuit breakers. By installing reactors, the short-circuit requirements can be reduced to avoid replacing the breakers.

Another benefit of limiting fault-current magnitude is smaller bus voltage drop during a short circuit, minimizing its effect on other parts of the

system. It is desirable to maintain close-to-normal voltage on parts of the system remote from the fault, both to prevent tripout of undervoltage devices and to maintain stability. Reactors properly applied, along with fast and highly selective relay coordination, can segregate the short-circuited part of the system with minimum disturbance elsewhere. Furthermore, proper load division in proportion to feeder capacity (especially with parallel-connected feeders) often can be obtained with reactors.

Because system stability is influenced by reactors, they should be applied with caution: Increased reactance between machines decreases the limit of their stability. A particular re-

actor application may improve stability between certain parts of the system, but may decrease it between other parts. A balance must be found between system stability and the economies and other benefits of reactors.

Application and location of current-limiting reactors in industrial power systems are shown in Fig 1.

Feeder reactors are inserted in outgoing feeders from major station or substation buses to permit both lighter construction of feeder circuits and use of circuit breakers with lower interrupting capacity, as well as to reduce damage at the fault point. Breaker short-circuit duty is reduced only if the reactor is placed between bus and feeder breaker.

Relay selectivity is improved by both the voltage drop across the reac-

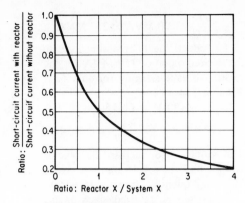

3—**Reduction** in short-circuit current from use of reactors follows this curve

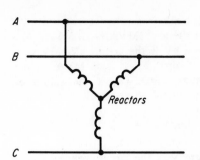

5—**Shunt reactors** are used to balance out leading currents due to capacitance of long power lines. They prevent undesirable voltage rises caused by charging current

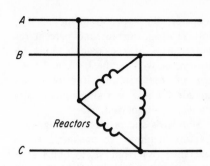

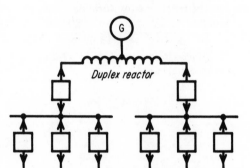

4—**Duplex reactor** gives low reactance in normal operation, high with a fault

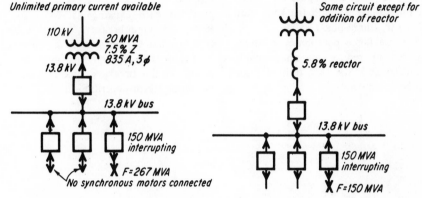

6—**Example** shows how reactors can reduce higher interrupting duty imposed on existing breakers when larger transformer increases available short-circuit current

tor and the difference between short-circuit currents available at its incoming and outgoing terminals. Thus, the difference in current magnitude between a bus fault and a feeder fault permits high relay selectivity.

Synchronizing and bus-tie reactors are used when several important feeders and power sources are concentrated on a single bus, and it is desirable to sectionalize the bus so that a fault will not take the entire station out of service. Additional incoming sections can be added and the system expanded, provided the bus voltage and source voltage are the same.

Several methods of connection are depicted in Fig 2. Simplest one shown is **A,** but its shortcoming is that a fault on one of the inner bus sections will leave the station in two separate parts. **B** has a ring-bus arrangement to hold the station together if a fault occurs in any of the sections. Isolation of one bus section does not remove the remaining power sources.

The star-bus arrangement **(C)** features a separate synchronizing bus connected to each of the bus sections through a current-limiting reactor and

a circuit breaker. The star bus is applied in large industrial systems. If any one section is cut out, power is transferred automatically to that section from the remaining sections.

Generator series reactors are used mainly with steam-turbine generators —which usually have low reactance— to reduce 3-phase short-circuit stresses. Generator stability, however, is somewhat reduced. Consequently, reactors are seldom used with salient-pole generators, which have a higher inherent reactance.

A duplex reactor (Fig 4) is used with a generator to provide low reactance under normal operating conditions and high reactance under fault conditions. The reactor coils are so wound that, when normal current is flowing, the magnetic fluxes produced in the two sections are in opposition and the effective reactance between the generator and each bus is reduced. When a fault occurs, the high fault current flows only through half the coil. Since there is no equal opposing flux from the other section, the fault current is limited by the relatively high reactance it encounters.

Grounding reactors, placed in the neutral circuit of a system, reduce the line-to-ground fault current to a value that will not damage the generator or transformer windings—usually less than 40% of the 3-phase current value. Grounding reactors are applied mainly to generators supplying a four-wire utility distribution at 12.47Y/7.2 kV or 4.16Y/2.4 kV The ohmic value of the reactor should be selected to avoid a circuit which produces damaging oscillatory overvoltages.

Motor-starting reactors reduce inrush current. As an example, a 10% reactor used with a motor taking 6 to 7 times normal current at start, can reduce the starting current to about 40% with a full-load voltage drop of only 5%.

Other applications of reactors include shunt reactors, Fig. 5.

Selection of current-limiting reactors is based on the *percent reactance* to be introduced into a circuit. Percent reactance is the ratio of the voltage drop across the reactor to the voltage between line and neutral in 3-phase circuits and between lines in single-phase circuits. To select a reactor properly, the type, frequency, kVA, voltage drop, current and percent reactive drop of the reactor must be known, as well as the kVA and voltage of the circuit. Reactor types include 3-phase and single-phase, air-cooled, oil-immersed, etc.

Standards and product catalogs rate reactors in ohms. To convert a given reactance (X) from % to ohms at a given voltage and selected kVA base:

$$X \text{ (ohms)} = \frac{X(\%) \times (kV \text{ base})^2 \times 10}{kVA \text{ base}} \quad (1)$$

In a three-phase circuit, the kV will be the line-to-line kV and the kVA base will be the three-phase value.

The reactance per phase, in ohms, required to reduce an unacceptable symmetrical MVA to a desired value can be found from:

$$X \text{ (ohms)} = (kV)^2 \times (1/MVA_d - 1/MVA_e) \quad (2)$$

where kV is the circuit kV, MVA_d is the desired MVA and MVA_e is the existing value. Or, if the values of symmetrical short-circuit current are known,

$$X \text{ (ohms)} = (V/\sqrt{3}) \times (1/I_{scd} - 1/I_{sce}) \quad (3)$$

where V is the circuit voltage, I_{scd} is the desired and I_{sce} the existing current values in amperes.

Assume that a larger, 20-MVA, 3-phase transformer at 110 to 13.8 kV supplies a 13.8-kV switchgear that is provided with existing 150-MVA-interrupting rated breakers, and that it is connected to the system as shown in Fig 6. The interrupting duty imposed on the breakers (without synchronous motor contribution) is

$$\frac{100}{7.5 \, X\%} \times 20 \, MVA = 267 \, MVA$$

To reduce the interrupting duty to the desired value of 150 MVA for the existing breakers, apply formula (2):

$$X \text{ (ohms)} = (13.8)^2 \times (1/150 - 1/267)$$
$$= 190.44 \times \frac{117}{150 \times 267} = 0.56 \text{ ohms}$$

The voltage drop across the reactor will be 835 A × 0.56 ohms = 467.6 V. Consequently, three single-phase reactors will be selected, each having 0.56 ohms per phase and a rating of 835 × 467.6/1000 = 390 kVA. Each reactor is capable of introducing a percent reactance (by formula 1) of:

$$\frac{\text{(ohms)} \times kVA}{kV^2 \times 10} = \frac{0.56 \times 20,000}{(13.8)^2 \times 10}$$

= 5.8% in a 20-MVA, 13.7-kV, three-phase circuit.

2

The Engineering Basics of Power Factor Improvement

2.1 Fundamental Considerations of System Power Factor Improvement

Modern electrical power plants at industrial sites have steadily increased system reactances (kilovar, or kvar) because of the continually growing use of equipment producing inductive loads. Some of the sources of these loads are induction motors, (especially when operated at less than full load), transformers, arc welders, rectifiers, arc furnaces, fluorescent lamps and various types of electronic equipment.

The electric utility has to supply the active (usable) power and also the reactive (unusable) power that these inductive loads require. This constitutes an extra load on the utility system's capacity.

The cost of system losses due to kilovar flow is an important economic factor, one that should not be overlooked—for if the necessary kilovars required by these loads are not supplied by some other means, the reactive flow of current in the system uses up the thermal and voltage capabilities of the line and equipment.

An industrial plant operating at a low power factor can:

• Reduce system capacity and performance by overloaded cables and transformers.

• Increase copper losses.

• Reduce voltage level, adversely affecting the efficiency of motor operation.

• Reduce incandescent lamp illumination.

• Increase power cost where utility power-factor clauses are enforced.

The reactive current also introduces higher losses in the generator, transformers and the lines through which it flows. The generator and lines are overloaded unnecessarily by the reactive current, which requires larger generators, transformers and heavier lines.

Utilities usually compensate for revenue losses caused by low power factor at a customer's plant by including a charge in the rate schedule. Improving power factor leads to important savings in power cost and improved plant efficiency. Capacitors, synchronous motors and synchronous condensers are the most common methods used to improve a plant's power factor.

How capacitors improve PF

Using capacitors is the simplest and most economical method of improving power factor in plants that do not require additional large motor drives. When properly applied to the system, capacitors supply the reactive magnetizing current and remove the reactive current from the plant circuit. This improves the overall power factor. Capacitors also improve a plant's efficiency by releasing electrical system capacity (kva), by raising the voltage level and reducing system losses so that additional loads can be added to the same system.

Here's how improving the power factor can save money. Assume that a plant's load is 1,500 kw at 0.75 power factor and the utility has a cost-rate schedule based on $2/kva, with a maximum billed power factor of 0.9.

The billed kva is:

$$\frac{1,500 \text{ kw}}{0.75 \text{ PF}} = 2,000 \text{ kva}$$

The utility demand charge is: 2,000 kva × $2/kva = $4,000 a month.

The minimum kva on which the plant's 1,500 kw demand cost can be based is:

$$\frac{1,500 \text{ kw}}{0.9 \text{ PF}} = 1,667 \text{ kva}$$

Single Phase Power Factor

The demand charge at 1,667 kva would be $3,334 a month (1,667 kva × $2/kva).

This means that by improving the power factor from 0.75 to 0.9, the demand charge will be reduced $666 a month ($4,000 − $3,334 = $666).

(Tables showing the necessary kvar of the capacitors to improve the power factor from 0.75 to 0.9 will be shown in detail in the next section (2.2). The tables also provide multiplying factors for kw in order to obtain necessary kvar at different power factors.)

At 1,500 kw with 0.75 power factor, the reactive kva (kvar) is 1,500 kw × 0.882 (the multiplying factor) = 1,323 kvar. At 1,500 kw with 0.9 power factor the kvar is 1,500 kw × 0.484 (the multiplying factor) = 726 kvar. The required corrective capacity is 597 kvar (1,323 kvar − 726 kvar). The present cost of 480/600-v static capacitors is approximately $10/kvar, or $5,970 for the 597 kvar capacitors needed for the example. At a savings of $666 a month the initial cost of the capacitors is amortized in less than nine months. After the first nine months, however, the $666 savings continues each month. (The amount saved varies with the location of the power utility and its rate schedule.)

The capacitor method of improving power factor is most economical where synchronous motors are not applicable. During the last 20 years the cost per kvar of capacitors has continually decreased compared to other means of kvar supplies—i.e., synchronous generators or condensers.

The main applications of synchronous motors to improve power factor are in plants that require new large motor drives. In most other cases, however, capacitors are the best bet.

A synchronous condenser is a rotating machine, somewhat similar to the synchronous motor. The synchronous condenser, however, improves the power factor but drives no load. Synchronous condensers are used mainly by electric utilities and are seldom a practical solution in industrial plants.

Power factor fundamentals

Induction loads, such as induction motors, transformers, induction furnaces, welders and fluorescent lights, require two kinds of current, *magnetizing current* and *power-producing current.*

Magnetizing current—also known as *wattless, reactive* or *nonusable* current—is necessary to build up the flux for the magnetic field of inductive devices. Without magnetizing current, electric energy cannot flow through the core of transformers or across the air gap of induction motors.

Generators and synchronous motors, however, are magnetized by direct current, from their DC exciters. Induction motors and transformers are magnetized from the AC power line system causing a *lagging component* in the current. Energy spent in building up the magnetic field flows back and forth between the generator and the load. This magnetizing current is the real cause of low power factor in the power system.

The unit of measurement of the magnetizing volt-amperes is the kilovar. The instrument showing kilovars is called a kilovarmeter. Kilovar readings are more useful than power-factor readings because they indicate the actual value of the magnetizing components.

Power-producing current—also known as *active, working* or *usable* current—is converted into useful work, such as rotating a fan, heating or pumping water. The unit of measurement of the active power produced is the kilowatt.

The *total current* is the current read on an ammeter in the circuit and is made up of both the magnetizing current and the power-producing current.

The total volt-amperes, also known as *apparent power,* is expressed in kva.

Active and reactive current

Inductive loads require two current components—the magnetizing current (reactive current) and the power-producing current (active current). These two components of current are vectorially represented at 90 deg to each other in Figure 1.

The total current can be determined from the expression:

1. total $current^2$ = active $current^2$ + reactive $current^2$

At a common voltage point, kva and kw are proportional to current. Therefore:

2. $kva^2 = \overline{kw^2} + \overline{kvar^2}$

Or, apparent $power^2$ = active $power^2$ + reactive $power^2$, as shown in Figure 2.

What is power factor?

Power factor is defined as the ratio of active power (kw) to the total apparent power (kva):

3. $PF = \dfrac{kw}{kva}$ or $kva \times PF = kw$

Trigonometrically the $PF =$

$\dfrac{kw}{kva} = Cosine\ \theta$

Power factor can also be defined as the factor to multiply apparent power in order to obtain active power. For example, assume a load on a 460-v, 3-phase system. The ammeter indicates 200 amp and the wattmeter reads 120 kw. What is the power factor of the load?

The apparent power for a 3-phase circuit is given by the expression:

4. $kva = \dfrac{E \times I \times \sqrt{3}}{1,000}$

$= \dfrac{460\ volts \times 200\ amp \times 1.73}{1,000}$

$= 159.2\ kva$

Substituting in Formula 3:

$PF = \dfrac{kw}{kva} = \dfrac{120}{159.2}$

=0.75, or 75 percent.

Power factor is often stated as a percentage, but since it is a ratio it is better expressed a decimal form and is usually found that way in formulas and tables. The 75 percent power factor in the example is stated at 0.75 and unity power factor as 1.

The following formulas are derived from Formulas 1, 2, 3 and 4 and will be

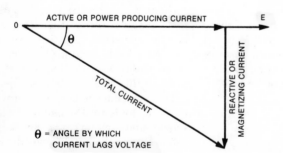

FIGURE 1   COMPONENT CURRENTS IN
AC INDUCTIVE LOADS

ACTIVE OR POWER PRODUCING CURRENT

θ

0

E

TOTAL CURRENT

REACTIVE OR MAGNETIZING CURRENT

θ = ANGLE BY WHICH
CURRENT LAGS VOLTAGE

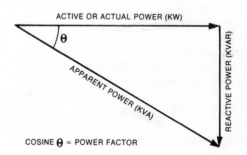

FIGURE 2   COMPONENTS POWER IN
AC INDUCTIVE LOADS

ACTIVE OR ACTUAL POWER (KW)

θ

APPARENT POWER (KVA)

REACTIVE POWER (KVAR)

COSINE θ = POWER FACTOR

used in the future sections.

Formulas 3 and 4:

5. $kw = \dfrac{1.73 \times E \times I \times PF}{1,000}$

From Formulas 2, 4 and 5:

6. $kvar = \dfrac{1.73 \times E \times I \times \sqrt{1\text{-}PF^2}}{1,000}$

As shown in Figure 1, θ is the angle by which the current lags the voltage and can be expressed trigonometrically as:

7. $Cosine\ \theta = \dfrac{kw}{kva} = PF$

This means the power factor of a circuit can be expressed by the cosine of the angle by which the current lags (or leads) the voltage in that circuit.

Voltage and current relationship

In an AC circuit the voltage has a sinusoidal form at 60 Hz. In a pure resistive load, such as a heater or an incandescent light, the current is in phase with the voltage. This means the current passes through zero, maximum and minimum values in the same instant as the voltage does, as shown in Figure 3. At any instant, the watts are equal to the volts times the amperes.

When the current and the voltage are positive at the same instant, the wattage is positive. When they are both negative at the same instant, the wattage is positive $(W = -E \times -I)$.

In inductive loads, however, the current and voltage are not in phase. The current is lagging the voltage, as shown in Figure 4. The current reaches zero, maximum and minimum after the voltage does. Here the current and the voltage are not always both positive or negative at the same instant.

When current and voltage are positive or negative at the same instant, the wattage or power is also positive. When one is positive and the other is negative, the power is negative, as shown in Figure 4.

The net actual or usable power is the difference between the positive area above and the negative area below the zero-line axis. The power factor, defined by Formula 3, is the ratio of this difference to the total kva. In this case, the power factor is a lagging power factor. The power factor is lagging when the load requires kvar (inductive loads). It is leading when the load furnishes kvar (capacitive loads).

Induction motors have a lagging power factor because their magnetizing current must be supplied by the power source. The reactive component drops off only slightly with a load decrease. The in phase, or real-power component, drops in almost direct proportion to a decrease in load. This means that a lightly loaded induction motor has a large lagging component as the ratio of reactive kva to kw becomes quite high. It is important, therefore, to make sure that all induction motors are loaded as fully as possible to their nominal ratings.

Kilovar generators

Capacitors have a leading power factor because they can supply kvar. The leading power factor of capacitors and unity, or leading, power factor of synchronous motors can be used to improve the lagging power factor of the inductive loads that will improve the plant's overall power factor.

Capacitors also can be considered as kilovar generators because they can supply the required magnetizing current of inductive loads. This can be explained in terms of stored energy. A capacitor installed in the same circuit with an induction motor has the effect of an exchange of reactive current between them. The leading current taken by the capacitors then supplies the lagging current required by the induction motor.

Figure 5a shows an induction motor without power factor correction. The motor draws only 80 amp for its working load. Because of the 60-amp magnetizing current required by the motor, the supply circuit must carry:

$\sqrt{80^2 + 60^2} = 100$ amp
(See Formula 1)

FIGURE 3   VOLTAGE, CURRENT AND POWER RELATIONSHIP IN A PURE RESISTANCE LOAD

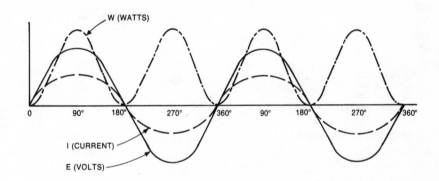

FIGURE 4   VOLTAGE, CURRENT AND POWER RELATIONSHIP IN AN INDUCTIVE LOAD

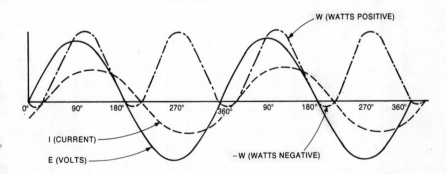

The supply feeder is loaded with the working current and also with the nonworking magnetizing current. After a capacitor is installed at the motor to supply the motor's magnetizing requirements, as shown in Figure 5b, the supply circuit has to carry and deliver only 80 amp for the same work done by the motor. The supply circuit now carries working current only. This permits the use of more electrical equipment on the same circuit and reduces electricity costs where power factor rates are enforced.

Limiting kw and kva

Turbine generators and engine/generator sets have a kw limit for the prime mover and kva of the generator. If the set is rated at the nominal kw value at unit-power-factor operation, the kw limit corresponds to the kva rating of the generator. Intermediate kw values, usually between 0.8 and 1.0 power factor operation, are dictated by the power factor and kva rating at the generator so that neither the kw nor

kva load exceed the generator kva rating.

Consequently, an improvement of the power factor releases both kw and kva capacity. The higher the power factor, the lower the kva for any given load. A high power factor means less kva in installed generators and transformers and smaller main and branch circuit feeders.

By improving the power factor from 70 percent to 90 percent, the current along the circuit is reduced by 28 percent for the same kw load. The approximate effect of a lagging power factor load on the permissible output of a standard 0.8 power factor generator can be seen in Figure 6. The effect of low power factor on the kilowatt-carrying capacity of transformers (rated in kva) can be seen in Figure 7.

Every year, millions of dollars are wasted in industrial plants because of the lack of understanding of benefits obtained from power factor improvement. The waste is incurred by

unnecessary capital investment for increased kva facilities and power factor penalty charges imposed by utilities.

On the other hand, it is generally neither economical nor necessary to improve power factor to 1. Capacitors or synchronous motors supply part of the necessary kvar required by reactive loads. The remainder is taken from the supply system to meet the power factor imposed by utility rates.

The exact amount of power factor improvement depends on the original combined power factor of group loads and the type of utility rate structure. Each of these factors should be individually studied before reaching any decision. A rough rule that has been used is to improve power factor to .9-.95.

FIGURE 5   INDUCTION MOTORS

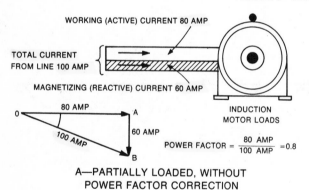

WORKING (ACTIVE) CURRENT 80 AMP

TOTAL CURRENT FROM LINE 100 AMP

MAGNETIZING (REACTIVE) CURRENT 60 AMP

INDUCTION MOTOR LOADS

POWER FACTOR = $\frac{80 \text{ AMP}}{100 \text{ AMP}}$ = 0.8

A—PARTIALLY LOADED, WITHOUT POWER FACTOR CORRECTION

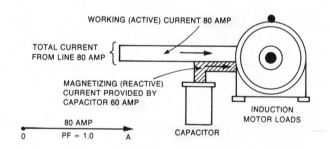

WORKING (ACTIVE) CURRENT 80 AMP

TOTAL CURRENT FROM LINE 80 AMP

MAGNETIZING (REACTIVE) CURRENT PROVIDED BY CAPACITOR 60 AMP

INDUCTION MOTOR LOADS

CAPACITOR

PF = 1.0

B—CAPACITOR INSTALLED NEAR SAME MOTOR TO SUPPLY MOTOR'S MAGNETIZING CURRENT REQUIREMENT

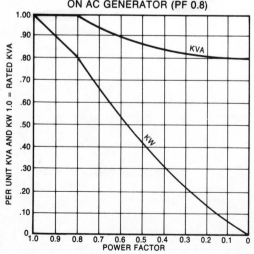

FIGURE 6   EFFECT OF LAGGING POWER FACTOR ON AC GENERATOR (PF 0.8)

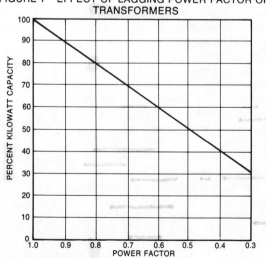

FIGURE 7   EFFECT OF LAGGING POWER FACTOR ON TRANSFORMERS

2.2 Desired Power Factor Improvement and the Power Factor for a Group of Loads

Section 2.1 discussed power factor fundamentals and formulas showing the relationship between kilowatts, kilovars and power factor. This part deals with the combined power factor of group loads, numerical and graphical representation of group loads, as well as the calculation of required kvar for a desired power factor improvement. (Figures, formulas and tables are numbered chronologically.)

The first section explained why induction motors, transformers, arc welders, induction furnaces, fluorescent lamps, electronic equipment, etc., can cause low lagging power factor. Improving low power factor by means of capacitors and synchronous motors can raise voltage level, reduce system losses and release electrical system capacity. Another important reason for improving power factor is the reduction of electricity costs where utilities enforce power factor schedule rates.

The power factors of individual loads are usually known and can be closely estimated. Table 1 gives typical high, leading and lagging loads and their power factors.

The power factors of individual loads can be used to calculate the power factor for a group of different loads. This is done by using the formulas in the first section. The method consists of adding the kw numerically and the kvar algebraical-

ly. The two components are then combined vectorially. The power factor for a group of loads, each with a different power factor, also can be obtained by a graphical method.

As an example of a combined power factor for a group of loads, assume that a substation supplies three different types of loads—leading, lagging and unity power factor—as shown in Figure 8.

The numerical method for calculating the overall substation power factor uses the total kw and kvar of the three various loads as follows:

50-kw lighting load: incandescent lights are a unity power factor load, and all the current is kw current.

Since kva = kw, then

50 kva = 50 kw

150-kva-connected induction motors operating at a lagging power factor of 0.8:

$$\text{kw} = \text{kva} \times \text{PF} = 150 \text{ kva} \times 0.8$$
$$= 120 \text{ kw} \qquad \text{(Formula 3)}$$

$$\text{kvar} = \sqrt{\text{kva}^2 - \text{kw}^2} =$$
$$\sqrt{150^2 - 120^2} =$$
$$\sqrt{22{,}500 - 14{,}400} = \sqrt{8{,}100}$$
$$= 90 \text{ kvar} \qquad \text{(Formula 2)}$$

TABLE 1 TYPICAL HIGH, LEADING AND LAGGING POWER FACTOR LOADS

High loads	Approximate PF
Incandescent lamps	1.0
Fluorescent lamps	
(with built-in capacitors)	0.95-0.97
Resistor heaters	1.0
Synchronous motors	1.0 or leading
Rotary converters	1.0
Leading loads	
Synchronous motors	0.9; 0.8; etc., leading, depending on rating
Synchronous condensers	Nearly 0, leading
Capacitors	0
Lagging loads	
Induction motors (full-load)	
Split-phase fractional hp	0.55 to 0.75
Split-phase (1-10 hp)	0.75 to 0.85
Split-phase condenser type	0.75 to 1.0
Polyphase squirrel-cage motors	
High speed (1 to 10 hp)	0.75 to 0.90
High speed (10 hp or more)	0.85 to 0.92
Low speed	0.70 to 0.85
Wound rotor	0.80 to 0.90
Groups of induction motors	0.50 to 0.85
Welders	0.50 to 0.70
Arc furnaces	0.80 to 0.90
Induction furnaces	0.60 to 0.70

75-kva synchronous motor with a leading power factor of 0.8:

kw = 75 kva × 0.8
= 60 kw (See Formula 3)

$$kvar = \sqrt{75^2 - 60^2} =$$
$$\sqrt{5,625 - 3,600}$$
$$= \sqrt{2,025} = 45 \text{ kvar (See Formula 2)}$$

If motor ratings are given in hp instead of kva, the ratings are converted to kva by using this formula:

8. $kva =$
$$\frac{hp \times 0.746}{\text{Efficiency (full load)} \times \text{PF (full load)}}$$

The kw that the substation must supply is obtained by adding: 50 kw (lights) + 120 kw (induction motor) + 60 kw (synchronous motor) = 230 kw.

The kvar that the substation must supply is obtained by adding: 0-kvar (lights) + 90 kvar (induction motor) −45 kvar (synchronous motor) = 45 kvar.

An overexcited synchronous motor (leading factor) has the ability to supply kvar in the same manner as a capacitor. This explains why the substation has to supply only 45 kvar.

of the 90 kvar the induction motors require. Overexcited synchronous motors (with leading power factor) perform useful work and improve the overall power factor. The overall plant power factor can be improved by putting unity or leading power factor synchronous motors in a circuit with a lagging power factor.

In the example, the total kva and overall power factor of the substation is:

$$kva = \sqrt{kw^2 + kvar^2} =$$
$$\sqrt{230^2 + 45^2}$$
$$= \sqrt{52,900 + 2,025} = \sqrt{54,925}$$
$$= 234 \text{ kva} \qquad \text{(See Formula 2)}$$

$$\text{Overall PF} = \frac{kw}{kva} = \frac{230}{234}$$
$$= 0.982 \qquad \text{(See Formula 3)}$$

The overall power factor of 0.982 shows how the synchronous motor helps to supply part of the reactive power required by the induction motors. The remainder of kvar requirements must be supplied by the substation.

If a synchronous motor is not required to supply active power, 45 kvar of capacitors can be used to

obtain the same power factor improvement. The various loads are added diagrammatically, as explained and shown in Figure 8.

The graphical method

The overall power factor and kva of the substation can be calculated by using the graph shown in Figure 9.

• On a convenient scale draw a horizontal line representing the 50-kw incandescent lighting load with a power factor of 1. (Line AB in Figure 9.)

• With B as the centerpoint draw a circle to the same scale representing the 150 kva of induction motors with lagging power factor.

• Continue Line AB after the 50-kw lighting load to include the 120 kw of induction motors (Line BD).

• Draw a vertical line from Point D to intersect with the 150-kva circle Point C below Line BD (lagging PF). Line DC represents the 90 kvar required by the induction motors.

• With C as the center, draw a circle (to the same scale) showing the 75-kva synchronous motor.

• Extend the horizontal line from Point D to F to represent the 60-kw synchronous motor.

• Draw a vertical line from Point F to intersect with the 75 kva circle at Point E above Line CG (leading PF).

Join A with E. Line AE, 234 kva, represents the overall kva of the substation. Line EF shows the overall improved 45 kvar demand that the substation has to supply.

By using Formula 7 from section 1.1 the overall improved power factor achieved by the synchronous motor and lighting load can be calculated.

$$\text{Overall PF} = \text{cosine } \theta =$$
$$\frac{AF}{AE} = \frac{230 \text{ kw}}{234 \text{ kva}}$$
$$= 0.982$$

This value also can be determined by measuring the angle θ between Lines AF and AE and finding out from trigonometric tables the cosine of this angle.

How much should PF be improved?

After calculating the overall power factor for a group of different loads with different power factors, the next step is to calculate the required kvar for the desired overall power factor improvement.

FIGURE 8 COMBINED POWER FACTOR OF A GROUP OF LOADS
WITH DIFFERENT PF'S

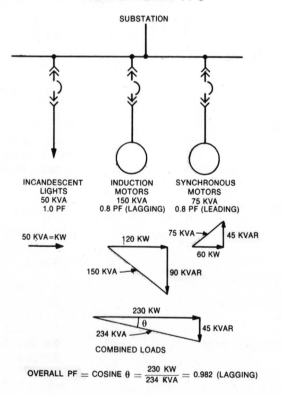

OVERALL PF = COSINE θ = $\frac{230 \text{ KW}}{234 \text{ KVA}}$ = 0.982 (LAGGING)

Reducing the kvar current amounts to reducing the total current. As usual the kw current does not change and the power factor will improve if kvar current is reduced.

If all the kvar current would be brought to zero, all current would be only kw current and the power factor would be 1.0 (100 percent). In actual practice, however, it is neither necessary nor economical to improve the power factor to 100 percent. Usually capacitors or synchronous motors are used to supply part of the load's kvar requirements up to an economical point. The supply system supplies the remainder.

There are four methods of calculating the desired power factor improvement: numerical, graphical, tables and curves.

As an example of the numerical method, assume the overall power factor of a group of 120-kw loads, calculated by the previous method, was found to be 80 percent (see Figure 10). The desired improved power factor dictated by the power factor rate schedule, however, is assumed to be 0.9.

If capacitors are used to improve the power factor to the 0.9 value, the magnetizing requirement furnished by the capacitors is calculated as follows:

kw = 120

$$kva = \frac{120}{0.9} = 133.3 \text{ kva (Formula 3)}$$

$$\text{Line kvar} = \sqrt{kva^2 - kw^2} =$$
$$\sqrt{133.3^2 - 120^2}$$
$$= \sqrt{17,768.89 - 14,400} =$$
$$\sqrt{3,368.89}$$
$$\cong 58 \text{ kvar} \qquad \text{(Formula 2)}$$

Since the load requirements are 90 kvar, and the line supplies 58 kvar, the capacitors must supply the difference, or 32 kvar. By installing 32 kvar of capacitors, the overall power factor is improved to 0.9 (90 percent) and the power bill is reduced. Also, 16.7 kva of transformer capacity has been made available for additional power needs. (150 kva − 133.3 kva = 16.7 kva.) The saving in power cost amortizes the cost of the installed capacitors in 9 to 10 months.

In fact, the calculating method previously described shows the influence of kvar on power factor improvement and how improved kva is

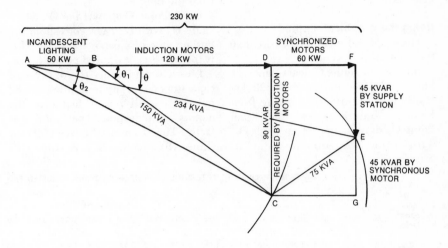

FIGURE 9   GRAPHICAL METHOD FOR DETERMINING COMBINED PF FOR GROUP OF LOADS

COSINE θ_1 =PF OF INDUCTION MOTORS=0.8

COSINE θ_2 =PF OF COMBINED LIGHTING AND INDUCTION MOTORS

COSINE θ =COMBINED PF OF LIGHTING, INDUCTION AND SYNCHRONOUS MOTORS=0.982

FIGURE 10   KVAR OF CAPACITORS REQUIRED TO IMPROVE A GIVEN PF TO A DESIRED VALUE

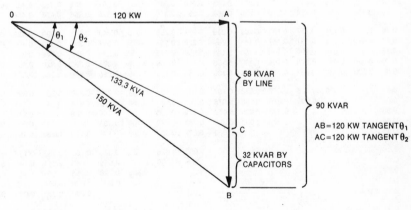

COSINE $\theta_1 = \dfrac{120 \text{ KW}}{150 \text{ KVA}} = 0.8 \text{ PF}$

COSINE $\theta_2 = \dfrac{120 \text{ KW}}{133.3 \text{ KVA}} = 0.9 \text{ PF}$

obtained by the right-triangle relationship and not by simple addition of kw and kvar. This method, however, is rather laborious for power factor calculations.

Using the graphical method

The graphical method is easier than the numerical method.

On a convenient scale draw a horizontal line representing 120 kw (Line, OA, Figure 10). Starting from Point A, draw a vertical line. From Point O, draw a line at an angle Θ_1, with Line OA, up to Point B.

Angle Θ_1 corresponds to Cosine Θ_1 = 0.8 or 80 percent. This is the existing overall power factor. Line AB represents the 90-kvar load requirement from the line.

From Point O draw Line OC at an angle Θ_2 with Line OA corresponding to the angle of Cosine Θ_2 = 0.9. This is the 90 percent desired power factor.

Line CB represents the 32 kvar of capacitors necessary to improve the 80 percent overall power factor of the motors to the desired 90 percent power factor. The difference between 90 kvar (Line AB) and the 32 kvar (Line CB)

supplied by the capacitors, or 58 kvar (Line AC), will be supplied by the line.

Handy table method

The easiest method is using tables that include a kw multiplier. The tables are convenient in finding out necessary capacitor or synchronous-motor kvar for a desired power factor improvement. Table 2 is based on the right-triangle relationship shown in Figure 10 as follows:

$$\text{Cosine } \Theta = \text{power factor} = \frac{kw}{kva}$$

(See Formula 3)

TABLE 2   KW MULTIPLIERS TO DETERMINE CAPACITOR KILOVARS REQUIRED FOR POWER-FACTOR CORRECTION

Original power factor	Corrected power factor																				
	0.80	0.81	0.82	0.83	0.84	0.85	0.86	0.87	0.88	0.89	0.90	0.91	0.92	0.93	0.94	0.95	0.96	0.97	0.98	0.99	1.0
0.50	0.982	1.008	1.034	1.060	1.086	1.112	1.139	1.165	1.192	1.220	1.248	1.276	1.306	1.337	1.369	1.403	1.440	1.481	1.529	1.589	1.732
0.51	0.937	0.962	0.989	1.015	1.041	1.067	1.094	1.120	1.147	1.175	1.203	1.231	1.261	1.292	1.324	1.358	1.395	1.436	1.484	1.544	1.687
0.52	0.893	0.919	0.945	0.971	0.997	1.023	1.050	1.076	1.103	1.131	1.159	1.187	1.217	1.248	1.280	1.314	1.351	1.392	1.440	1.500	1.643
0.53	0.850	0.876	0.902	0.928	0.954	0.980	1.007	1.033	1.060	1.088	1.116	1.144	1.174	1.205	1.237	1.271	1.308	1.349	1.397	1.457	1.600
0.54	0.809	0.835	0.861	0.887	0.913	0.939	0.966	0.992	1.019	1.047	1.075	1.103	1.133	1.164	1.196	1.230	1.267	1.308	1.356	1.416	1.559
0.55	0.769	0.795	0.821	0.847	0.873	0.899	0.926	0.952	0.979	1.007	1.035	1.063	1.093	1.124	1.156	1.190	1.227	1.268	1.316	1.376	1.519
0.56	0.730	0.756	0.782	0.808	0.834	0.860	0.887	0.913	0.940	0.963	0.996	1.024	1.054	1.085	1.117	1.151	1.188	1.229	1.277	1.337	1.480
0.57	0.692	0.718	0.744	0.770	0.796	0.822	0.849	0.875	0.902	0.930	0.958	0.986	1.016	1.047	1.079	1.113	1.150	1.191	1.239	1.299	1.442
0.58	0.655	0.681	0.707	0.733	0.759	0.785	0.812	0.838	0.865	0.893	0.921	0.949	0.979	1.010	1.042	1.076	1.113	1.154	1.202	1.262	1.405
0.59	0.619	0.645	0.671	0.697	0.723	0.749	0.776	0.802	0.829	0.857	0.885	0.913	0.943	0.974	1.006	1.040	1.077	1.118	1.166	1.226	1.369
0.60	0.583	0.609	0.635	0.661	0.687	0.713	0.740	0.766	0.793	0.821	0.849	0.877	0.907	0.938	0.970	1.004	1.041	1.082	1.130	1.190	1.333
0.61	0.549	0.575	0.601	0.627	0.653	0.679	0.706	0.732	0.759	0.787	0.815	0.843	0.873	0.904	0.936	0.970	1.007	1.048	1.096	1.156	1.299
0.62	0.516	0.542	0.568	0.594	0.620	0.646	0.673	0.699	0.726	0.754	0.782	0.810	0.840	0.871	0.903	0.937	0.974	1.015	1.063	1.123	1.266
0.63	0.483	0.509	0.535	0.561	0.587	0.613	0.640	0.666	0.693	0.721	0.749	0.777	0.807	0.838	0.870	0.904	0.941	0.982	1.030	1.090	1.233
0.64	0.451	0.474	0.503	0.529	0.555	0.581	0.608	0.634	0.661	0.689	0.717	0.745	0.775	0.806	0.838	0.872	0.909	0.950	0.998	1.068	1.201
0.65	0.419	0.445	0.471	0.497	0.523	0.549	0.576	0.602	0.629	0.657	0.685	0.713	0.743	0.774	0.806	0.840	0.877	0.918	0.966	1.026	1.169
0.66	0.388	0.414	0.440	0.466	0.492	0.518	0.545	0.571	0.598	0.626	0.654	0.682	0.712	0.743	0.775	0.809	0.846	0.887	0.935	0.995	1.138
0.67	0.358	0.384	0.410	0.436	0.462	0.488	0.515	0.541	0.568	0.596	0.624	0.652	0.682	0.713	0.745	0.779	0.816	0.857	0.905	0.965	1.108
0.68	0.328	0.354	0.380	0.406	0.432	0.458	0.485	0.511	0.538	0.566	0.594	0.622	0.652	0.683	0.715	0.749	0.786	0.827	0.875	0.935	1.078
0.69	0.299	0.325	0.351	0.377	0.403	0.429	0.456	0.482	0.509	0.537	0.565	0.593	0.623	0.654	0.686	0.720	0.757	0.798	0.846	0.906	1.049
0.70	0.270	0.296	0.322	0.348	0.374	0.400	0.427	0.453	0.480	0.508	0.536	0.564	0.594	0.625	0.657	0.691	0.728	0.769	0.817	0.877	1.020
0.71	0.242	0.268	0.294	0.320	0.346	0.372	0.399	0.425	0.452	0.480	0.508	0.536	0.566	0.597	0.629	0.663	0.700	0.741	0.789	0.849	0.992
0.72	0.214	0.240	0.266	0.292	0.318	0.344	0.371	0.397	0.424	0.452	0.480	0.508	0.538	0.569	0.601	0.635	0.672	0.713	0.761	0.821	0.964
0.73	0.186	0.212	0.238	0.264	0.290	0.316	0.343	0.369	0.396	0.424	0.452	0.480	0.510	0.541	0.573	0.607	0.644	0.685	0.733	0.793	0.936
0.74	0.159	0.185	0.211	0.237	0.263	0.289	0.316	0.342	0.369	0.397	0.425	0.453	0.483	0.514	0.546	0.580	0.617	0.658	0.706	0.766	0.909
0.75	0.132	0.158	0.184	0.210	0.236	0.262	0.289	0.315	0.342	0.370	0.398	0.426	0.456	0.487	0.519	0.553	0.590	0.631	0.679	0.739	0.882
0.76	0.105	0.131	0.157	0.183	0.209	0.235	0.262	0.288	0.315	0.343	0.371	0.399	0.429	0.460	0.492	0.526	0.563	0.604	0.652	0.712	0.855
0.77	0.079	0.105	0.131	0.157	0.183	0.209	0.236	0.262	0.289	0.317	0.345	0.373	0.403	0.434	0.466	0.500	0.537	0.578	0.626	0.685	0.829
0.78	0.052	0.078	0.104	0.130	0.156	0.182	0.209	0.235	0.262	0.290	0.318	0.346	0.376	0.407	0.439	0.473	0.510	0.551	0.599	0.659	0.802
0.79	0.026	0.052	0.078	0.104	0.130	0.156	0.183	0.209	0.236	0.264	0.292	0.320	0.350	0.381	0.413	0.447	0.484	0.525	0.573	0.633	0.776
0.80	0.000	0.026	0.052	0.078	0.104	0.130	0.157	0.183	0.210	0.238	0.266	0.294	0.324	0.355	0.387	0.421	0.458	0.499	0.547	0.609	0.750
0.81		0.000	0.026	0.052	0.078	0.104	0.131	0.157	0.184	0.212	0.240	0.268	0.298	0.329	0.361	0.395	0.432	0.473	0.521	0.581	0.724
0.82			0.000	0.026	0.052	0.078	0.105	0.131	0.158	0.186	0.214	0.242	0.272	0.303	0.335	0.369	0.406	0.447	0.495	0.555	0.698
0.83				0.000	0.026	0.052	0.079	0.105	0.132	0.160	0.188	0.216	0.246	0.277	0.309	0.343	0.380	0.421	0.469	0.529	0.672
0.84					0.000	0.026	0.053	0.079	0.106	0.134	0.162	0.190	0.220	0.251	0.283	0.317	0.354	0.395	0.443	0.503	0.646
0.85						0.000	0.027	0.053	0.080	0.108	0.136	0.164	0.194	0.225	0.257	0.291	0.328	0.369	0.417	0.477	0.620
0.86							0.000	0.026	0.053	0.081	0.109	0.137	0.167	0.198	0.230	0.264	0.301	0.342	0.390	0.450	0.593
0.87								0.000	0.027	0.055	0.083	0.111	0.141	0.172	0.204	0.238	0.275	0.316	0.364	0.424	0.567
0.88									0.000	0.028	0.056	0.084	0.114	0.145	0.177	0.211	0.248	0.289	0.337	0.397	0.540
0.89										0.000	0.028	0.056	0.086	0.117	0.149	0.183	0.220	0.261	0.309	0.369	0.512
0.90											0.000	0.028	0.058	0.089	0.121	0.155	0.192	0.233	0.281	0.341	0.484
0.91												0.000	0.030	0.061	0.093	0.127	0.164	0.205	0.253	0.313	0.456
0.92													0.000	0.031	0.063	0.097	0.134	0.175	0.223	0.283	0.426
0.93														0.000	0.032	0.066	0.103	0.144	0.192	0.252	0.395
0.94															0.000	0.034	0.071	0.112	0.160	0.220	0.363
0.95																0.000	0.037	0.079	0.126	0.186	0.329
0.96																	0.000	0.041	0.089	0.149	0.292
0.97																		0.000	0.048	0.108	0.251
0.98																			0.000	0.060	0.203
0.99																				0.000	0.143
1.0																					0.000

9. $\text{Tangent } \Theta = \dfrac{\text{kvar}}{\text{kw}}$

10. $\text{Sine } \Theta = \dfrac{\text{kvar}}{\text{kva}}$

Because the kw component is usually constant and kva and kvar change with the power factor, Formula 9 is the most convenient to use. This formula can be rewritten:

11. $\text{kvar} = \text{kw} \times \text{Tangent } \Theta$.

Based on Formula 11, the kvar at the original power factor Cosine Θ_1 and at the desired power factor Cosine Θ_2 are:

Kvar at original PF = kw × Tangent Θ_1

Kvar at desired PF = kw × Tangent Θ_2

The necessary capacitor rating for improving the power factor to the desired value is the difference of these two values, or

Capacitor kvar = kw × (Tangent Θ_1 − Tangent Θ_2)

This formula can be written simply as follows:

12. Capacitor kvar = kw × Δ Tangent

The required capacitor kvar rating for improving the power factor from Cosine Θ_1 to Cosine Θ_2 is based on a kw multiplier from Table 2. To obtain the required kvar, the constant kw of the system is multiplied by this factor.

By applying Table 2 to the previous numerical example in which a 120-kw load has an original 0.8 power factor and a desired power factor of 0.9, the kw multiplier from Table 2 is 0.266.

This number is found by locating 0.8 under "Original Power Factor." Read to the right until the number 0.90 is reached under "Corrected Power Factor." This number is 0.266.

Substituting this multiplier in Formula 12:

Capacitor kvar = 120 kw × 0.266 $\cong$ 32 kvar, which is the same as found by the numerical method.

Figure 11 shows a graph for determining the kvar of the capacitors to improve the power factor. To find the necessary kvar of the capacitors to raise the power factor from an initial value, Θ_1, to a final value, Θ_3, draw a horizontal line from the initial power factor value to the curve corresponding to the final value desired. From this point draw a vertical line to the horizontal axis. Read the multiplying factor for the kw load in order to obtain the necessary kvar for the capacitors.

For example, assume an initial

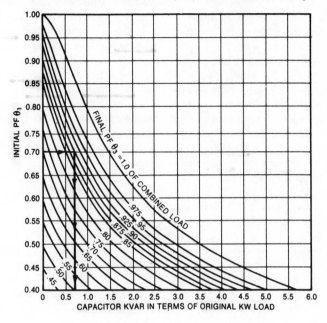

FIGURE 11   GRAPH FOR DETERMINING THE CAPACITOR KVAR, FOR IMPROVING INITIAL PF θ_1 TO FINAL DESIRED PF θ_3

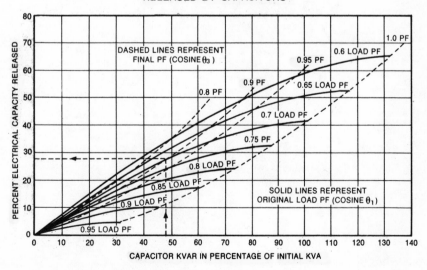

FIGURE 12   PERCENT OF ELECTRICAL SYSTEM CAPACITY RELEASED BY CAPACITORS

Source: *Independent Power Systems*, General Electric Co.

power factor of 0.7 for a 1,000-kw load. The desired power factor is 0.9. The multiplying factor determined by the graph method is 0.54. Therefore, the capacitor kvar required is 1,000 × 0.54 or 540 kvar.

Is it worth it?

There are many reasons for improving a plant's power factor by investing in capacitors:

• Generators are usually rated at 0.8 power factor. If the power factor is below 0.8, the kw output will be less than normal. The generator will not be able to carry the full-load line current because the lagging component of the poor power factor has a demagnetizing effect on the generator fields. This requires a large increase in the generator field current, which boils down to the fact that full-load kva cannot be carried at a low lagging power factor.

• Transmission and distribution lines carry a certain amount of current without overheating regardless of whether the current is active or reactive. The large reactive component at low power factor displaces the in-phase power current that could be doing useful work. Consequently there is a higher burden of line losses for each kw of useful power, or larger wires will be required for a given kw load at low power factor than would be required at high power factor.

• Voltage regulation of generators is impaired at low lagging power factors. Usually voltage regulation of an AC generator is about 25 percent at 1.0 PF and 40 percent at 0.8 PF.

• The extra current carried by feeders at a low power factor also has the disadvantage of a greater voltage drop than with high power factor loads.

• Capacitors or synchronous motors operating in a plant deliver kvar and furnish magnetizing current for motors and transformers. Less current is needed from the power supply. Less current means less kva or less load on transformers. This permits release of the system capacity.

Release in system capacity can be determined from Figure 12. Assuming a plant has a load of 1,000 kva at 70 percent power factor (Θ_1) and 480 kvar of capacitors are added, the system's capacity released is approximately 28.5 percent. This means the system can carry 28.5 percent more load at the same 70 percent power factor without exceeding the kva before the power factor was improved.

The final power factor (Θ_3) of the original load plus the additional load is approximately 90 percent.

• Power bills with power factor clauses are reduced, as shown by the example in section 2.1.

Once the importance of power factor improvement by capacitors and synchronous motors is understood and the required kvar for a desired power factor is calculated, where should the capacitors be installed to obtain their maximum benefit?

2.3 Plant Location of Capacitors and Synchronous Motors

Section 2.1 discussed power factor fundamentals and gave the formulas showing relationships between kilowatts, kilovars and power factor. Section 2.2 showed how to calculate combined power factor for group loads and the necessary kvar for a desired power factor improvement.

This section discusses the technical and economic aspects of capacitors and synchronous motors and where they should be located in the electrical power system to derive maximum benefits. (Figures, formulas and tables are consecutive.)

The engineer must consider several factors before deciding where to locate capacitors in an industrial plant. Variations in loads, load factor, load distribution, type of motors, constancy of load distribution, circuit layout, length of circuits, voltage condition— all influence capacitor location. Capacitors can be located to act as either a group correction or as a localized correction. (See Figure 13.)

A group correction can be made at the primary and secondary transformers or in the plant—e.g., at a main switchgear or motor control center bus. Group correction is necessary where loads shift radically between feeders and where motor voltages are low, such as 230 v.

In some cases the power flow from the main distribution center to various plant locations and to individual loads shifts frequently between feeders. In these cases it is necessary to make a correction in one part of the plant first and in another part later. It is more advantageous, however, to use a group capacitor located approximately the same distance from the loads at all times. This enables the operator to switch off portions of the centrally-located capacitors to meet specific varying load conditions.

If capacitors were connected at the individual motors, many diverse capacitors would be needed, resulting in greater cost. An exception arises where there are long feeders and where the gain from individual load application pays for the higher cost of the capacitors.

Where motor circuits are 230 v, at which voltage the cost of the capacitors is twice that of higher voltage units, it is more economical to use the group installation if it can be made on the primary 2,400-v or 4,160-v side. When capacitors are installed ahead of the main transformer bank, however, the transformer does not benefit from the use of capacitors, and no transformer kva is released. This is the reason for using 230-v capacitors, despite their higher cost, on feeders or near motors. Practical examples of group corrections are shown in the accompanying photos.

Localized corrections

Localized power factor correction can be made by placing capacitors on small feeders, on branch-motor circuits, or directly on motors or a group of motors and switched with the motors. To obtain the maximum benefits, capacitors should be connected as near as possible to the load or near the end of feeders. An accompanying photo shows a localized installation of capacitors switched with the motors through the motors' contactors.

When specifying equipment to improve power factor, the engineer should remember that the improvement takes place only from the point of application toward the source of power and not in the opposite direction.

Placing the capacitors at the loads reduces the losses in the circuits between the load and the metering point. The reduced losses can be determined by investigating the length of the circuits and transformations, the net gains in released transformer capacity, and loss reduction in transformers and circuits. Capacitors placed near loads can be reduced automatically as the loads drop off by switching them together with the loads.

Another advantage of placing capacitors near loads is a voltage increase. This results in better motor performance. The voltage increase, when compared to normal voltage, is practically constant from no load to full load of the feeder. The voltage at the point will rise or fall corresponding to the feeder voltage, but at a higher level. The voltage rise alone (maximum 4 to 5 percent) usually will not justify the cost of such improvement. It is, however, an attractive additional benefit.

Locating capacitors near motors

Capacitors frequently are installed across the induction motor terminals and switched as a unit with the motor. When connected in this manner, the amount of kvar should be limited to values that do not cause excessive voltage rise at the motor due to self-excitation when the breaker is opened. Tables 3 and 4 give the maximum recommended capacitor kvar for direct connection to the terminals of induction motors with normal starting torque (NEMA Design B) and with high starting torque (NEMA Design C).

When capacitors switched as a unit with the motors are located on the motor side of the overload relay, the line current actuating the relay will be lower in value than the motor current at all loads. When connecting capacitors in this manner, it is recommended that the size of the overload relay be based on the decreased value of line current. Hence, a smaller relay will be necessary. For example, the line current for full-load operation of the motor at the improved power factor is equal to:

Motor full-load current $\times \dfrac{\text{Cosine } \theta_1}{\text{Cosine } \theta_2}$

Where:

Cosine θ_1 = the motor full-load power factor

Cosine θ_2 = the corrected power factor.

The percent ampere reduction (AR) is equal to:

$$100 \left(1.0 - \frac{\text{Cosine } \theta_1}{\text{Cosine } \theta_2} \right)$$

The reduced motor-rated current can be calculated by using the Percent AR values in Tables 3 and 4.

When capacitors are divided into a number of banks and located on the feeders close to the motor, the voltage increase under no-load conditions will be smaller than if the capacitors would be located at one point on the main feeder. This means that it may not be necessary to switch the capacitors with the motors to avoid over-voltage at light load. In this case it would be better to distribute the capacitors on the smaller feeders branching out from the main source and keep them continuously connected.

Where to place synchronous motors

There is not as much freedom locating synchronous motors as there is capacitors. Synchronous motors usually have a larger hp rating than needed for economical operation at 240 or 480 v, the common utilization voltages in industrial plants. The same principle used in locating capacitors applies to synchronous motors— connect to the load bus whose power factor is to be improved.

Synchronous motors are available in standard ratings of 1.0 and 0.8 power factor. The 1.0-PF motor costs less. It also is more efficient for driving a given mechanical load and draws no lagging or leading current. The 0.8-PF motors operate at leading power factor. They are used to improve the overall power factor of the power line to which they are connected and to deliver rated-hp output.

With full excitation maintained while the motor operates at part load, the motor will operate at a more leading power factor. This provides more than the rated power factor improvement.

In the past, the synchronous motor has often been selected for "free" power-factor improvement where

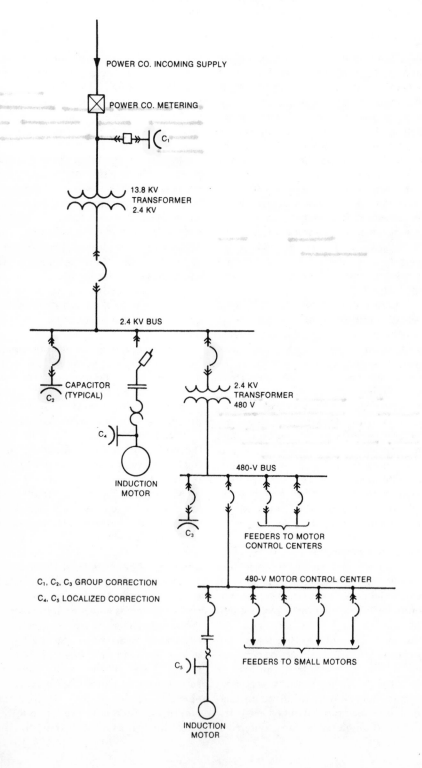

FIGURE 13   POSSIBLE LOCATIONS OF CAPACITORS IN INDUSTRIAL POWER PLANTS

POWER CO. INCOMING SUPPLY

POWER CO. METERING

C_1

13.8 KV TRANSFORMER 2.4 KV

2.4 KV BUS

CAPACITOR (TYPICAL) C_2

C_4

INDUCTION MOTOR

2.4 KV TRANSFORMER 480 V

480-V BUS

C_3

FEEDERS TO MOTOR CONTROL CENTERS

480-V MOTOR CONTROL CENTER

C_5

FEEDERS TO SMALL MOTORS

INDUCTION MOTOR

C_1, C_2, C_3 GROUP CORRECTION

C_4, C_5 LOCALIZED CORRECTION

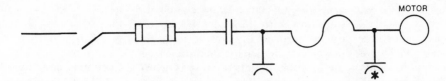

*If the capacitor is located on the motor side of the overload relay, a smaller relay may be necessary, since line current is reduced. This arrangement has the advantage of reduced fault current at the capacitor terminals due to the impedance of the overload relay.

TABLE 3 230-, 460-, AND 575-V MOTORS. OPEN—DRIP-PROOF TYPE K (NEMA DESIGN "B") NORMAL STARTING TORQUE AND CURRENT

Induction motor hp rating	Nominal motor speed in rpm and number of poles											
	3,600 2		1,800 4		1,200 6		900 8		720 10		600 12	
	kvar	% AR	kvar	% AR	kvar	% AR	kvar	% AR	kvar	% AR	kvar	% AR
2	1	14	1	24	1	28	2	42	—	—	3	50
3	1	14	2	24	2	28	4	42	3	40	4	49
5	2	14	2	21	3	26	4	31	4	40	5	49
7½	2	14	4	21	4	21	4	26	7.5	40	10	49
10	4	14	4	17	5	21	5	26	7.5	36	10	41
15	5	12	5	17	5	19	10	26	7.5	31	10	34
20	5	11	7.5	17	7.5	19	10	23	10	29	15	34
25	7.5	11	7.5	17	7.5	19	10	23	10	24	20	34
30	7.5	10	7.5	17	10	19	15	23	15	24	25	32
40	7.5	10	15	17	15	19	20	23	20	24	30	32
50	10	10	20	17	20	19	25	23	20	24	35	32
60	10	10	20	17	30	19	30	23	30	22	45	32
75	15	10	25	14	30	16	30	17	35	21	40	19
100	15	10	30	14	30	12	35	16	40	15	45	17
125	30	10	35	12	30	12	50	16	45	15	50	17
150	30	10	35	11	35	12	50	14	50	13	60	17
200	35	10	50	11	55	12	70	14	70	13	90	17
250	35	10	55	9	70	12	85	14	90	13	100	17
300	35	10	65	9	75	12	95	14	100	13	110	17
350	40	10	80	9	85	12	125	14	120	13	150	17
400	100	10	80	8	100	12	140	14	150	13	150	17
450	100	9	90	8	140	12	150	13	150	13	175	17
500	100	8	115	8	150	12	150	12	175	13	175	17

TABLE 4 230-, 460-, 575-V MOTORS, OPEN—DRIP-PROOF, TYPE KG (NEMA DESIGN "C") HIGH STARTING TORQUE AND NORMAL STARTING CURRENT

Induction motor hp rating	Nominal motor speed in rpm and number of poles											
	1,800 4		12,000 6		900 8		720 10		600 12	
	kvar	% AR	kvar	% AR	kvar	% AR	kvar	% AR	kvar	% AR
3	—	—	2	28	4	42	—	—	—	—
5	2	21	3	26	4	32	—	—	—	—
7.5	4	21	4	22	4	29	—	—	—	—
10	4	17	5	22	5	29	—	—	—	—
15	5	17	7.5	22	10	29	—	—	20	40
20	5	17	7.5	21	10	25	—	—	—	—
25	7.5	17	7.5	21	10	23	—	—	30	40
30	7.5	17	10	21	15	23	20	28	35	39
40	10	17	15	21	20	23	—	—	45	39
50	20	17	15	21	25	23	30	28	—	—
60	20	15	30	21	30	23	35	28	—	—
75	25	14	30	17	40	23	45	28	—	—
100	30	13	30	14	50	23	40	15	45	17
125	35	12	40	14	50	16	45	15	50	17
150	35	10	45	13	50	14	50	13	60	17
200	50	10	55	11	70	14	70	13	90	17

Source: GE Bulletin, 'How to Select Capacitors Rating for Induction Motors,' 6063-02, 1974.

power factor was the most important consideration. In these cases, however, it may be more economical to install an induction motor and capacitors. Installed cost is the main factor in deciding between a synchronous motor and an induction motor with capacitors. Sometimes the type of drive and the required characteristics of the motor dictates the selection.

Synchronous motors supply smoothly varying values of kvar, and the kvar output can be changed by adjusting the field rheostat. So far as losses are concerned, the two methods are almost equal. One disadvantage of the synchronous motor, however, is that is must be in operation to produce kvar. Using the induction motor and

capacitor combination, it is not necessary to connect and switch the capacitors with the motor. Capacitors can be permanently connected to the power system. This is important from the loss standpoint, because synchronous motors may be operated only to produce kvar. Synchronous motors cost more to maintain—because of their exciters and more complicated control—than the induction motor/capacitor combination.

The synchronous motor equipment is less costly for 2.3- or 4-kv service than the induction-motor equipment, considering the entire hp and speed ranges. This is assuming that a power circuit breaker is used for switching the capacitors. The induction-motor

arrangement becomes less expensive, however, if the capacitors can be located on the 460- or 575-v systems to give full benefits.

Economic considerations

Although maximum overall operating benefits are obtained by connecting capacitors directly at the loads, it is not always practical or economical to do so. In some applications, it is more economical to take advantage of load diversity and to locate the capacitors farther back on the system to obtain the greatest return on capacitor investment.

Industrial plants usually have a number of small loads. Since capacitors are manufactured in standard sizes, it is impractical to use the correct size capacitor at each load. Also, all these small loads are not on all the time. Because of this diversity it is more advantageous to install a single capacitor at a central location, which may be the main bus of a switchgear or motor control center.

In most processing plants only 60 percent of the total connected motor load is operating at the same time—40 percent is standby. This means a group capacitor located at the main bus would have to be only 60 percent of the total kvar necessary for capacitors located at individual loads.

The system operating voltage also has an influence on the economics of capacitor location. This is because 230-v capacitors cost approximately twice as much as 460- or 575-v capacitors. An economic comparison also should include the capacitor's switching device. The higher the voltage, the more expensive the switching device. For example, although 2.4-kv or 4.16-kv capacitors are the most economical (nearly half the price of 460-v capacitors), the proper switching device costs more than the 460- or 575-v switching devices.

A careful analysis of all technical and economical aspects—including local utility-rate schedules, released kva, reduced losses, voltage improvement, prices of power factor corrective devices based on the previous consideration—will dictate the best selection and location of power factor improvement methods.

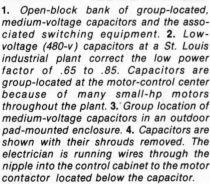

1. *Open-block bank of group-located, medium-voltage capacitors and the associated switching equipment.* 2. *Low-voltage (480-v) capacitors at a St. Louis industrial plant correct the low power factor of .65 to .85. Capacitors are group-located at the motor-control center because of many small-hp motors throughout the plant.* 3. *Group location of medium-voltage capacitors in an outdoor pad-mounted enclosure.* 4. *Capacitors are shown with their shrouds removed. The electrician is running wires through the nipple into the control cabinet to the motor contactor located below the capacitor.*

2.4 Variables Influencing the Economic Analysis of Power Factor Improvement

Section 2.3 of PF Improvement discussed the technical and economic considerations for properly locating capacitors and synchronous motors in industrial plants. This section discusses the different economic aspects of power factor improvement. The question of how much power factor correction is justified calls forth different answers depending on the nature and content of each plant.

Such factors as the original power factor, loads suited for synchronous motor drive, hours of operation each month, load factor, distribution voltage and purchased or generated power may influence the amount of power factor improvement. A rough rule of thumb is to improve power factor to .90-.95.

(Figures, formulas and tables are numbered consecutively.)

When power is purchased the question of whether power factor correction pays generally depends on the utility's rate structure.

In the first section (2.1) a numerical example showed how to determine the amount and cost of capacitors needed for a desired power factor correction and the rate of return using the power company's utility-rate schedule. In that example, the savings in electric power costs paid for the capacitors in less than nine months. Since every utility, according to its location and price policy, has different rate schedules and different power factor penalties, each plant must be treated individually.

The rate of return on a capacitor investment depends not only on the utility's rate structure but also on the utility's method of measuring power factor. The same rate structure may be used for all cases, but the method of measuring the power factor can be different in each case. The type of rate clause may be based on the power factor measured at the time of maximum kw demand or during normal load periods. In other cases, the utility might use the average monthly power factor.

Sometimes the utility's rate structure is independent of power factor. In these cases, no rate of return on capacitor investment can be determined from the utility's billing. More often, however, rates are affected by the billing demand and, therefore, by power factor. Utilities using power factor clauses adjust the kw demand for billing purposes by multiplying the measured demand by the ratio of an imposed power factor to the actual power factor of the plant:

Billing demand = measured kw demand (imposed PF ÷ actual PF of plant)

The accompanying photos show three examples of how capacitors can save money where the utility rates include penalty charges for low power factor.

Synchronous motors or capacitors?

If loads are required that might be driven by synchronous motors, the improvement in power factor and reduction in demand charge could be calculated for both a unity power factor and a .8 leading PF motor. The monthly saving compares to the cost of a synchronous motor and a comparable induction motor with the proper capacitors and respective switching equipment.

Some industrial plants use their own generating facilities. The generating equipment's capacity is generally based on .8 lagging PF. If the plant power factor drops below .8, it is usually advisable to take corrective steps to prevent unnecessary voltage drops in feeders, excessive RI^2 losses, and reduced generating plant capacity and efficiency. Corrections above .95 PF, however, are seldom justified, because the amount of capacitor correction increases very rapidly after .95 PF is reached. This makes improvement in distribution losses, voltage regulation and generating capacity for such a correction uneconomical.

If the plant load consists mainly of groups of small motors, capacitors are the most economical type of correction. If a very large load operates continuously, synchronous motors with 1 or .8 leading PF should be considered. Large compressors or pumps usually can be advantageously driven by synchronous motors. Synchronous motors with less than .8 leading PF are seldom justified because power factors of 1 and .8 are standard. At leading power factors lower than .8, motor efficiency drops off rapidly and the exciter sizes become large and uneconomical. Rather than use a synchronous motor with a leading power factor less than .8, the combination of a .8 leading PF motor plus capacitors may be more economical.

Synchronous motors deliver an increasing amount of kvar as line voltage drops, raising the power factor and voltage. The synchronous motor, therefore, has the advantage of acting as a voltage regulator as well as a power factor controller.

Synchronous condensers

The use of synchronous condensers is rarely justified in industrial plants. There is not much cost difference between synchronous condensers and capacitors up to ratings of several thousand kva. The higher losses of synchronous condensers also make them undesirable on the basis of power factor correction alone. Synchronous condensers are better for voltage regulation because they can be better controlled than capacitors.

The economic effect of power factor is most significant in power cost reduction, released capacity, loss reduction and voltage improvement.

The most economical value at which power factor should be improved is established by comparing the anticipated power bill reduction to the installed cost of capacitors, which is approximately $10 to $15/kvar for 480-v and 600-v systems, $20 to $30/kvar for 240-v systems and $5 to $10/kvar for 2,400-v to 13,800-v systems.

Table 2 in section 2.2 showed the kw multipliers to determine capacitor kvar required for a desired power factor improvement. As an example, assume a plant has 1,000 kw and 1,300 kva demand and a power contract calling for an energy charge based on kwh and a demand charge based on kva. Except for the loss reduction a higher power factor will produce, the energy will be unaffected by power factor. The kva demand, however, can be reduced if the power factor is improved. The demand charge imposed by the utility is assumed to be $1/kva/month. The amount of capacitor kvar to be added is determined by checking the saving that can be realized by improving the power factor. Usually .95 is an economical power factor. The present power factor is:

$$PF = \frac{kw}{kva} = \frac{1.000}{1.300} = .77$$

Referring to Table 2, the multiplier required for .77 to .95 is .5. It follows that the kva required is .5 × 1,000 kw = 500 kvar of capacitors. The installed cost of 500 kvar of capacitors for a

1. *This installation of a 90-kvar bank of capacitors is in a machine shop and welding plant with utility service at 240 v, 60 Hz, 3-phase. The 90-kvar capacitor bank cost $1,510 (plus installation.) The average reduction in power costs is $130 every month or $1,560 yearly. This means the capacitor cost is recovered in less than 12 months.* **2.** *The capacitor installation here is for a black-top and gravel plant with 480-v, 60-Hz, 3-phase service. The 320 kvar was installed at cost of $2,245 (plus installation). The average electricity bill reduction is $285 every month or $3,420 yearly. Recovery is accomplished in less than eight months.* **3.** *These pole-mounted capacitors with fuse cutouts are used by a manufacturer of large blowers. Service is 14.4 kv, 60 Hz, 3-phase and the 150 kvar was installed at a cost of $675 (plus installation). The average monthly electric bill reduction is $172.91 or $2,073 yearly. A recovery in less than 4 months. (All photos courtesy of Federal Pacific Electric Co.)*

480-v system is estimated at 500 kvar × $10 = $5,000.

This means the new kva demand is:

$$kva = \frac{kw}{PF} = \frac{1.000}{.95} = 1.053 \text{ kva}$$

The saving in demand charge is:
(1,300 kva − 1,053 kva) × $1 = $247/month, or $2,964/year

The cost of the 500 kvar of capacitors is amortized in 20 months.

Releasing existing-system capacity

System capacity can be released by power factor improvement, because the higher the power factor the lower the kva for any given kw load. Adding capacitors to an existing system is the cheapest way to obtain the system capacity necessary to serve additional loads. The amount of power factor correction justified for releasing capacity depends on the cost of additional system equipment per kw or kva compared to the cost of capacitors per kvar.

Use Figure 14 to determine the amount of additional system capacity obtained after a certain power factor correction. Locate the intersection of the original power factor and additional system capacity desired and then read at the bottom the corrected power factor required. Use Table 5 to find how many kvar of capacitors are required per kva of released capacity.

To determine if power factor correction is the most economical means of additional capacity, compare the cost of the capacitors required to the cost of the substation and distribution equipment needed to increase system capacity by the same amount. For example, a fully loaded system operates at .75 power factor and requires an additional capacity to serve 20 percent more load. Figure 14 shows that 20 percent released capacity can be obtained by correcting the present load to .93 power factor. Table 5 shows that 1.797 kvar of capacitors are required per kva of released capacity. If the estimated cost of installed capacitors is $10/kvar, the released capacity obtained from correcting the power factor to .93 will cost approximately $18/kva.

To determine if this is the most economical means of obtaining additional capacity, the $18/kva should be compared to the cost per kva of alternate means of obtaining the same additional capacity.

Releasing new-system capacity

A new industrial power distribution

FIGURE 14   ADDITIONAL SYSTEM CAPACITY AFTER PF CORRECTION

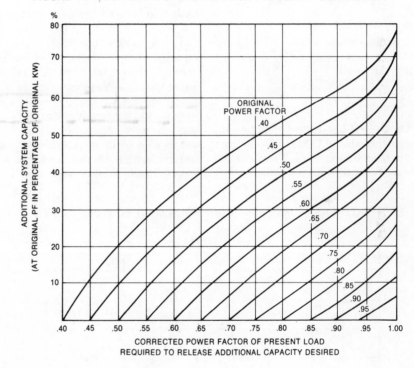

TABLE 5   KVAR/KVA OF RELEASED CAPACITY
Final PF of original load

Original PF	.90	.91	.92	.93	.94	.95	.96	.97	.98	.99	1.00
.95							3.374	3.587	3.873	4.314	5.947
.94						3.058	3.210	3.397	3.644	3.816	5.366
.93					2.824	2.934	3.110	3.233	3.451	3.779	4.909
.92				2.633	2.723	2.825	2.946	3.094	3.287	3.575	4.541
.91			2.487	2.553	2.635	2.727	2.835	2.968	3.143	3.395	4.229
.90		2.346	2.407	2.479	2.553	2.638	2.739	2.858	3.011	3.240	3.970
.89	2.243	2.296	2.332	2.413	2.475	2.558	2.649	2.757	2.896	3.100	3.742
.88	2.195	2.241	2.293	2.350	2.413	2.484	2.566	2.665	2.792	2.974	3.543
.85	2.053	2.098	2.140	2.186	2.238	2.293	2.354	2.431	2.524	2.661	3.068
.80	1.878	1.909	1.939	1.969	2.002	2.041	2.083	2.133	2.196	2.283	2.528
.75	1.735	1.753	1.775	**1.797**	1.820	1.846	1.876	1.910	1.952	2.008	2.164

system is most economical when the necessary power factor correction is considered in the design. The most economical power factor can be calculated by the formula:

$$PF = \sqrt{1 - \left(\frac{C}{S}\right)^2}$$

Where: C = cost of capacitors per kvar; S = cost of system equipment per kva.

This formula is plotted in Figure 15.

As an example, assume a new power distribution system is designed to serve a 1,300 kva-load at .7 power factor. The system requires a 1,500-kva load-center substation that costs about $60,000. The cost of the system is:

$$\frac{\$60,000}{1,300 \text{ kva}} \text{ or } S = \$46/\text{kva}.$$

Assume the distribution system has a nominal voltage of 480 v. The cost of the capacitors can be estimated at $10/kvar, or

$$\frac{C}{S} = \frac{10}{46} = .217$$

On the left-hand scale of Figure 15, locate the value of C/S = .217 and trace a horizontal line until it crosses the curve. From this point draw a vertical line down to the power factor line and find the *most* economical power factor which is .98. Since this is above the usually economical .95 limit, reduce the correction from .7 to .91, which will reduce the load to 1,000 kva:

$$\frac{1,300 \text{ kva} \times .7 \text{ original PF}}{.91 \text{ improved PF}} = 1,000 \text{ kva}$$

This means a smaller rated standard load-center substation of 1,000 kva instead of 1,500 kva can be used to serve the ultimate 910-kw load (PF × kva = .7 × 1,300 kva = 910 kw) at an improved power factor of .91. If the load grows, additional capacitors can be installed later to keep in step with the load growth.

Reducing loss and raising voltage

The return from loss reduction alone may not justify the installation of capacitors but it may be an additional benefit along with power factor improvement. The power distribution losses in kw = RI² vary approximately from 2.5 to 7.5 percent of the load kwh depending on the hours of full-load and no-load plant operation, wire sizes and the length of main-and branch-feeder circuits. Losses are proportional to the square of the current and, as the current is reduced, in direct proportion to the power factor improvement. It follows that the losses are inversely proportional to the square of the power factor. The formula used to calculate the power loss reduction is:

$$\text{kw losses} = \frac{(\text{original PF})^2}{(\text{improved PF})^2}$$

and

$$\text{loss reduction} = 1 - \frac{(\text{original PF})^2}{(\text{improved PF})^2}$$

Capacitors also raise voltage level, but it is seldom economical to use them in industrial power systems only for this reason. Voltage improvement by capacitors is another side benefit.

The approximate equation used to calculate the voltage drop in an electrical circuit is:

$$e = RI \cos\theta + XI \sin\theta$$

Which can be written:

e = R (kw current) + X (kvar current)

This expression shows that kvar current operates on reactance, and since capacitors reduce kvar current they also reduce voltage drop by a value equal to the capacitor current multiplied by the reactance. The voltage rise caused by capacitors in a modern distribution system with "only on" transformation is not too great and does not exceed 4 percent.

The most economical way to use capacitors to improve voltage is in plant distribution circuits with high reactances and low system voltage, such as 240 v, and long runs of open wires with large spacing between phase wires. In 480- or 600-v distribution systems the voltage improvement is small.

All these economic considerations show how many variables and possible advantages must be weighed in making a study and reaching a final decision regarding power factor correction in any one plant. The sound knowledge of the basic fundamentals discussed will be of value to the engineer who makes the final economical analysis.

FIGURE 15   CURVE FOR DETERMINING MOST ECONOMICAL PF

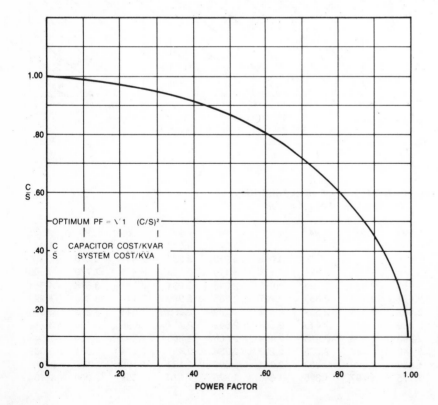

OPTIMUM PF = √1 (C/S)²
C   CAPACITOR COST/KVAR
S   SYSTEM COST/KVA

POWER FACTOR

2.5 Shapes, Sizes, and Forms of Capacitors; Their Application and Specification

Section 2.4 covered the economic aspects of power factor improvement. This section discusses types of capacitors designed to meet various conditions and code requirements.

(Figures, formulas, and tables are numbered consecutively.)

Capacitors are manufactured for different voltages and types of enclosures and for indoor or outdoor use. Low-voltage exposed-bushing capacitor units are suitable for indoor or outdoor applications on 240-, 480- or 600-v systems. Medium-voltage exposed-bushing capacitor units are suitable for indoor or outdoor application and for voltages ranging from 2,400 v to 14,400 v.

2.4 kv and above units can be connected in series, to equal the line-to-neutral voltage of the circuit. The minimum number of series sections is usually the best.

Dust-proof units are designed to meet the requirements of Class 2 (Div. 2) and Class 3 locations as defined in Article 500 of the National Electrical Code.

Weatherproof units are designed for use in the Class 2 (Divs. 1 and 2) and Class 3 locations. Dust-proof capacitors have a cover for the bushing terminals and fuses and knockouts for cable entrances. "Live" parts of a weatherproof capacitor are completely enclosed in a heavy-gage steel terminal compartment bolted to the top of the unit. A neoprene rubber gasket seals

the joint of the terminal box and the top of the capacitor case. The cover is pulled tightly over the gasket by trunk-style latches that can be padlocked. Conduit can be connected to the terminal compartment by weatherproof pipe nipples.

A bank of capacitor units should be supported by rugged structural members to permit individual unit replacement without disturbing adjacent units (see accompanying photo). Solderless ground terminals are provided inside the bus compartment for cable grounding and on the base of the side sheet for connection to system ground. Solderless connectors make it easier to connect to the line. Capacitor units are individually grounded to the frame through their mounting bolts.

For all capacitors, the maximum and minimum allowable ambient temperatures are:

- Single-tier equipment—maximum 115 F (46 C)
- Multitier equipment—maximum 104 F (40 C)
- Minimum energizing temperature is −40 F (−40 C).

Table 6 lists the standard ratings for individual capacitor units. Some manufacturers have additional ratings, usually in unit sizes from 1 to 10 kvar for small-motor applications. Capacitor equipment assemblies are manufactured in multiples of individual capacitor units.

Table 6 shows that the standard capacitor voltages correspond to the system's operating voltages. This is because the actual plant operating voltage is less than the supply voltage by the amount of voltage drop from the supply point to the load. For example, in a nominal 480-v system, motors are rated 460 v. Generally, the low voltage in industrial plants, under normal load

conditions, operates at about 460 v, corresponding to the capacitor-rated voltage for that service. This means the capacitor operates at or near rated voltage and output, which contributes to the unit's long life.

Capacitors are designed to operate at comparatively high electrical stresses and continuous full load; so definite overvoltage limits must be allowed. Consequently, capacitors are manufactured for operation at a terminal-to-terminal voltage, including harmonics, at a maximum 110 percent of rated voltage for continuous or short-time operation, exclusive of transients.

Industry standards include a 35 percent kvar margin. This allows for increased output even when operating above the manufacturer's rated voltage, harmonic currents and kvar tolerances.

Fuses are the most economical means of protecting the capacitor bank from possible consequences of a capacitor unit failure. Proper fuse selection should be based on the following considerations:

- Service continuity
- Personnel safety
- Minimum loss of capacitor kvars
- Switching transients
- Visual indication for locating the failed unit.

Factory-assembled capacitor equipment is furnished with individual capacitor-unit fuses based on the foregoing considerations. The specific type of fuse depends on equipment design and connection.

High-interrupting current-limiting fuses have been developed for use with capacitors. Two fuses are used for each 3-phase capacitor unit. Each fuse is equipped with a pop-up button to indicate a blown fuse. The interrupting capacity of these fuses is in the order of 200,000 amp. The current-limiting action assures fuse operation in systems with high short-circuit currents.

Open-rack, bus-mounted expulsion fuses with high interrupting capacity usually are used for outdoor installations. (Individual capacitor-unit fusing is usually not economical for medium-voltage pole-top equipment.) The units in each phase are group-protected by a fuse in each of the line connections. Factory-assembled equipment normally is furnished without fuses. Users prefer to select the type and rating of fuses adequate for the particular installation. The continuous current rating of the fuse is approximately 1.65 times the rated bank current, especially for grounded-wye switched banks.

What the NEC says

NEC Article 460 gives the requirements for capacitor installations. These requirements refer to means and time of discharging capacitors, conductor rating, overcurrent protection, disconnecting means, grounding, mechanical considerations and capacitor rating for capacitors switched as a unit with the motor.

For capacitors rated 600 v and less, the residual voltage must be reduced to 50 v or less within one minute after disconnecting the capacitor from the source of supply. For capacitors rated above 600 v, the reduction to 50 v may occur in five minutes or less. The discharge circuit may be permanently connected to the capacitor bank terminals, or it may be provided with automatic means of connection to the terminals of the capacitor bank on voltage removal from the line.

The NEC states that the power factor correction for motor circuits switched as a unit with capacitors "shall not exceed the value required to raise the no-load power factor of the motor to unity." The code also says,

TABLE 6   STANDARD RATINGS FOR 60-CYCLE SHUNT CAPACITOR UNITS*

kvar ratings

Capacitor rated voltage	Indoor enclosed units	Indoor or Outdoor nonenclosed units	Outdoor units	Phase
230	.5, 1, 2.5, 5, 7.5, 10, 15	2.5, 5, 7.5, 10, 15	5, 7.5, 10, 15	1 and 3
460	1, 2, 5, 7.5, 10, 15, 20, 25.	5, 7.5, 10, 15, 20, 25	7.5, 10, 15, 20, 25	1 and 3
575	1, 2, 5, 7, 10, 15, 20, 25	5, 7.5, 10, 15, 20, 25	7.5, 10, 15, 25	1 and 3
2,400	—	—	25, 50, 100	1
4,160	—	—	25, 50, 100	1
4,800	—	—	25, 50, 100	1
7,200	—	—	25, 50, 100	1
13,200	—	—	50, 100	1
13,800	—	—	50, 100	1
14,400	—	—	50, 100	1

*Includes some ratings not listed by National Electrical Manufacturers Assn.
Table courtesy General Electric Co.

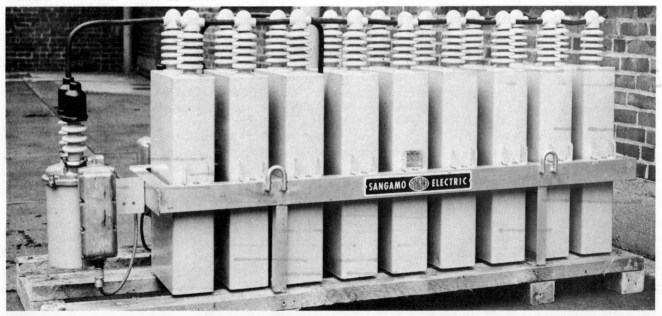

This bank of medium-voltage exposed-bushing capacitor units is supported by heavy-duty structural members. This permits the individual units to be replaced without disturbing other units.

"The ampacity of capacitor circuit conductors shall not be less than 135 percent of the rated current of the capacitor" or the capacitor bank. In addition, the "ampacity of conductors that connect a capacitor to the terminals of a motor or to motor circuits shall not be less than ⅓ the ampacity of the motor circuit conductors and in no case less than 135 percent of the rated current of the capacitor."

According to the code, overcurrent protection devices must be provided in each ungrounded conductor for each capacitor bank.

Since power capacitors for industrial service are designed to be used in a maximum ambient temperature of 115 to 140 F (40 to 45 C), the cables and disconnecting devices should be selected for these conditions. The specifying engineer must give even more attention to selecting cable sizes for capacitors than for the usual distribution feeders because the load factor of an energized capacitor is 100 percent.

In low-voltage circuits (600 v and below), air circuit breakers or fused

TABLE 7   GUIDE FOR SELECTION OF CABLE, CONDUIT AND SWITCHING DEVICES

| Capacitor Rating | | Minimum cable and conduit sizes | | Switching devices—minimum current ratings | | | | |
| | | | | Safety switch | | Contactor | Molded-case ACB | Magnetic AC |
kvar	amps	AWG or MCM	Conduit in.	Rating amps	Fuse amps	NEMA size	Trip-rating amps	Trip-rating amps
				240-v, 3-PHASE SERVICE				
5	12.0	10	¾	30	20	2	20	20
7.5	18.0	8	¾	30	30	2	30	30
10	24.1	8	¾	60	40	2	40	40
15	36.1	6	1	60	60	3	70	50
30	72.2	2	1¼	200	125	4	125	100
60	144	4/0	2½	400	250	5	225	200
90	217	500	3	400	400	6	350	300
120	289	(2) 4/0	(2) 2½	600	500	6	500	400
180	433	(2) 500	(2) 3	800	800	7	700	600
270	650	(3) 500	(3) 3	1,200	1,200	8	—	1,000
				480-v, 3-PHASE SERVICE				
5	6.01	12	½	30	15	2	15	15
7.5	9.02	12	½	30	15	2	15	15
10	12.0	10	¾	30	20	2	20	20
15	18.0	8	¾	30	30	2	30	30
20	24.0	8	¾	60	50	2	40	40
25	30.1	8	¾	60	50	3	70	50
40	48.1	3	1¼	100	90	3	90	70
50	60.1	2	1¼	200	125	4	100	90
80	96.2	1/0	2	200	175	4	150	150
120	144	4/0	2½	400	250	5	225	200
160	192	350	3	400	350	5	300	300
240	289	(2) 4/0	(2) 2½	600	500	6	450	400
360	433	(2) 500	(2) 3	800	800	7	700	600
				600-v, 3-PHASE SERVICE				
5	4.81	14	½	30	10	2	15	15
10	9.62	12	½	30	20	2	15	15
15	14.4	10	¾	30	25	2	30	20
20	19.2	8	¾	60	35	2	30	30
25	24.1	8	¾	60	40	2	40	40
40	38.5	6	1	100	70	3	70	50
50	48.1	4	1¼	100	80	3	90	70
80	77.0	1	1½	200	150	4	125	125
120	115	3/0	2	200	200	5	175	175
160	154	250	2½	400	300	5	250	225
240	231	500	3	600	450	6	350	350
360	347	(2) 350	(2) 3	600	600	6	550	500

Notes:
1. Cable and conduit sizes are based upon three single-conductor, 600-v cables, (Type RH, RH-RW, RHW rubber and THW, THWH thermoplastic insulation) for each conduit.
2. The switching device should be selected for the fault duty of the system on which it will operate.
3. For kvar ratings in excess of table, consult manufacturer.
Table courtesy Federal Pacific Electric Co.

safety switches are specified for manual switching, and air circuit breakers or contactors for electrical switching of capacitors. In medium-voltage circuits (2,400 to 13,800 v), power circuit breakers are almost always specified. Switching devices used with capacitors must have a current rating in excess of the rated capacitor current to provide for overcurrent because of overvoltage at fundamental frequency and harmonic currents.

Disconnecting the bank

Disconnecting means have to be provided for each capacitor bank. The continuous ampacity of the disconnecting device cannot be less than 135 percent of the rated capacitor-bank current. The disconnecting means must have a short-circuit interrupting-capacity rating adequate for the system to which it is connected.

The National Electrical Manufacturers Assn.'s standards require fusible safety switches to have a current rating not less than 165 percent of the rated capacitor current. Contactors and low-voltage-power circuit breakers also must have a current rating not less

than 135 percent of the rated capacitor current. Molded-case circuit breakers, however, require a minimum continuous rating of 187 percent of rated capacitor current. Enclosed contactors require a rating 150 percent of the rated capacitor current.

The setting of the overcurrent device for motors switched as a unit with the capacitor connected on the load side of the overcurrent device is given in Tables 3 and 4 of section 2.3. The tables permit proper selection or setting of the overload relay based on a decreased value of line current, reduced by the % AR value in the tables.

Capacitor cases and enclosures have to be grounded in accordance with NEC Article 250. Table 7 shows the selection of cable, conduit and switching devices for 240-, 480- and 600-v, 3-phase capacitors based on the NEC requirements. Table 8 shows the kvar multiplying factors used to obtain the ampere rating for 3-phase capacitor-switching devices, which also must be selected to withstand the fault duty of the system to which they are connected.

TABLE 8   APPROXIMATE CAPACITOR KVAR MULTIPLIERS TO OBTAIN
AMPERE RATING OF SWITCHING DEVICE (3-PHASE SERVICE)
(Enclosed rating and 40 C (104 F) ambient temperature)

Type of switching device	Nominal system voltage		
	230	460	575
Magnetic-type circuit breakers	3.38	1.69	1.35
Contactors	3.76	1.88	1.5
Safety switches	4.14	2.07	1.65
Molded-case circuit breakers (maximum)	4.68	2.34	1.87

Table courtesy General Electric Co.

2.6 Variable Power Factor Adjustment by Static Switches

Section 2.5 of P.F. Improvement discussed the economic aspects of power factor improvement. This section explains how solid-state technology has led to new concepts for variable kvar supply.

Shunt capacitors, rotating synchronous condensers and synchronous motors are used to supply the kvar necessary for a desired power factor improvement. Each of these devices has its advantages, disadvantages and limitations.

Synchronous motors can be made to operate at either leading or lagging power factors by varying the field currents. Also they can draw leading or lagging currents, in addition to the load currents. Synchronous motors, in addition to performing useful work, also vary the power factor of the system on which they operate.

A rotating synchronous condenser is a synchronous motor used primarily for power factor correction or voltage regulation. On large power systems these machines are essential to regulate the voltage at the receiving stations.

At times of heavy load, the synchronous condensers are over-excited and draw leading current over the lines. This holds the receiver voltage or supplies a part or all of the lagging current required for the load. At times of light load, the synchronous condensers are under-excited and draw lagging currents from the lines. This combines with the lagging currents required by the reduced load and holds the receiver voltage down to its normal value.

Synchronous condensers are usually operated without mechanical loads. Their use for power factor correction in industrial plants is limited because of their high cost, size, losses and maintenance.

Synchronous motors also continuously adjust kvar supply by excitation control but are uneconomical for power factor control only. They become economical in industrial plants when applied to perform work. The most economical method for power factor improvement is shunt capacitors as compared to synchronous condensers and motors. Shunt capacitors, however, cannot continuously adjust to varying power factor compensation requirements, unless switched as a unit with the motors.

The recent higher currents and voltage capabilities of silicon-controlled rectifiers (SCRs) has provided new methods for variable power factor improvement. Other solid-state devices, *thyristor switches,* have features that combine the advantages of rotating synchronous condensers, synchronous motors and static capacitors.

A review of the basics of thyristor operation is helpful in understanding how these solid-state devices provide automatic variable power-factor correction.

Diodes and thyristors

Semiconductors, called *diodes,* are two-terminal solid substances that when electrically energized, exhibit an *anode* and a *cathode,* permitting current flow in the forward direction, from anode to cathode and blocking the reverse current flow. All activity in these solid-state devices occur inside the material without any parts movement.

Semiconductor cells are composed of silicon or germanium and are formed by the junction of N (negative) and P (positive) crystals. A voltage applied across this junction makes the current flow through the junction. If the polarity of the applied voltage is reversed, then the current flow is blocked. A silicon diode offering a low forward voltage drop and a very small reverse current is suited perfectly to act as a rectifier. A typical power diode, diagram symbol and voltage-vs.-current curve of a silicon diode is shown in Figure 16.

A *thyristor,* or silicon-controlled rectifier (SCR), is also a semiconductor device. Current in the SCR is blocked in both directions, until a logic-signal voltage is applied to a control terminal called a *gate.*

Thyristors are formed by a junction of four layers of crystals (P-N P-N). The gate is connected to the second layer. The gate, or trigger current has a relatively low value. The thyristor blocks current in both directions but has a forward break-over voltage (V_0), at which point it behaves as a diode. A typical thyristor diagram symbol and voltage-vs.-current curve of an SCR is shown in Figure 17.

In the reverse direction, the thyristor has the same operating characteristics as a diode. In the forward direction, it blocks the voltage until the breakover voltage point is reached. At this point, the thyristor breaks down and the current increases from low to very high value, limited only by the circuit impedance. If the load current drops below the holding current level, forward blocking is restored.

With a gate signal of sufficient

magnitude, forward blocking is ineffective and the thyristor behaves like a diode. Applying a voltage to the SCR's gate causes the breakdown to occur at a lower value, V_1, instead of V_0, as shown in Figure 17.

If an AC voltage is applied, the thyristor automatically turns off at each half cycle when the voltage reaches zero. In a DC circuit the thyristor is turned off by auxiliary devices that reduce the voltage to zero or reduce the current below the holding value.

The life expectancy of a completely sealed silicon cell is believed to be unlimited provided it is properly applied. When a thyristor is used for AC switching, rectification of AC is avoided by connecting two thyristors in reverse-parallel as shown in Figure 18. This connection prevents commutation and allows the AC flow through the static switch. The gated SCR No. 1 allows the positive half of the AC wave to flow while SCR No. 2 allows the negative wave to flow because of the reverse-parallel connection of SCR No. 1 and No. 2. The firing logic sets the timing and the duration of the

energization of SCR No. 1 and No. 2 and consequently the flow of AC current through the static switch. To provide a continuously varying compensation for power factor correction, two thyristors are connected in reverse-parallel (to form the static switch) in series with an inductor and all are connected in parallel with a capacitor.

This scheme, as shown in Figure 18, can be used to provide unity power factor at full load if the inductor and capacitor are properly selected and rated for the maximum kvar required by the system. At the maximum capacitor kvar demand, the static switch opens and full capacitive current is drawn from the lines.

When the kvar demand is zero, the static switch closes, the inductor cancels the capacitor effect and the net current provided is zero.

Between these two extreme conditions the switch is *phase controlled*. The inductor, in series with the phase-angle-controlled static switch, acts as a variable inductor with a time response of one half of a cycle interval. This means the angle θ between

voltage and current can be set to open the static switch through the firing logic at every half cycle and allow the capacitor to provide the required kvar. When power factor reaches the desired value, say 0.95, which corresponds to $\theta = 18$ deg, the firing logic closes the static switch and the inductor cancels the capacitor effect.

The principle of operation for variable power factor adjustment is shown by the circuit and vector diagram of Figure 19.

The main current I has three components:

$$I_1 = \frac{E}{R} \text{ in phase with E}$$

$$I_2 = \frac{E}{X_L} \text{ in quadrature behind E}$$

$$I_3 = \frac{E}{X_c} \text{ in quadrature ahead of E}$$

Where:

R = circuit resistance in phase with E

X_l = inductive reactance

X_c = capacitive reactance

From the vector diagram:

$$I = \sqrt{I_1^2 + (I_2 - I_3)^2} =$$

FIGURE 16   TYPICAL POWER DIODE, DIAGRAM SYMBOL AND VOLTAGE VS. CURRENT CURVE OF SILICON DIODE

FIGURE 17 TYPICAL THYRISTOR, DIAGRAM SYMBOL AND VOLTAGE VS. CURRENT CURVE OF SCR

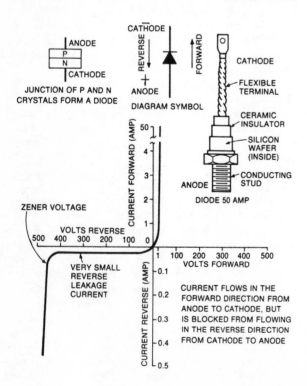

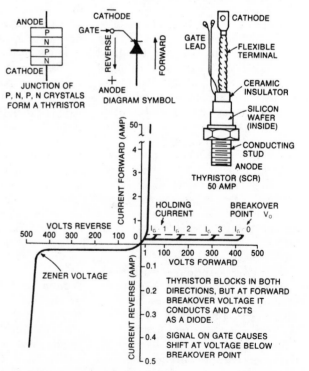

Figures from article *The What, Why, Where And How Of UPS—Pt. 2* (p. 140, June, 1969 ASE).

FIGURE 18 SYSTEM OF CAPACITOR, INDUCTOR AND THYRISTOR SWITCH TO PROVIDE UNITY POWER FACTOR AT FULL LOAD

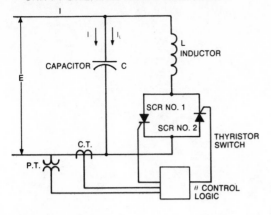

FIGURE 19 CIRCUIT AND VECTOR DIAGRAM FOR VARIABLE POWER FACTOR ADJUSTMENT BY STATIC SWITCH

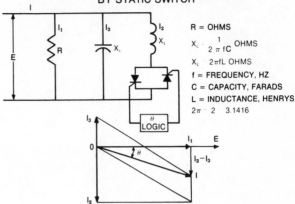

R = OHMS

$X_C = \dfrac{1}{2\pi fC}$ OHMS

$X_L = 2\pi fL$ OHMS

f = FREQUENCY, HZ

C = CAPACITY, FARADS

L = INDUCTANCE, HENRYS

$2\pi = 2 \times 3.1416$

$$E\sqrt{\frac{1}{R^2} + \left(\frac{1}{X_L} - \frac{1}{X_C}\right)^2}$$

$$\text{Tangent } \theta = \frac{I_2 - I_3}{I_1} = \frac{\dfrac{1}{X_L} - \dfrac{1}{X_C}}{\dfrac{1}{R}} =$$

$$\frac{\dfrac{1}{2\pi fL} - 2\pi fC}{\dfrac{1}{R}}$$

and the current is in phase with the voltage. This means cosine θ = PF = 1. When this condition occurs the thyristors are fired and the static switch closes circuit X_1.

To complete this condition, capacitor (C) and inductor (L) have to be selected to satisfy the equation

$$\frac{1}{2\pi fL} = 2\pi fC. \quad \frac{1}{2\pi fL} = 2\pi fC$$

This means the inductor should be selected to be:

$$L = \frac{1}{(2\pi f)^2 C} \quad \text{when } \frac{1}{2\pi fL} = 2\pi fC,$$

$$\text{then } t_g\theta = 0; \ \theta = 0$$

The capacitor is then selected for the maximum kvar required by the system.

When capacitive current is required, the logic senses the increased angle θ - between voltage and current and opens the X_1 circuit. This leaves only the capacitors to act. This shift in paralleling the capacitor with the inductor by automatically closing or opening the static switch, may occur as often as every half cycle according to varying power factor improvement requirements. This arrangement has the effect of continuously adding or subtracting leading kvars to or from the system.

The static system for power factor improvement overcomes the main

FIGURE 20 SINGLE-PHASE SYSTEM, WITH LARGE CAPACITOR BANK NEXT TO THYRISTOR SWITCH. TUNED FILTERS (L₁-C₁-L₂-C₂ AND L₃-C₃) SUPPRESS HARMONICS

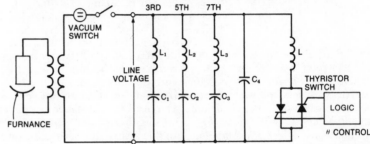

limitation of static capacitors by offering a continuously varying compensation. This method was first used in arc furnace systems. The static method of kvar supply was used because of its lower cost and operating advantages as compared to synchronous condensers. Also operating voltage levels used in arc furnaces have been matched by the progress in thyristor switching technology.

In arc furnace applications, high-speed power factor control, as well as flicker reduction, are of great importance. It is here that the static kvar supply successfully solves the problem. The static solid-state system operates on a completely different principle than its conventional counterpart, the synchronous condenser. Variations in furnace arc resistance are large and erratic during the initial melting period. This causes fluctuations in magnitude and phase angle, for the current drawn from the supply line.

The operating principle of the static-switch correcting system provides instantaneous compensation for the impedance changes in the furnace

circuit. This means the reactive load on the power system is maintained at a power factor of 0.95 or better. The static system operates as a variable capacitor with a response as fast as half a cycle. This eliminates flicker and improves power factor instantaneously.

The fast control of the phase angle, however, may generate harmonics that are functions of the angle θ. The three significant harmonics of the fundamental current are the third, fifth and seventh. The maximum amplitudes are 13.63 percent, 5.04 percent and 1.31 percent respectively. These harmonics must be filtered.

Filtering is obtained by placing appropriate inductors in series with capacitors all connected in parallel with the main capacitor, as shown in Figure 20. Filtering also protects the static switch against voltage transients and faults.

Similar to the arc furnace, the static kvar-supply system could be used in industrial plants where frequent and rapid variations in power-factor correction are a problem.

49

2.7 Series Capacitors and Their Application

Section 2.6 of P.F. Improvement explained how solid-state technology has led to new concepts for variable kvar supply. This section 2.7 on power factor improvement, discusses series capacitor fundamentals and applications. (Figures, formulas and tables are numbered consecutively.)

Shunt capacitors are universally applied on power systems. Series capacitors, however, are a more specialized type of device and are used to a limited extent on distribution and subtransmission circuits. The two main uses of series capacitors are to compensate system reactance for voltage regulation improvement and to improve the power factor for certain types of loads, such as resistance welders, arc furnaces and high-frequency generators.

A series capacitor is merely a capacitor connected in a series. The shunt capacitor, described in the previous sections is connected in parallel. The terms "shunt" and "series" only imply the type of connection, not the type of capacitor. The capacitor is the same in both cases, as shown in Figure 21. It can be seen from the two vector diagrams that the way the same capacitor is connected in the circuit determines the different functions it performs.

The shunt capacitor is a capacitive reactance in shunt (parallel) with the load or system and is basically used to improve power factor. The results—released system capacity, improved voltage level, reduced system (RI²) losses, lower power bills when power factor clauses are enforced by utili-ties—are all additional benefits derived from power factor improvement. The unswitched shunt capacitors do not improve the voltage regulation caused by changes in load, but they increase the normal voltage level.

Unlike the shunt capacitor, a series capacitor can be visualized as a negative (capacitive) reactance in series with the line. The voltage rise across the capacitor, which is a function of the circuit current, is practically instantaneous, depending on circuit resistance and inductance. In this respect the series capacitor may be considered primarily as a voltage regulator. The series capacitor differs from an induction or step-voltage regulator in that it does not compensate for voltage variations originating in the supply source.

At rated load, the series capacitor provides power factor improvement to the same degree as do the same kvars of shunt capacitors. The series capacitors provide power factor improvement by an out-of-phase *voltage* component. Shunt capacitors accomplish the same improvement by an out-of-phase *current* component. These two methods are illustrated in the two vector diagrams in Figure 21. In the usual application for power service, the series capacitor kvar rating is much too low to improve the power factor significantly.

The operating principle

The series capacitor can be thought of as a negative reactance that neutralizes the system inductive reactance. Other devices produce a voltage rise 180 deg out of phase with the system reactive drop.

When a series capacitor is inserted in a feeder or a transmission line, the inductive reactance between two points including the capacitor is reduced by the amount of the capacitive reactance of the capacitor.

The net effect of the series capacitor is a reduction in voltage drop caused by inductive reactance in the feeder or line. The resulting effect is that the line appears to be of lower inductive reactance.

The series capacitor acts as a voltage regulator, giving a voltage boost proportional to the magnitude and power factor of the through current. This constitutes the main difference between the effects of a series and a shunt capacitor. The shunt capacitor gives a constant voltage boost that is independent of the through current so long as the through current causes no appreciable voltage change.

If the load current causes appreciable voltage drop, the voltage boost of the shunt capacitor decreases, a change to an undesirable direction. A shunt capacitor, therefore, may make the voltage regulation worse. On the other hand, the series capacitor gives a voltage rise that increases as the load increases. In addition, at lower power factors, which would cause more line voltage drop, the series capacitor gives more net voltage rise. This is why a series capacitor can be considered a voltage regulator.

The voltage across a series capacitor is a function of its reactance and current:

13. $E_c = IX_c$

The effect of the series capacitor, however, on the circuit voltage depends on the power factor of the load current:

14. $e_c = IX \sin \Theta$

From the vector diagram in Figure 22, the voltage drop formula for a 3-phase service can be written:

15. $e = IR \cos \Theta + I(X_L - X_c) \sin \Theta$

Where:

E_s = sending-end voltage
E_r = receiving-end voltage
e = circuit voltage drop or change in volts

e_c = circuit voltage rise due to the series capacitor

E_c = voltage across the series capacitor only

I = total current in amp

Θ = power factor angle

R = resistance in ohms

X_c = capacitive reactance in ohms

X_L = inductive reactance in ohms

(X_L is positive and X_c negative in accordance with accepted terminology).

Formula 15 shows that the voltage drop, and therefore the voltage regulation, are reduced when the reactive drop IX is reduced. In industrial power systems this is usually the largest part of the voltage drop.

The effect of the negative reactance of a series capacitor on voltage regulation is illustrated by the schematic and vector diagram shown in Figure 23. In this vector diagram, the vector voltage at the receiving end, E_r, is taken as reference.

The voltage regulation of a system without a series capacitor is large. This can be seen from the relative length of the voltage vectors E_r and E_s.

With a series capacitor of $X_c = X_L$, the capacitor neutralizes the system reactance and the regulation is considerably reduced as indicated by vector E_{s1}. This reduction can be further improved by overcompensation if X_c is selected to be larger than X_L. This achieves zero regulation, in which case $E_{s2} = E_r$.

In the power system operation, however, the less the voltage regulation, the stiffer the system is electrically. This means the system has a higher interrupting duty. A system with zero voltage regulation can be visualized as the equivalent of an infinitely large power system. It is advisable to compensate the reactance in many industrial systems so that the voltage regulation is only that caused by the resistance component, which amounts to a few percent.

The series capacitor stiffens the electrical system. This is beneficial for starting large motors from an otherwise weak system. It reduces voltage drop and light flicker caused by large load fluctuations.

Using series capacitors

The instantaneous and automatic response of the series capacitor is perfectly suited for compensation of voltage drop fluctuations caused by suddenly applied loads, such as electric welders, arc furnaces and motor-starting conditions. The explanation for the application of the series capacitor can be derived by examining Formula 15 and the relative values of the resistance (RI) and reactance (IX) components.

In most industrial power systems the reactance is much higher than the resistance, and the ratio X_L/R ranges from 3 to 10. If the power factor is low (sine Θ is large), as in the case of motor starting, then the IX drop will be the largest portion. It follows that the series capacitor will help in reducing the voltage drop.

In general, a series capacitor is effective in an electric circuit, when the reactance is greater than the resistance or when the load power factor is low. The optimum application is when the capacitive reactance completely neutralizes the inductive reactance, leaving only the resistance component. In this case, fluctuating loads will have little effect on voltage drop.

If the power factor varies appreciably, overcompensation with series capacitors may cause voltage rise. That is why such overcompensation applications should be carefully studied to make sure that the overall resulting voltage is not harmful to the equipment.

When properly applied, series capacitors reduce line impedances and thereby raise the delivered voltage. The effect is an increase in the kva capacity of a radial feeder; and for the same delivered kva load, the line current is slightly reduced. Evidently a series capacitor is not a substitute for line copper.

Series capacitors are used in subtransmission lines to change the division load between parallel lines or to reduce voltage regulation. Series capacitors also are used in radial circuits to supply loads of about .70 to .95 lagging power factor. Below .70, shunt capacitors are more advantageous (provided the power factor does not change over a wide range, making it impossible to switch shunt capacitors fast enough to supply the kvar required by the load). Applications on radial circuits supplying loads of .70 to .90 power factor are most likely to be successful.

Series capacitors affect power factor to a limited extent, compared to shunt capacitors, because the kvar in series

FIGURE 21   SHUNT AND SERIES CONNECTIONS OF CAPACITORS AND VECTOR DIAGRAMS SHOWING HOW POWER FACTOR IS OBTAINED

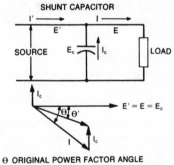

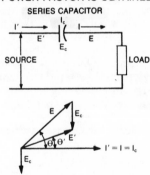

Θ ORIGINAL POWER FACTOR ANGLE
Θ' POWER FACTOR ANGLE WITH CAPACITOR

FIGURE 22   VOLTAGE DROP IN A CIRCUIT WITH RESISTANCE, IMPEDANCE AND CAPACITANCE

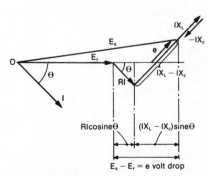

FORMULA 15
$e = IR\cos\Theta + I(X_L - X_c)\sin\Theta$

FIGURE 23   DIAGRAM SHOWING HOW A SERIES CAPACITOR REDUCES VOLTAGE REGULATION

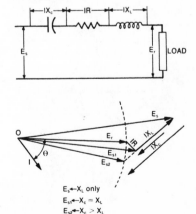

$E_s \leftarrow X_L$ only
$E_{s1} \leftarrow X_c = X_L$
$E_{s2} \leftarrow X_c > X_L$

capacitors is usually much smaller, being a fourth to a half the shunt capacitor kvar for the same change in load voltage. Also, the series capacitor contributes its kvar to the system as the square of the load current:

$$\text{Series capacitor kvar} = \frac{3I^2X_c}{1,000}$$

Series capacitors are particularly effective in radial circuits with lamp-flicker problems, repetitive load fluctuations, motor-starting voltage dips, rapidly varying motor loads, electric welders and arc furnaces.

Voltage drops that cause light flicker are produced by rapidly fluctuating currents flowing through the impedance of the power system. The voltage drop can be reduced by reducing the impedance of the system. If the character of the impedance system is a lagging one, the addition of leading reactive impedance by series capacitors can neutralize the lagging reactive instantaneously. This reduces the system reactive drop to practically zero. Shunt capacitors cannot be switched fast enough to prevent lamp flicker—in fact, shunt capacitors might even aggravate the situation.

One of the most important applications of series capacitors is in supply lines to electric welders. Resistance welders operate at a low power factor (.25 to .50). Consequently, they draw considerable reactive current, causing large voltage drops. In addition, by the nature of their intermittent operation, the welders produce rapid fluctuations in voltage and annoying light flicker. Voltage dips also can spoil welds. A series capacitor with a proper rating can produce a voltage rise to offset the drop across the circuit inductive reactance.

The voltage rise across the series capacitor and the voltage drop across the system reactance are both proportional to current flow. It follows that the drop across the circuit reactance with a series capacitor is instantly cancelled out for all values of current. The instantaneous and automatic response in voltage rise of the series capacitors also makes them suitable for voltage compensation of voltage dips caused by motor starting or fluctuating motor loads, as is the case in saw mills and rubber mills.

Locating series capacitors

The location of series capacitors should be carefully worked out. Figure 24 shows a series capacitor located at the primary of a unit substation. Heavy currents drawn by welders, cause voltage drops in the transformer and in the primary system. The series capacitor, however, maintains the voltage at the low-voltage bus at practically a constant level. It can be seen that voltage fluctuations in the primary system are not corrected by the series capacitor.

The capacitors should be selected to improve the power factor instantly to about unity at full output. The improved power factor decreases the voltage dip at the bus.

A word of caution

Although series capacitors have many desirable characteristics, there is the possibility of undesirable phenomena occurring.

The prediction of circuit performance during transient conditions—e.g., loads suddenly applied or removed, motor starting, welder operation—is not as simple as indicated by the steady-state conditions expressed in Formula 15. The difficulty arises when circuit constants become nonlinear. In these cases a great many data are necessary, and even then the prediction is difficult without the aid of a network or differential analyzer. Therefore, the practical solution for most applications of series capacitors is based on experience.

Some of the main difficulties that may occur are self-excitation of induction and synchronous motors during starting that causes motors to lock in step at subsynchronous speed; excessive vibration or large current pulsations; hunting of synchronous motors during normal operation; and ferroresonance in transformers. Although these abnormal operations can be eliminated, it is advisable that each series capacitor application be thoroughly studied and checked and suitable precautions taken to make the installation practical.

To make the proper selection and application of series capacitors, it is necessary to have complete information about the system and the loads to which series capacitors are applied. In this way the electrical engineer can specify the most economical equipment.

The engineer should obtain the following information:
- Complete one-line diagram of the electrical system, including circuit voltages, description, rating, and so on of transformers, motors, etc.
- Normal and maximum load and power factor—the momentary rather than the normal current, which determines capacitor rating.
- Maximum short-circuit current of the system at the location of the series capacitor in order to determine if voltage protective equipment is necessary.
- Rating of the capacitor in ohms or equivalent information for determining this rating, such as transformer nameplate data, wire size, type of cable or overhead wire spacing, etc., or fault duty at incoming power source.
- Frequency of power supply.
- Number of phases (single or three).
- Ambient operating temperature.
- Purpose or function of the series capacitor.

Power capacitors are rated in kvars. This is related to the Farad unit by the equation:

$$16. \quad \text{kvar} = \frac{E^2 \times 2\pi f\, C(10^{-6})}{1,000}$$

Where:
E = rated rms voltage
f = frequency in cycles/sec (Hz)
C = capacitance in microfarads

The kvar is the convenient term for the power industry since load is usually expressed in kilowatts and kilovars.

FIGURE 24 SERIES CAPACITOR LOCATED AT THE PRIMARY OF A UNIT SUBSTATION

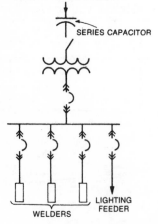

SERIES CAPACITOR

WELDERS

LIGHTING FEEDER

2.8 Automatic Switching of Capacitors

Section 2.7 of P.F. Improvement discussed series capacitor fundamentals and applications. (Figures and tables are numbered consecutively.)

Automatic switching of capacitors is employed in industrial plants for a number of reasons:

To prevent overvoltages at light loads. Shunt capacitors raise the voltage level the same amount regardless of whether they are under light or full loads. For this reason, the capacitance required to improve the power factor to a desired level at full load may result in overvoltage at light load, particularly when the system reactance is high.

An example will point this out. Assume that at a generated voltage of 2,400 v, the light-load voltage at the utilization bus is 2,360 v. Suppose also that the full-load bus voltage is only 2,140 v and power factor improvement capacitors are added with the side effect of raising the bus voltage to 2,300 v. If the capacitors remain connected at light load, the voltage will be 2,360 + (2,300 − 2,140) = 2,520 v. This is an overvoltage of 5 percent, and it may be advisable to switch off the capacitors to prevent overvoltage to lights or other voltage-sensitive equipment.

To provide voltage regulation. Voltage can be regulated by switching shunt capacitors in steps in response to voltage changes at the load bus. This kind of voltage regulation is not smooth enough, however, since the smaller the size of the steps, the less economical the system.

To avoid utility penalties for leading power factor. These penalties are seldom enforced, and when they are, utilities permit power factors as low as 95 percent leading without penalty. Sometimes penalties for leading power factor are applied to discourage greater losses in the utility lines and possible instability of the generating system connected to higher leading power factors.

To reduce system losses at light loads. At full load, capacitors supply the required kvar at the utilization bus. Under light load, capacitors supply kvars back to the utility system, and this unnecessary flow of reactive current increases the losses. These losses can be eliminated by automatically switching off capacitors during light loads.

To prevent generator instability. Generators operated at leading power factor must have the excitation reduced. As a result, the generators become unstable, and an unstable generator has a tendency to pull out of step when transient power swings take place. The general characteristics of the generator and its system excitation dictate how far the leading power factor can be made before instability occurs. When instability results because of the number of capacitors in the system, means should be provided for switching off part or all of the capacitors.

To prevent circuit overloading. Heavily loaded circuits, operating at low power factor, carry reactive current that loads the circuit but does not produce useful power. When capacitors are switched on, the load power factor is improved immediately and the reactive current is removed from the circuit. The result has the effect of reducing the circuit loading. To avoid capacitor current loading the circuit at light loads, the capacitors can be automatically switched off to reduce losses and overvoltages.

The most common types of automatic switching controls for capacitors in industrial plants are time-clock, voltage-sensitive, current-sensitive, kilovar-sensitive, and voltage-current-compensated. The control receives the signal (intelligence), interprets it and initiates capacitor switching into or out of the circuit. The standard switching control contains a master element that can be responsive to voltage, current, time or kvars.

A time-delay device is used to avoid unnecessary operation for only momentary signal changes. A sequencing device is necessary only for a multistep control where the sequencer must determine the order in which capacitors are switched in and out of service. Usually, this device is a motor-operated selector switch.

In addition to the basic control devices, other miscellaneous components might be desired in the control system. These could include auxiliary relays, automatic to manual transfer switches, close and trip switches, and the like. The number and types of miscellaneous devices depend on the refinement and desired flexibility.

The type of intelligence used for a specific application depends on cost, bank location, number of switching steps, daily load cycles and the purpose of the capacitor application.

Types of controls most frequently used for existing switched capacitors are time controls for pole-mounted banks in feeders and voltage controls for distribution substation banks.

The time-switch or time-clock control is the most common type of control used with switched capacitor banks on distribution systems. This control switches on the capacitor bank at a certain time delay and takes it off at a later preset time. It is used frequently with single-step banks, 150 to 600 kvar, located on primary feeders, where the daily load cycle is known and the load remains fairly constant for long periods and has a load pattern that repeats over a period of time. The greatest advantage of the time-switch control is its low cost and the fact that it does not require coordination with other voltage-regulating equipment.

A disadvantage of the time-switch control is that its operating sequence is the same under both normal and unusual load conditions. If a power failure occurs on a feeder, part of which is temporarily connected to an on-line adjoining feeder, the capacitor should be in the circuit to maintain proper voltage levels with the additional load. If a failure occurs when the capacitors are normally off the circuit, a special trip must be made to the capacitor location to switch them on.

Voltage control alone can be used as a source of intelligence only when switched capacitors are applied at points where circuit voltage decreases with an increase in circuit load. If capacitors are applied at points where the circuit voltage increases with the load, then a second source of intelligence must be used. Voltage-current and the voltage-time controls

FIGURE 25 ELECTRICAL LOCATION OF CAPACITORS AND POINT-OF-SIGNAL MEASUREMENT

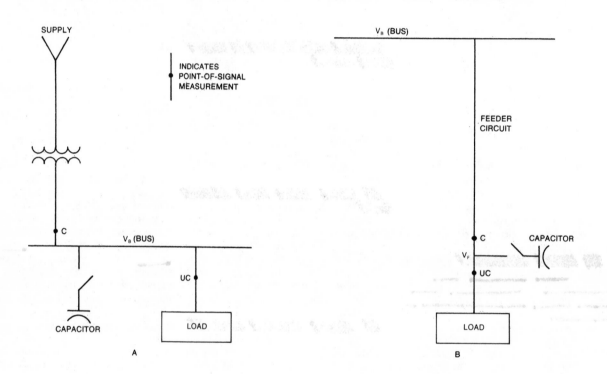

TABLE 9 SELECTION OF MASTER CONTROL ELEMENT FOR AUTOMATIC CONTROL EQUIPMENT

Purpose	Bus voltage conditions	Preferred master control element	Location of capacitors and point-of-signal measurement*	
			See Figure 1 (a)	See Figure 1 (b)
Remove capacitors at light load	V_B Constant	Voltage multistep		C or UC
		Voltage single-step		C or UC
		Kilovar single-step	C or UC	C or UC
		Kilovar multistep	C	C
		Current single-step	UC	UC
	(Note: Current control applicable when power factor is reasonably constant with load variations.)			
Remove capacitors at light load	V_B variable	Kilovar multistep	C	C
		Kilovar single-step	C or UC	C or UC
		Current single-step	UC	UC
Remove capacitors at light load	V_B variable because of switching capacitors on adjacent feeders	Kilovar multistep		C
		Kilovar single-step		C or UC
		Current single-step		UC
Regulate feeder voltage	Bus voltage reasonably constant	Voltage multistep		C
Regulate kilovars	Not important	Kilovar multistep	C	C

*C refers to corrected load measurement, i.e., with effect of capacitors included. UC refers to uncorrected load measurement.
From "Industrial Power Systems Handbook" D. Beeman—*McGraw-Hill* 1968.

are two such intelligence sources.

Extensively used in substation applications, voltage control has the advantage of initiating a switching operation only when the circuit voltage condition requires it and it is independent of the load cycle. The band width of the voltage setting depends on the rating of the capacitor bank, the number of steps and whether other voltage-regulating equipment is applied on the same circuit. A time delay is always used before any switching operation to prevent unnecessary switching triggered by transitory disturbances.

Current control alone is used only where voltage is not a satisfactory signal. Primary applications for this type of control are on feeders or substations where voltage increases with the load or where voltage reduction at load increase is not enough for effective relaying. To obtain an effective current control, the load change should be such as the ratio of maximum to minimum demand is three or more. A time delay is always used with current control to prevent excessive operations due to momentary load disturbances.

Kilovar controls are contact-making zero-center varmeters. They have a range adjustment from 66 percent lagging to 32 percent leading. In practice, two var-sensitive relays are used, one for the on setting and the other for the off setting when more than a single-step control is wanted.

The voltage-sensitive current-compensated control has a contact-making voltmeter that functions as the ordinary voltage type for all values of current below a preset value. When the line current exceeds this value, it activates a relay that raises the voltmeter calibration and causes it to "see" a lower voltage and switch on the capacitor. At currents higher than the preset value, the capacitors will be on unless the circuit voltage rises enough to offset the change of the voltmeter calibration. This type of control keeps capacitors on the system when needed most—say, during periods of low voltage due to system disturbances.

The master element should obtain its signal from a point of signal that includes the effect of the capacitor. An exception is the current control where the uncorrected load measurement must be used. Kilovar-responsive controls and multistep voltage controls should always obtain their signals from the corrected load measurement. Table 9 and Figure 25 show the point-of-signal measurement for various types of controls.

Manual switching is the least expensive switching control. It is usually used in attended substations where switching operations are performed daily. Some large capacitor banks are switched remotely by the load dispatcher over the supervisory control according to requirements. The main purpose for these large banks is kvar supply rather than voltage control.

Capacitor switching devices

Special consideration should be given to the devices used for switching capacitors because switching capacitors imposes a particular duty on a switch or breaker. A device that performs satisfactorily under normal load and fault duty may be wholly inadequate for capacitor switching. (Manufacturer's advice should always be obtained before applying breakers for switching large banks of capacitors.)

Two factors contribute heavily in causing the capacitor switching action to impose a severe duty on the switching device.

The first factor is due to the 90-deg phase relationship between the system voltage and the capacitor current. The switch interrupts the capacitor current at a normal current zero, but this leaves a trapped voltage on the capacitor as high as the system crest voltage. When the system voltage reaches the crest of the opposite polarity a half cycle later, the voltage across the switch contacts is at least twice the system crest voltage. Unless the switch recovers the insulation strength between the contacts very quickly, reignition or restrike is apt to occur.

The second factor is associated with the high-frequency transient currents that flow into a capacitor bank when it is energized, or when restrike occurs during a switch opening. The magnitude of the transient current may be severe, and restriking in a circuit breaker can build up transient overvoltages on the power system and possibly lead to an explosion inside the breaker.

With proper precautions and recognition of basic limitations, standard magnetic air breakers may, in general, be used for shunt capacitor switching. As a rule, maintenance for magnetic breakers increases with the size of capacitor banks. For larger banks and higher voltages, it is generally necessary to use supplementary protective means by inserting resistors in the switching circuit.

Addition of the series resistance during opening or closing constitutes a critically damped RLC circuit, and the transient currents and voltage are greatly reduced. The effect of the restrike is also appreciably reduced.

Complete installation details must be known before a switching device can be specified and applied. To select the right breaker, it is necessary to know the maximum kvar rating of the bank and the maximum short-circuit capacity. The continuous-current rating must be at least 135 percent of the rated current of the capacitor bank.

General considerations

This concludes the series on power factor improvement by means of capacitors. In general, it can be said that the shunt capacitor has become increasingly important in industrial power substation design. In power distribution, capacitors reduce peak-load feeder voltage drops, allow greater feeder loads to be carried, increase feeder capacity, and release substation and generation capacity.

Many variables and some intangible advantages must be weighed in making any decision relative to power factor correction. A knowledge of the basic fundamentals of power factor (as described in the series) will facilitate such study.

Here are some things the engineer should keep in mind:

Capacitor applications should be checked closely to make sure that the voltage will not rise excessively during light-load periods, especially if the feeder is not regulated. Consideration must be given to any change that might be made (after capacitors are applied) in turn ratios of transformers and voltage regulators located between the generator and the load. Transformer taps could be changed after capacitors are applied and could result in a reduction in both the active and reactive components of current. This additional reduction in current would bring about additional system benefits on the source side of the transformer where tap changes are made.

3

The What, Why, Where, and How of UPS

3.1 Basic Systems Available

Today's complex electrical and electronic critical systems often require a carefully monitored and controlled uninterrupted power supply (in addition to a backup system) to prevent shutdowns in case of main power failures. Examples of critical load systems include computers; flame failure and boiler controls; electronic process control instruments; critical communications equipment; relays, solenoids, turbine-trip circuits that trip when de-energized; and critical alarms, instruments, analyzers, potentiometers, etc.

Within the last decade electric devices have utilized solid-state components, making possible a whole new class of equipment. Transistors, diodes, silicon controlled rectifiers etc., have brought about a new approach in industry to uninterrupted power supply by creating static rectifiers, inverters and switches.

To determine the appropriate UPS system for a particular critical load, the following questions have to be investigated and answered:

■ Will a power failure damage the critical equipment?
■ If so, what can be the extent of the damage, how long will it take to repair it and how much will it cost?
■ Will the power failure endanger the safety of personnel?
■ Are spare parts readily available, and what do they cost?
■ Will the computer memory be lost because of power failure?
■ If a standby emergency source is necessary, what is its steady-state output and for how long?
■ Can momentary outages be tolerated, and if so, for how long? (Timing is an important factor in selecting the right UPS.)
■ What is the critical tolerance imposed by the critical load in percent of voltage regulation, frequency variation and harmonic distortion?
■ Does the critical load require a square or a sine wave shape?

A solid-state uninterrupted power system (as shown in this section's diagrams) is basically composed of a solid-state rectifier-charger, a battery and a static inverter. Sometimes a static switch is connected to the output for added protection. These systems are intended to provide uninterrupted AC power to critical-load systems that cannot tolerate even a fraction of a cycle interruption from the incoming utility supply sources.

No Disturbance Allowed

Voltage dips, frequency variations and momentary or sustained disturbances of utility power supply can cause malfunction or complete outage of critical loads. Power loss during critical loads results in production downtime and costly recycling of equipment or possible equipment damage.

If voltage dips exceed stringent imposed values, computers may lose their stored information or create errors in computation. Computers controlling manufacturing processes or boiler flame failure devices can lose control or generate wrong commands if interruptions of even a fraction of a cycle occur.

The answer to these problems is a UPS system, which uses static devices to operate as buffers between the utility power feeder disturbances and the customer's critical loads. A variety of buffer systems have been introduced or proposed, some with different combination of turbine and/or motor-generator sets, some with flywheels, some with electro-mechanical transfer switches.

For systems requiring 25- or 50-kw units, the installed cost for static units may become prohibitive. Rotating-type uninterrupted power supplies effectively serve large loads, though the more advantageous solid-state systems are now gaining favor. The rotating types of UPS systems are based on inertial systems (flywheel with or without Eddy current coupling) of various combinations of rotating equipment driven by synchronous or induction motors.

Solid-state devices provide fast response transients, stable output frequency, high efficiency and relatively quiet operation (60 db). Solid-state equipment using silicon-controlled rectifiers and static switches isolates utility power line voltage transients, frequency variations and high-low voltage conditions from the AC critical load. In other words, the devices and solid-state circuitry act as a line filter and voltage regulator and provide no-break power during normal power outages. In addition to these advantages, the cost per kva of UPS systems is decreasing because of technical advances and improvements in solid-state technology.

Two Standby Systems

Based on transfer-time characteristics, there are two types of standby systems, the wave shapes of which are shown in the diagram on this page.

Type 1 standby systems are used mainly for critical controls and instruments, lighting, and secondary communication systems that can stand a time-delay of several cycles. The transfer can be made by electro-mechanical transfer switches that transfer loads in as low a range as 2 to 4 cycles, though it is more common for switches to be in the 8-to-10-cycle range.

Type 2 standby systems, which are the major focus of this article, are used mostly for such critical loads as boiler-flame detectors, computers and electronic process-control instrumentation, in which an outage of even a fraction of a cycle cannot be tolerated.

UPS Components

The continuous or float-type UPS system is simple, popular and inexpensive. It is composed of a solid-state rectifier-battery charger, a DC storage battery and a solid-state inverter assembled, as shown in the diagram on this page.

During normal operation the AC input feeds the solid-state rectifier converting AC to DC and float-charges the battery. At the same time, the rectifier supplies DC to the static inverter. The solid-state inverter converts DC to AC at the desired load voltage. The AC square wave is converted to an approximate AC sine wave by using a ferro-resonant transformer and solid-state circuitry located in the inverter enclosure.

When the AC supply fails, the battery supplies the necessary DC power, thus providing the alternate source operating the inverter. This assembly constitutes a complete no-break system without any loss in switching time because there is only a change in DC voltage source to the inverter. In addition, this combination acts as a buffer system converting incoming power, regardless of continuity or quality, to a continuous power that meets the critical-load specifications.

The battery support-time, in case of a line failure, varies from 10 to 60 min, depending on the amp-hr capacity of the selected battery. If the outage lasts longer, a generator set having as prime mover a turbine or a diesel-engine begins supplying power to the rectifier and at the same time re-

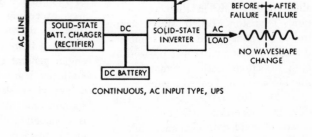

SOLID-STATE UNINTERRUPTED POWER SYSTEM

CONTINUOUS, AC INPUT TYPE, UPS

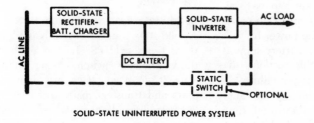

WAVESHAPE OF STANDBY SYSTEMS

In Type 1, a brief time interval may be allowed between failure of primary power source and transfer to secondary standby source (4 to 12 cycles). In Type 2, no load interruption and no major transients in wave form may be tolerated during the transfer from primary source to the secondary standby source.

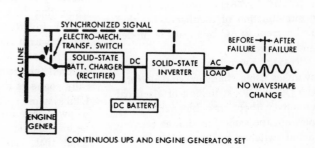

CONTINUOUS UPS AND ENGINE GENERATOR SET

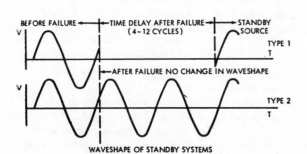

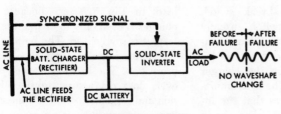

CONTINUOUS FLOAT TYPE

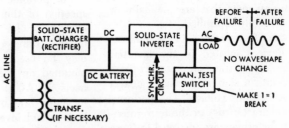

CONTINUOUS UPS WITH MANUAL MAKE 1=1 BREAK SWITCH

charges the battery. A careful analysis of the load requirements will show the break-even point at which an engine-generator would also have to be considered, all resulting in a lower cost than a larger, long-time battery.

A New Type

The AC-input type of UPS is a recent development of the continuous float type system and is shown in the diagram on page 65. In this type of UPS the normal AC line feeds into a recti-

---

GLOSSARY OF BASIC TERMS

SOLID-STATE COMPONENTS are electrical devices within which all activity takes place in a solid block of material without moving parts. In energy systems they are known as semiconductors. These solid substances, called diodes, permit the flow of current in one direction and block the flow in the reverse direction. Silicon is used almost exclusively in their composition. Thyristors, called silicon controlled rectifier (SCR), are semiconductors in which current is blocked in both directions until a signal is applied to a terminal called a gate.

STATIC RECTIFIERS are electrical devices converting AC to DC by means of solid-state elements such as diodes.

STATIC INVERTERS perform the opposite function of rectifiers, changing DC current to AC by means of diodes and thyristors.

STATIC SWITCHES are solid-state switches using thyristors and perform the ON or OFF switching of electrical circuits without movable parts. They perform the same function as conventional switches and contactors but do not have movable parts.

ELECTRO-MECHANICAL TRANSFER SWITCHES transfer loads from normal to emergency sources or vice-versa. They have movable parts actuated by electro-magnets that are manually or automatically controlled.

FERRO-RESONANT TRANSFORMERS are devices located in the inverter, which besides transforming the square wave into a sine wave also regulates the AC-output voltage. The performance characteristics of the ferro-resonant transformers are identical to those of the conventional constant voltage transformers extensively used in industry.

---

fier panel located in the inverter cabinet. The battery is paralleled with the rectifier panel, and, if the AC input line fails, no-break is assured.

The line DC voltage and the battery DC voltage are compared continuously, and the highest source is selected to supply the critical load with no interruption. The load sees only the AC voltage produced by the inverter, and there are no switching transients or synchronization variations. When the AC input goes directly into the inverter, it reduces the required size of the battery inverter-charger. The battery charger in this system is sized only for battery charging and not for the critical load supply through the inverter. The AC input type of UPS usually proves economical in systems of 3 kva and above.

For Good Measure . . .

An engine-generator set can be combined with a float-type continuous UPS to provide backup power for failures exceeding the battery-support time, as shown in this section's diagrams. If there is a power failure, the engine-generator manually or automatically starts after a preset time-delay, which depends on the battery support-time. After normal frequency is obtained within ±2 percent, the electro-mechanical transfer switch is manually or automatically transferred, connecting the engine-generator to the battery inverter-charger. The operation acts as if the AC power line had been restored. When normal power is restored the transfer switch automatically connects the AC line bus to the UPS system.

Power line frequency stability for the load is assured by a synchronizing signal that maintains the inverter's phase and frequency output at the same level as in the incoming line. The inverter's voltage regulator maintains the AC load voltage constant.

For periodic maintenance and inspection of the inverter and battery charger or for battery servicing, a manual transfer make-break switch may be used. This switch, usually mounted on the inverter door, connects the AC critical load to the AC incoming line bypassing the charger battery and inverter. The synchronizing signal circuit assures that the inverter output and the AC line are in phase at the transfer time as shown in the make-break diagram. A transformer is used in the bypass if the line AC

---

voltage differs from the load AC voltage.

The DC power of the battery can be used for instrumentation control. The recommended battery voltage is usually 125-v DC. The reason for this voltage is the reduction in amperage for the charger required and, hence, a lower price for the static battery charger. Sometimes 12-, 24- or 48-v DC is required for instrumentation control. This usage is possible even with a 125-v DC battery.

One way of obtaining different DC voltage sources is from the inverter itself. The inverter transforms DC current from one voltage to another. The 125-v DC battery current is inverted into a square wave, fed through a transformer inside the inverter, and then rectified to the desired 12-, 24- or 48-v DC as required. (See the various DC voltage supply diagrams in this section.)

Solid-State Transfer Switch UPS

A solid-state transfer switch is used in these types of UPS. It is a double-throw transfer switch. Being solid-state it does not have any moving parts and transfers loads within 0 to ¼ cycle depending on where in the cycle power is interrupted. A synchronizing signal circuitry between the inverter and the AC incoming line keeps the transferred load in step through the solid-state transfer switches. This type of transfer can be used effectively for critical loads such as flame-failure devices and computers.

The static transfer-switch UPS may be one of three kinds: forward system, reverse system or reverse system combined with engine-generator backup.

The forward system uses a static transfer switch in addition to the basic continuous system. The load usually is fed directly through the static transfer switch from the line or through a transformer if the voltage of the incoming load is different from the AC load voltage. If there is a power failure, the static switch transfers the AC load to the inverter. Because the charger is used only to charge the battery, it is small sized. The battery and the static inverter form the backup protection. The forward system, however, does not assure transient isolation and regulation from AC incoming line. This condition is not required in all critical loads, though.

The reverse system is used if a better continuous supply regulation and transient isolation are required. The AC normal line power feeds the battery charger, which floats the battery and supplies power to the critical load through the inverter and the static switch. This system has the same reliability as the simplest and best continuous system, as shown in lower left diagram, plus the following advantages: no voltage disturbances and no frequency variations can be transmitted from the input line to the critical load. The assembly battery charger, battery and inverter with its input filter form a perfect buffer to absorb these disturbances. Because of the added static transfer switch, if any component of the reverse system fails, the load is transferred in 0 to ¼ cycle to the backup line supply. The reverse system costs more than the continuous system because of the larger rectifier.

The reverse system combined with engine-generator set offers double backup protection. The engine-generator set offers added protection against line failures exceeding the battery supply time. The starting and connecting of the engine generator set can be made either manually or automatically after a preselected time delay following power failure. When synchronization with the power line is required, a synchronization switch is inserted into the engine-generator transfer switch to bypass synchronization when the emergency source is in operation. The frequency and voltage stability of the generator set must match the requirements of the critical load. This system provides power-line frequency stability to the critical load during normal operation and inverter controlled frequency during emergency operation. The electro-mechanical transfer switch must not transfer the engine-generator before a normal frequency of ±2 percent is obtained. This limit is obtained through the frequency regulator of the engine-generator set interlocked with the electro-mechanical transfer switch. If the frequency and voltage stability of the engine-generator do not meet the requirements of the critical load, then a continuous system is recommended. (The forward, reverse and reverse

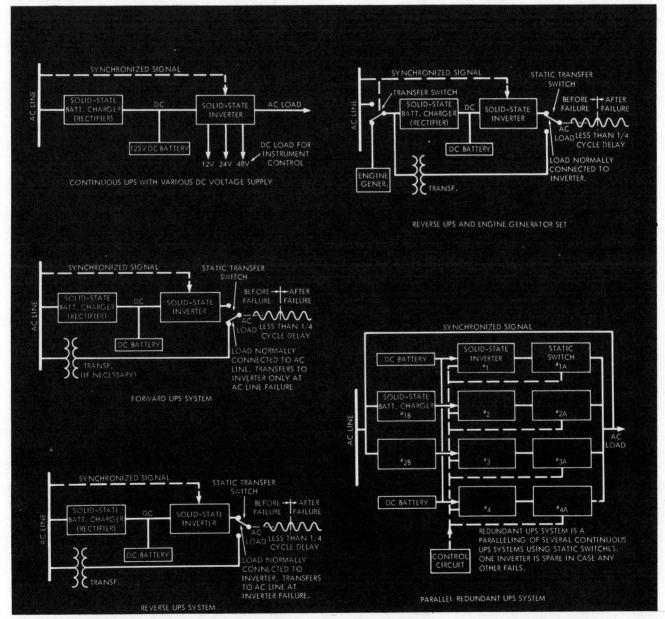

CONTINUOUS UPS WITH VARIOUS DC VOLTAGE SUPPLY

REVERSE UPS AND ENGINE GENERATOR SET

FORWARD UPS SYSTEM

REVERSE UPS SYSTEM

PARALLEL REDUNDANT UPS SYSTEM

with engine-generator set are shown in diagrams.

Parallel Redundant UPS Systems

From the standpoint of reliability, continuous or floated battery systems can be classified in two categories: nonredundant and parallel redundant.

The nonredundant system consists of one rectifier, one battery and one inverter. This system is the simplest in operation, the lowest in cost and has good reliability.

The more reliable and sophisticated parallel redundant system is a combination of two or more nonredundant UPS systems connected in parallel (see diagrams). Each branch of the paralleled UPS systems can be isolated from the critical bus by a static switch. A failure in one paralleled UPS system is isolated from the critical load before it can affect the remaining ones.

The nonredundant system is reliable for approximately 40,000 hr mean time between failures. The mean time between failures (MTBF) is the average time between several failures of the UPS system experienced over a period of time with that particular system. The redundant system has attained an 80,000 hr mean time between failures. The cost for the same kva load for a redundant system, however, is more than double the nonredundant. The reliability required by the critical load, therefore, dictates which system should be installed. The effect of the line frequency and voltage dip variations also must be compared with the potential cost in wasted manpower, damaged equipment and the importance of the critical load.

These systems may consist of two parallel rectifier-chargers each being capable to carry the full load, one or two sets of batteries and four parallel inverters, three of which carry the full load and the fourth inverter is a spare. This arrangement can operate with one inverter and/or charger out of service. The static switch instantly isolates the failing inverter from the critical load before the voltage dips out of the critical value and is replaced with the spare unit.

Isolation and replacement are accomplished in less than a quarter cycle before the failing inverter can develop a complete short-circuit and before the remaining inverters can see the short. The parallel redundant UPS provides improved reliability over the nonredundant system. Such systems up to 1,000 kva have been successfully used for large computers and have provided fast transient responses and stable frequency.

A comparison of types, merits, costs and applications of the UPS systems is charted on this page.

COMPARISON OF STATIC UPS SYSTEMS					
Type of UPS			System	Outage after power failure (cycles)	Equip. relative cost %*	Application
U.P.S. with no load interruption	non redundant (non paralleled) systems	without static switches	Continuous AC Line input at battery charger	0	100% (taken as base)	Protection against power line failures and when load power requirements are not compatible with line voltage and frequency variations. Line back-up protection when UPS fails is not provided.
			Continuous with engine-gen. set through transfer-switch	0	100% + eng-gen. + transfer switch	Same as continuous AC line input at battery charger and when power failure may last more than battery support time. (10 to 60 min)
			Continuous AC line input at inverter	0	Over 100% for less than 3 kva Less than 100% for more than 3 kva.	Same as continuous AC line input at battery charger but less economical for loads below 3 kva.
		with static switches	Forward normal operation through AC line	0-¼	93-108% + cost of static switch	Protection against power line failures and when load power requirements are compatible with line voltage and frequency variations. Back-up protection with UPS is provided.
			Reverse normal operation through inverter	0	108-125% + cost of static switch	Same as continuous AC line input at battery charger. Line back-up protection is provided through static switch in case of UPS (inverter, rectifier, battery) failure.
			Reverse with eng-gen. set through transfer-switch	0	108-125% + eng-gen. + static switch	Same as reverse normal operation through inverter and when power failure may last more than battery support time (10 to 60 min)
			Paralleled reverse system (redundant)	0	Approx. 200%	Most reliable for very critical loads. Same as continuous AC line input at battery charger but paralleled with one or more UPS units. Failure of one unit is replaced with spare unit in less than ¼ cycle.

*Prices for each UPS system vary with their kva rating, characteristics.

3.2 A Discussion of Uninterrupted Power Supply

Section 3.1 of uninterrupted power supply discussed the general theory and operation of uninterrupted power supply (UPS) systems. This section gives a detailed discussion and illustration in diagrams of the basic solid-state hardware—transistors, thyristors and diodes — that control power in a UPS system.

Advancements in the semiconductor field during the last decade have led to the development of solid-state devices with greater reliability, longer life and shorter response time than the electronic and electro-mechanical devices. Solid-state devices have made possible the industrialization of static rectifiers, inverters and switches that are the basic components of static uninterrupted power supply systems.

Diodes, Thyristors And Transistors

Semiconductors, called diodes, are two-terminal solid substances that when electrified, exhibit an anode and a cathode, permitting current flow in the forward direction, from anode to cathode, and blocking reverse current flow. This property is due to the internal behavior of the atoms and electrons. All activity in these solid-state devices takes place inside the material and without any movement of parts.

Semiconductor elements are composite substances made of two layers of crystals, one of which has slight impurities. Silicon or germanium is used in their composition.

Semiconductor cells are formed by the junction of N (negative) and P (positive) crystals. Voltage applied across their junction current flows through the junction. If the polarity of the applied voltage is reversed, then the current flow is blocked.

A silicon diode offers a low forward voltage drop and a very small reverse leakage current. The diode is perfectly suited to act as a rectifier. The volt-ampere relationship of a diode, is shown in Fig. 1.

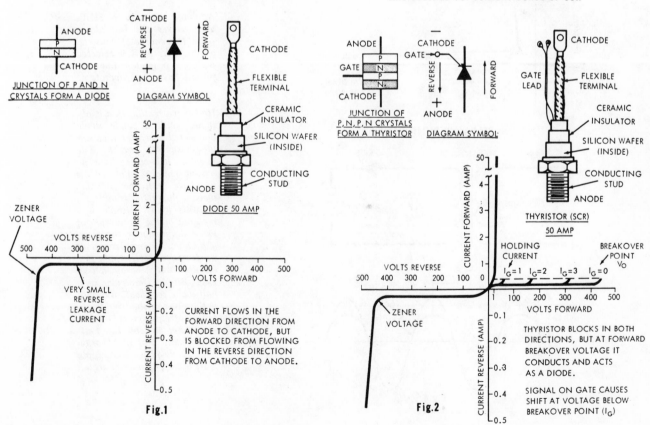

TYPICAL POWER DIODE, DIAGRAM SYMBOL AND VOLTAGE VS. CURRENT CURVE OF SILICON DIODE

Fig.1

TYPICAL THYRISTOR, DIAGRAM SYMBOL AND VOLTAGE VS. CURRENT CURVE OF SCR

Fig.2

If a positive voltage is applied, the current through the diode can reach high values, unless limited by external impedances. The diode, therefore, offers low resistance in the positive direction. If, however, the voltage polarity is reversed, the opposite effect occurs: as voltage increases in the negative direction, the current becomes extremely low, because the diode offers high resistance, thus blocking current flow.

Diodes are manufactured up to 550 amp half-wave maximum per diode at peak reverse voltages up to 1,200 v.

A thyristor, or silicon-controlled rectifier (SCR), also is a semiconducting device in which current is blocked in both directions until a signal voltage is applied to a control terminal called the gate. The thyristor is formed by a junction of four layers of crystals (P-N-P-N), with the gate connected to the second P layer. The gate or trigger current has a relatively low value. The thyristor blocks current in both directions but has a forward breakover voltage (V_0), at which point it behaves as a diode. The volt-ampere relationship of a thyristor (SCR) is shown in Fig. 2.

In the reverse direction, the thyristor has the same operating characteristics as a diode. In the forward direction, it blocks the voltage until the breakover voltage point is reached. When this point is reached, the thyristor breaks down, and the current increases from low to very high value, limited only by the circuit impedance. If the load current drops below the holding-current level, forward blocking is restored. With a gate signal of sufficient magnitude, forward blocking is ineffective, and the thyristor behaves like a diode. Applying a voltage to the SCR's gate causes the breakdown to occur at a lower value, V_1, instead of V_0, as shown in Fig. 3.

If an AC voltage is applied, the thyristor automatically turns off each half cycle when the voltage reaches zero. In a DC circuit, the thyristor is turned off by auxiliary devices that reduce the voltage to zero or reduce the current below holding value.

Diodes and thyristors have almost

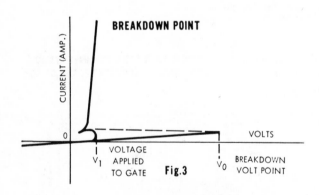

BREAKDOWN POINT

Fig.3

HALF-WAVE RECTIFICATION

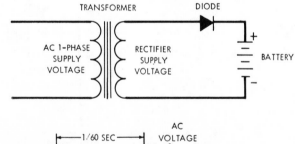

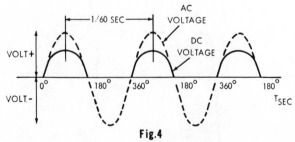

Fig.4

1. *Typical power diode.*

2. *Typical thyristor.*

3. *Applying voltage to SCR's gate causes the breakdown point to occur at V, instead of Vo. The SCR is selected with a Vo greater than expected in normal operation.*

4. *Half-wave rectification is obtained with a single diode connected in series with a single-phase AC circuit. The negative half-cycles have no output voltage. The DC is in phase with the AC sine wave voltage for completely resistive loads. Ripple is a measure of the fluctuation of DC voltage about the average value. A rectifier circuit producing a high ripple factor does not generate a true DC. Ripple frequency in a half-wave rectification circuit is the same as the fundamental AC frequency, i. e., 60/ sec. That is why the half-wave method of rectification with single-phase AC supply isn't used in power charging.*

no overload capability compared to familiar electric equipment. The peak reverse voltage (PRV) is the maximum voltage the cell can withstand in the reverse operation condition. All silicon static devices have thermal limitations. Diodes and thyristors are sensitive to excessive voltage or current beyond their nominal values.

The life expectancy of a completely sealed silicon cell is believed to be unlimited, if it is properly applied.

Transistors are obtained by adding a third layer of either germanium or silicon to a diode. A separate voltage source applied to the third middle layer assists or retards the flow of current through the other two layers. The transistor thus becomes an amplifier that can multiply an applied signal a hundredfold or more. With suitable resonant circuitry, the transistor can generate its own sine wave, the frequency of which depends on the constants of the resonant circuit. In this case, the transistor acts as an oscillator and is used as such in solid-state inverters.

These principal solid-state elements are used in the manufacture of the UPS's main components: rectifier-chargers, inverters and solid-state switches.

Rectifier Connections

Today's solid-state rectifier chargers more efficiently provide the desirable charge characteristics that previously were available only from motor-generator sets. There are three basic methods of battery charging: constant-current, two-rate and self-tapering. The self-tapering method is best because the charge rate diminishes as the battery charge increases. Rectifiers are usually fed by the AC-power source of the plant.

The solid-state element most often used in modern chargers is the silicon diode; its characteristics are best suited for non-aging and for high-operating temperature.

To obtain conversion from AC to DC, three basic circuits are commonly used: the half-wave rectification circuit (the simplest of the three), the center-tap full-wave circuit and the full-wave bridge circuit. Diagrams showing DC voltage resulting from these three types appear in Fig. 4.

High-power rectifiers are usually 3-

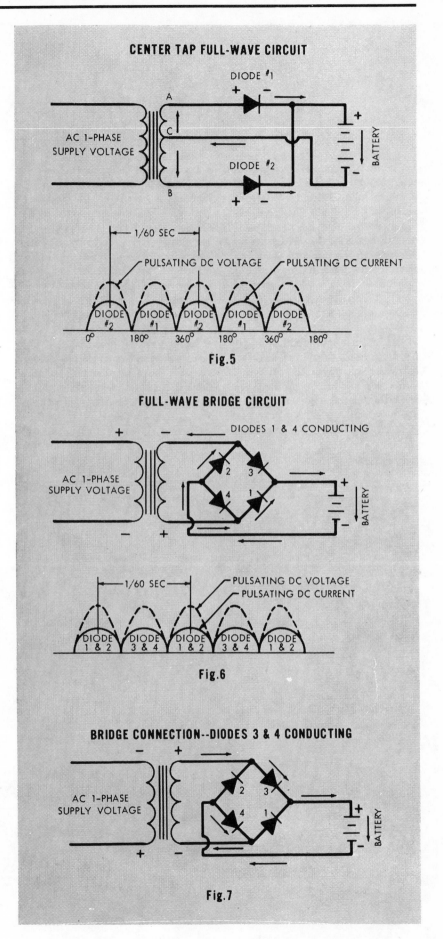

CENTER TAP FULL-WAVE CIRCUIT

Fig.5

FULL-WAVE BRIDGE CIRCUIT

Fig.6

BRIDGE CONNECTION--DIODES 3 & 4 CONDUCTING

Fig.7

5. The Center-tap full-wave connection is extensively used in today's single-phase chargers. Silicon rectifiers are capable of sustaining several hundred amperes per cell, and their construction is compact and relatively simple. In this method of connection, only two diodes are required for a single-phase AC supply. The full-wave rectification is obtained by the two diodes. One of them conducts during the positive half-cycle and the other during the negative half-cycle. Current flow is rectified as follows: when the induced voltage in the transformer secondary is from A to B, the current flows from C to B through Diode 2, the battery and then back to C. After a half cycle, when the voltage reverses, the current flows from C to A and through Diode 1, the battery and then back to C. This repeats every cycle, and full-wave rectification is obtained. The ripple frequency on a single-phase full-wave rectification is twice the fundamental frequency or 120/sec.

6. The full-wave bridge connection produces a ripple frequency twice that of the fundamental frequency. To follow the flow of current being rectified, the polarity during half a cycle is assumed. The flow of current is from positive to negative.

The arrows in the diagram indicate the flow of current through Diode 1, the battery, through Diode 2 and then back to the negative polarity of the transformer secondary.

7. This diagram shows what happens in the second half of the cycle when the polarity of the secondary reverses.

In the second half of the cycle, the flow of current is again from positive to negative through Diode 3, the battery, through Diode 4 and then back to the negative polarity of the transformer secondary. The bridge connection requires four diodes instead of two, as in the center-tap connection. The bridge connection has some advantages over the center-tap since sometimes the input transformer may not be necessary. For the same output voltage, the bridge diodes block only half the reverse voltage of diodes in the center-tap method. Higher operating voltages are possible with the bridge connection method.

8. Ripple frequency of pulsating DC is 180/sec. Output DC current is smoother than in one-phase half-wave circuit.

9. The 3-phase full-wave or 3-phase bridge connection has two diodes connected in each 3-phase branch. Output DC voltage has six ripples per cycle, resulting in a low ripple factor. Operation sequence: Assume Phase A positive, B negative and C neutral. Current flows from Phase A through Diode 1 to the positive of battery. The current is blocked from flowing to the negative of the battery by Diodes 2, 3 and 5. The only way the current can flow is through the battery and back to Phase B through Diode 4. This repeats six times per cycle with different phase combinations. A 1-cycle sequence would be Phases A to B, A to C, B to C, B to A, C to A, and C to B; then again A to B, etc.

THREE-PHASE HALF-WAVE CONNECTION

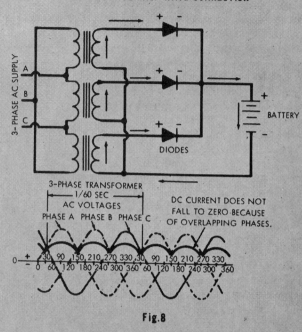

Fig.8

THREE-PHASE FULL-WAVE CONNECTION

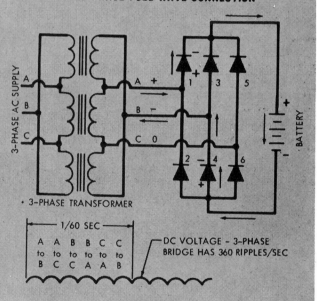

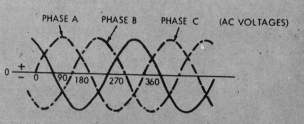

Fig.9

phase. A typical 3-phase half-wave connection is shown in Fig. 8. The ripple frequency is three times the AC current frequency, or 180/sec. The 3-phase full-wave connection, or 3-phase bridge circuit, is very often used in battery-charging equipment. The diagram of the 3-phase full-wave connection in Fig. 9, shows that the ripple frequency is six times the alternating current frequency, or 360/sec.

SCR's are used in modern rectifiers to regulate the output DC voltage within ± 0.5 percent with line voltage variations of ± 10 percent and frequency variations of ± 5 percent at 60 cycles. The rectifier charger is usually provided with low DC voltage relay to detect loss of AC power to charger, with ground-indicating lights, float-equalizing switch, ammeter and voltmeter. These last devices are optional.

Cooling of the rectifier for smaller units (1 to 100 kw) is accomplished by natural convection. For larger units (40 to 300 kw) forced-air cooling is assured by a fan driven by a 3-phase totally enclosed motor. Ratings for silicon AC-to-DC conversion units are available from 1 through 750 kw.

A diagram for a typical automatically regulated constant-voltage silicon battery charger is shown in Fig. 10. The diagram shows a 3-phase charger manufactured as a self-contained unit in a floor-mounted, motor-ventilated steel cabinet. The silicon rectifier has a full-wave bridge connection using hermetically-sealed silicon rectifier diodes.

The regulated DC output of the charger is obtained by SCR's controlled by a transistorized regulator. The transistorized regulator consists of a voltage section and a current limiting section.

Constant voltage is assured by comparing the DC output voltage with a Zener diode constant-voltage reference bridge. Any AC or DC voltage variation due to change in DC load generates an imbalance in the voltage reference bridge. This signal pulses the gate circuit of the SCR so as to maintain a DC voltage setting. The voltage is regulated between no load and full load to ± 0.5 percent, with a line voltage variation of ± 10 percent at 60 cycles. Efficiency is as high as 93 percent, and the current-limiting section of the transistorized regulator

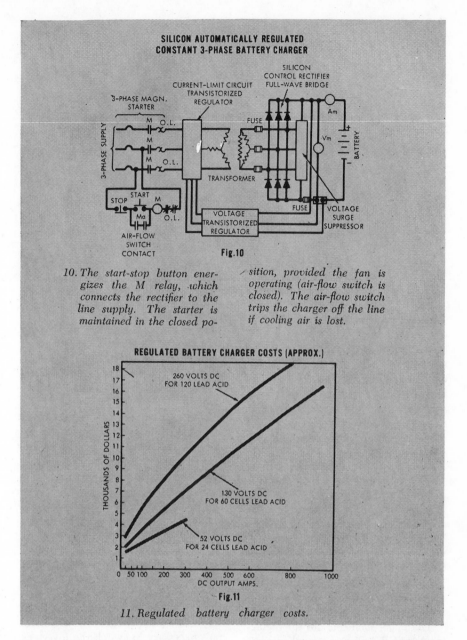

SILICON AUTOMATICALLY REGULATED CONSTANT 3-PHASE BATTERY CHARGER

Fig.10

10. The start-stop button energizes the M relay, which connects the rectifier to the line supply. The starter is maintained in the closed position, provided the fan is operating (air-flow switch is closed). The air-flow switch trips the charger off the line if cooling air is lost.

REGULATED BATTERY CHARGER COSTS (APPROX.)

Fig.11

11. Regulated battery charger costs.

protects the charger by automatically limiting the current to safe values if an overload occurs. A voltrap surge suppressor for over-voltage protection is also provided.

These self-contained units are manufactured for 208-, 230-, or 460-v, 3-phase AC, 60-cycle input and for loads of 25 to 1,000 amp. (The approximate costs of such battery chargers are shown in Fig. 11.)

How To Size A Battery Charger

To select the correct battery charger for an application, the following formula may be applied to determine the ampere requirement:

$$A = \frac{AH \times 1.15}{T} + L$$

A = minimum rated ampere charger capacity—in any case not less than 20 percent of the 8-hr rate of discharge of the battery.

AH = ampere hours discharged from the battery.

T = time allowed for recharge, in hours.

L = continuous connected load on the battery in amps.

1.15 = efficiency charge factor.

Example: If a 200 AH battery is 50 percent discharged and it must be recharged in 10 hours, the charger must supply a continuous load of 6 amp:

$$A = \frac{(200 \times 0.5) \ AH \times 1.15}{10} + 6 = 17.5 \ amp$$

Since 17.5 amp is not a standard rating, the nearest rating must be selected, but not less than 95 percent of the calculated value required.

3.3 Operating Theory of Static Inverters; Operational Block and Wiring Diagrams

The two previous sections (3.1-3.2) discussed the general theory and operation of UPS systems and described the basic solid-state hardware that control power in the system. This third section (3.3) defines and describes the basic, simplified operating theory of statics inverters, including operational block and wiring diagrams.

The most important component in an uninterrupted power supply system, the inverter, performs the opposite function of a rectifier: it changes DC produced by rectifiers, or batteries, into AC, which feeds the critical load.

An inverter is composed of three major elements, each performing a basic function, as shown in Figure 1.

The major elements are the oscillator, the SCR (silicone-controlled rectifier) inverter (power switching section) and the regulating filter (ferroresonant transformer).

The oscillator determines the operating frequency in the limits of $\pm\frac{1}{2}$ of 1 percent to 1 percent Hz over operating conditions. By synchronizing the oscillator to an external signal or to another inverter frequency, the line synchronization, or the parallel operation with another inverter, may be controlled. A basic oscillator wiring diagram is shown in Figure 2. It is a saturateable core-transformer type of transistorized oscillator, with a frequency proportional to the applied DC voltage.

The principle of operation is that of a tuned resonant circuit, with oscillations sustained by pulses of DC fed through the transistor during a small portion of each cycle. The output frequency of the oscillator is adjusted by tuning the resonant circuit (self-induction [L] and capacitor [C] load). A variable resistance control on the front panel does this.

Once the resonant circuit is tuned, the frequency remains stable and independent of the load or input voltage.

This is not the case, however, with similar rotating devices, which have a variation of frequency.

Because of the oscillator function, the pulse width—extent of cycle duration—and the desired frequency of the inverter output can be kept constant. The oscillator provides the basic frequency and produces the logic signals necessary to switch the inverter's thyristors correctly (firing, gating).

Most Critical Element

The SCR inverter, also called power switching section, is the most critical of the major elements. It operates as a switching circuit, the oscillator square wave output triggering the SCR's alternately. The inverter output is also a square wave with an amplitude proportional to the DC voltage input.

The thyristor (SCR) in the inverter blocks the current in the forward direction until a trigger signal is applied to its gate (see secton 3.2). The thyristor is easily turned on by a timed pulse (square wave) from the oscillator. It is not so simple to turn it off, however.

To turn it off, the thyristor current must be driven to zero, after which it acts as an open switch. With alternating current (as in the rectifiers), the thyristor is turned off at the instant the AC reaches zero. To turn off a thyristor fed by DC, the forward current must be reduced to zero in one element and the reapplication of forward voltage to this element must be delayed until its forward blocking capability is regained and the forward direction flow of the next element is triggered. This operation is called "commutation."

Commutation is achieved with a capacitor that stores energy for a half cycle and is discharged in the reverse direction at the beginning of the next, driving the thyristor current to zero.

The single-phase inverter, shown in Figure 3, is the simplest center-tapped circuit using only two thyristors (A and B in the figure) as switches.

Forced commutation is accomplished by adding a capacitor (C), inductor (L) and two blocking diodes (DA and DB).

The principle of operation is as follows:

Thyristor A is conducting, and capacitor C has been charged with positive polarity (see Figure 3a). After a half cycle, when Thyristor B is fired by the oscillator (see Figure 3b), the energy the capacitor stored during the first half cycle is discharged in the reverse direction at the beginning of the second half cycle. The energy in the capacitor maintains the load current until Thyristor A regains its blocking ability. The diodes block the turn-off energy from going through the trans-

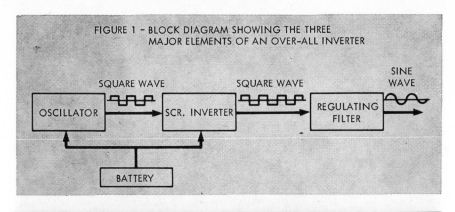

FIGURE 1 - BLOCK DIAGRAM SHOWING THE THREE MAJOR ELEMENTS OF AN OVER-ALL INVERTER

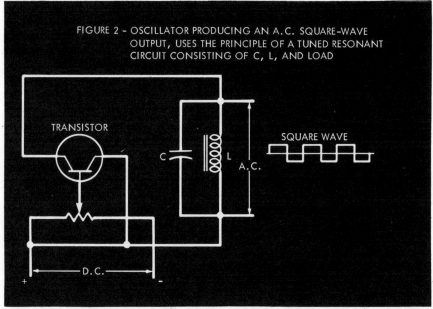

FIGURE 2 - OSCILLATOR PRODUCING AN A.C. SQUARE-WAVE OUTPUT, USES THE PRINCIPLE OF A TUNED RESONANT CIRCUIT CONSISTING OF C, L, AND LOAD

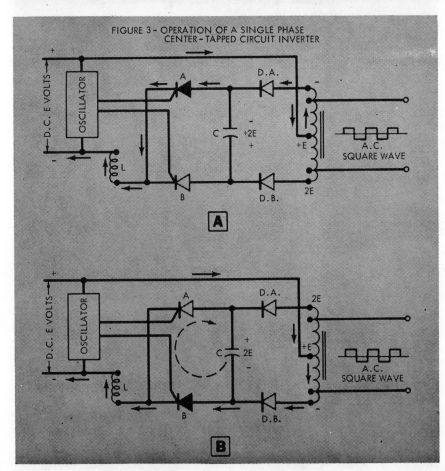

FIGURE 3 - OPERATION OF A SINGLE PHASE CENTER-TAPPED CIRCUIT INVERTER

former. The inductor limits the current during the transient turn-off interval. When Thyristor B conducts, the capacitor is charged again, but with opposite polarity, and the output voltage reverses its polarity (as indicated by the arrows showing current flow in Figure 3a).

After one cycle, Thyristor A is again triggered by the square wave impulse of the oscillator, and the sequence of operation repeats itself as long as the thyristors are fired and turned on by the alternate impulses of the oscillator.

By transformer action, the output voltage is an alternating square wave with a frequency set by the rate of switching and an amplitude set by the transformer ratio and the DC input voltage.

The single-phase, center-tapped autotransformer inverter is for ratings between 1 and 10 kva and is used mainly for source potentials of 12, 24 and 48 v DC.

The single-phase, bridge-circuit inverter is usually used for ratings of 10 to 50 kva and mainly for source potentials of 120, 240 and 600 v DC. The circuit uses four thyristors as switches to connect the load alternately from plus to minus and back to plus across the DC input source.

The inverter frequency is set by the rate of switching. By using the bridge connection, a better wave form is obtained. For this reason, some manufacturers use the SCR bridge-circuit inverter for units above 2 kva.

The three-phase inverter is usually used for 50 kva and more but is also manufactured for ratings as low as 10 kva. It is a combination of three basic single-phase inverters. Their output transformer secondaries may be delta or wye to supply the three-phase inverter, as shown in Figure 4.

Bridge-Circuit Operation

The operation of the single-phase bridge-circuit inverter is shown in Figure 5. In this operation, Thyristors A and D are fired by the oscillator and turned on. The DC voltage causes the current to flow from positive through the load, through D and then back to the negative source. The current through the load is in positive direction, as shown in Figures 5a and 5e. Before the end of the half cycle, switching Thyristors A and B will produce zero current output (Figures 5b and 5e). At the end of the positive half-cycle firing of the gates of B and C, full DC voltage is applied in the

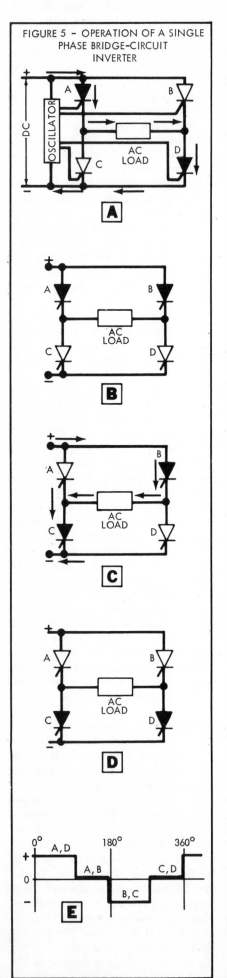

FIGURE 5 – OPERATION OF A SINGLE PHASE BRIDGE-CIRCUIT INVERTER

A

B

C

D

E

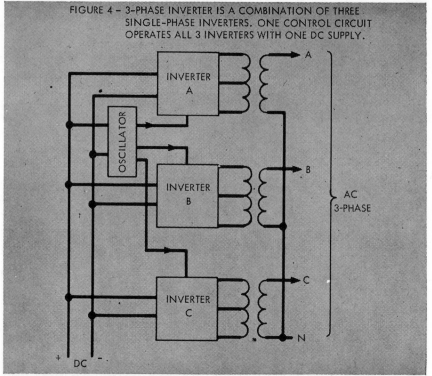

FIGURE 4 – 3-PHASE INVERTER IS A COMBINATION OF THREE SINGLE-PHASE INVERTERS. ONE CONTROL CIRCUIT OPERATES ALL 3 INVERTERS WITH ONE DC SUPPLY.

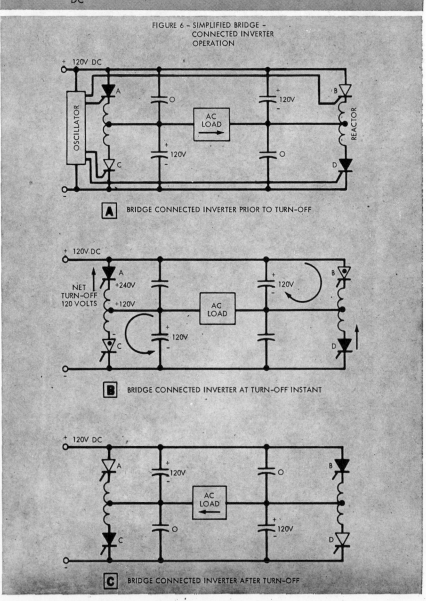

FIGURE 6 – SIMPLIFIED BRIDGE - CONNECTED INVERTER OPERATION

A BRIDGE CONNECTED INVERTER PRIOR TO TURN-OFF

B BRIDGE CONNECTED INVERTER AT TURN-OFF INSTANT

C BRIDGE CONNECTED INVERTER AFTER TURN-OFF

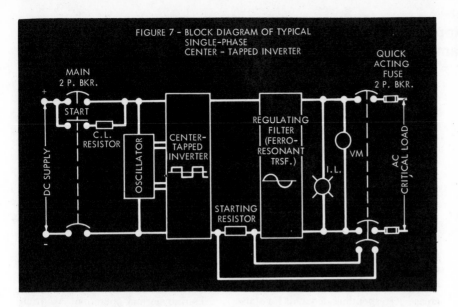

FIGURE 7 – BLOCK DIAGRAM OF TYPICAL
SINGLE-PHASE
CENTER – TAPPED INVERTER

negative sense and causes current to flow from positive through B, through the load in the opposite direction, through C and then to negative source (Figure 5c and 5e). Likewise, before the end of this second half-cycle firing, Thyristors C and D will produce zero current output (Figures 5d and 5e). The resulting wave form is a square wave with a frequency determined by the timing of switching on A and C, while the voltage is determined by the timing of switching on B and D. The square-wave output has the shape shown in Figure 5e.

Again as in the single-phase center-tapped circuit inverter, the commutation problem must be taken care of. Commutation is achieved, as shown in Figure 6, in this way:

A 120-v DC supply is connected (Figure 6a), and Thyristors A and D are conducting current through the load. Capacitors B and C are charged up to 120 v. The other capacitors are shorted out by the conducting of Thyristors A and D. At the instant of commutation (Figure 6b), Thyristors B and C are gated on, and the effect is to connect the capacitor voltage to the midpoint of the center-tapped reactor. By action of an autotransformer, the upper end of Reactor AC rises to +240 v. The line side of Thyristor A is at a potential of 120 v. The effect is a net voltage of 120 v across Thyristor A in the reverse direction, which drives its current to zero and turns it off. A similar action

also takes place at Thyristor D.

After commutation, Thyristors A and D have recovered their blocking condition, and Thyristors B and C are carrying the load current. The other capacitors, A and D, have charged up to the line voltage and are ready for the next commutation. (Figure 6c.) This connection fulfills the condition that any thyristor should be turned off by the firing of its mate.

If proper commutation does not occur, then the thyristors and their mates will be on, resulting in a short-circuit across the DC source. This is called "misfire," causing the protective fuse to blow. Misfiring is a result of overloading inverters beyond the current that can be safely commutated.

The Regulating Filter

The regulating filter in the inverter output limits inverter output current, preventing inverter overloading.

The filter is basically a ferro-resonant transformer similar to the constant-voltage transformer extensively used in industry. The filter converts the square-wave output of the inverter into a sine wave of low harmonic content, 5 percent from 25 percent to 100 percent load. The filter also regulates the output voltage to ±2 to 3 percent under all operating conditions and provides overload and short-circuit protection for the inverter.

When abnormal loads are applied, or when the output is short-circuited, the current-limiting circuit in the regulating filter electronically reduces

the rated output current until the overload or short-circuit is removed, at which time the inverter returns to normal.

The output current of a filtered inverter is limited on an instantaneous basis to not more than about 150 percent of full output current even when short-circuited. This is achieved by sensing the rectified output current signal with a transient monitoring circuit. When 150 percent of transient set-point is exceeded, the phase angle between square wave power stages is forced to 180 deg, producing zero output voltage at the regulating filter input.

It is advisable to divide critical instrument loads into many branch circuits protected individually with high-speed fuses of small sizes. This type of fuse provides fast opening on fault currents. The clearing time must be almost instantaneous to avert disturbances that affect the remainder of the instrument system.

The circuit breaker should not be used as branch circuit protective devices for critical instrumentation circuits fed by single-phase inverters 1 to 10 kva, 120 v, sine wave output. Instead, quick-acting fuses rated for coordination in the branch circuits and the UPS or inverter should be used, thus preventing loss of inverter output voltage and power outages in the instrumentation circuits. The use of such fuses is a result of successful field experience.

Inverter Operation

A block diagram and the operation of a typical single-phase inverter are shown in Figure 7. To start the inverter, a start push-button connects the input voltage through a circuit-limiting resistor to reduce starting inrush. When the indicating light is on, the main input breaker is closed, applying full voltage and starting the inverter.

The regulating filter has also a starting resistor in the primary to limit magnetizing inrush current. When the output breaker is closed, the resistor is shorted out and the load is connected for full capacity.

3.4 Static Switches, Their Application to UPS; Block and Wiring Diagrams

This section (3.4) on UPS describes the static switches, their application to UPS and their block and wiring diagrams.

The behavior of diodes, transistors and thyristors (SCR) and their operation in the rectifier charger and inverter components were discussed in sections 3.2 and 3.3.

Technological advances in semiconductors during the last decade have resulted in a switching device without movable parts—the static switch. Its application in uninterrupted power supply systems and a resistance heater controller and a static motor controller is growing.

The cost of the static switch is several times higher than its electromechanical counterpart because of the high cost of semiconductors. The advantages of the static switch, however, may well justify the cost. Solid-state devices are maintenance-free, but more important, they perform the switching in $\frac{1}{8}$ cycle (2 millisec), which is of paramount importance for critical loads. Moreover, because manufacturing techniques are always improving, the cost of the static switch and static controller is likely to decrease and, it is hoped, reach a level not exceeding 20 percent to 50 percent more than the cost of silicon cells. Currently, they cost 200 to 250 percent more than silicon cells.

Static switches that detect overloads and phase failures, that can reverse power and phase sequence and that can act from a low energy input will soon play a greater part in controlling electrical loads. The demand for higher productivity, greater reliability and low maintenance will increase corresponding demands for static switches and controllers.

The application of solid-state switches will benefit many industries, including textile, natural gas, oil, mining, chemical, glass and steel, where computer operations demand their use.

Switching And Rectifying

A silicon-controlled rectifier blocks current in each direction until a signal is applied to a control terminal, called a "gate." The cell of an SCR uses a four-layer wafer, P-N-P-N, the gate being connected to the second P layer, as shown in Figure 1. When the gate is energized by an oscillator circuit or by any logic-control circuitry, the current flows in only one direction, the same as in a diode. If the SCR is connected to AC, rectification takes place. Conversely, if the circuit is DC, the SCR operates as a switch, except that once energized, it does not turn off readily.

To turn off the thyristor, an additional circuit is necessary. This circuit includes a capacitor providing the turn-off current of the thyristor. The operation of this circuit is called commutation. In fact, the thyristor can be considered as a combined switch and rectifier.

Because thyristors function as switches when combined with suitable circuitry, they can do the job of conventional switches and contactors.

As an application to uninterrupted power supply, static switches are connected at the inverter output. They switch the AC; rectification is avoided by connecting two thyristors in reverse parallel. This connection prevents commutation and permits the flow of AC through the static switch toward the load, as shown in Figure 2.

During normal operation, AC from the line source energizes the battery charger, which floats the battery and powers the static inverter. The inverter is connected to the critical load through the static switch and is synchronized with the AC power line.

The normally gated SCR No. 1 allows the positive half of the AC wave to flow while SCR No. 2 allows the negative wave to flow because the two thyristors of the static switch are connected in reverse parallel. This also permits the inverter output current to flow through the static switch toward the load. The other SCR's, No. 3 and No. 4, when energized, likewise permit AC to flow—from the line source to the load.

The inverter voltage will decide through the firing logic whether SCR's No. 1 and No. 2 or No. 3 and No. 4 should be energized.

If the inverter voltage drops below a predetermined value, the power-line SCR's are gated-on by the static-switch logic board, and thus the power line will supply the critical load. If the power line voltage drops below a predetermined value, the inverter takes over. The SCR's stop conducting each time the AC voltage wave goes through zero. That is why no commutating capacitors are used, as they would be in DC. The switching time is 2 millisec. To enable so quick a switching, the power factor of the load must be close to unity, otherwise the current and voltage would not cross the zero axis at the same time.

When the power factor of the critical load is not unity power-factor, correcting capacitors bring the power factor close to unity. The simplified schematic of a reverse UPS filtered static-switch system is shown in Figure 3.

Sensing Trouble

The static switch can sense troubles at the rectifier, DC bus and failures that can cause the inverter to malfunction and can transfer the critical load to the AC supply line. The transfer time may be fast enough to keep most critical loads from trouble. The static switch ensures a back-up protection. Continuous power can thus be supplied with minimum or no interruption, regardless of whether AC is fed from the inverter or from the AC power line and regardless of whether the fault is in the critical branch circuits, in the static UPS components or in the AC power line.

If a fault occurs in a branch circuit of the critical load, the output voltage will drop in the inverter's current-limiting output filter. Sensing variations in current or voltage, the static switch will transfer the AC load from the inverter to the AC line, providing more current to clear the fault.

After clearing the fault, the static switch can then retransfer the load to the inverter. Likewise, any failure in the inverter would permit the AC load to be retransferred to the AC line. The very fast transfer of the static switch will keep most sensitive critical loads operating.

The transfer time is shown in Figure 4.

Any of the branch circuits of the critical load may short circuit, disturbing the UPS output voltage bus. Loads supplied by the inverter may de-energize and drop out. This is possible if the fault is not quickly cleared. When this happens, the faulted branch circuit may overload the inverter, causing its output filter to limit current.

To prevent this, protecting devices must clear any faults in branch circuits. Circuit breakers are too slow; quick-acting fuses should be used. Small loads should make up the branch circuits. The clearing time of the fuses must be coordinated with the available current from the inverter and with the disturbance time that the load permits. Inverters, high-impedance devices, may, while limiting current, supply only 150 percent of their full load current into a bolted fault.

If large fuses are necessary and if they cannot coordinate with the avail-

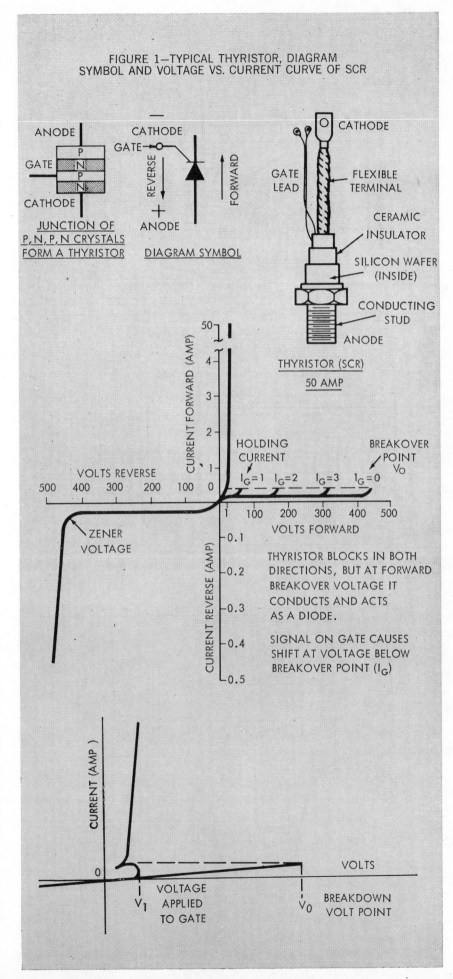

FIGURE 1—TYPICAL THYRISTOR, DIAGRAM SYMBOL AND VOLTAGE VS. CURRENT CURVE OF SCR

THYRISTOR BLOCKS IN BOTH DIRECTIONS, BUT AT FORWARD BREAKOVER VOLTAGE IT CONDUCTS AND ACTS AS A DIODE.

SIGNAL ON GATE CAUSES SHIFT AT VOLTAGE BELOW BREAKOVER POINT (I_G)

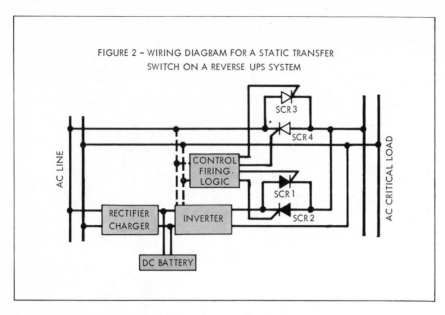

FIGURE 2 - WIRING DIAGRAM FOR A STATIC TRANSFER
SWITCH ON A REVERSE UPS SYSTEM

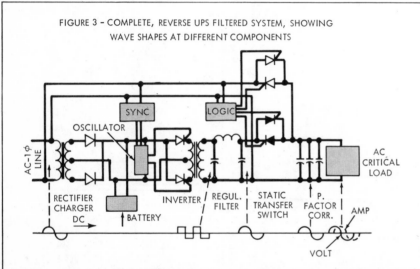

FIGURE 3 - COMPLETE, REVERSE UPS FILTERED SYSTEM, SHOWING
WAVE SHAPES AT DIFFERENT COMPONENTS

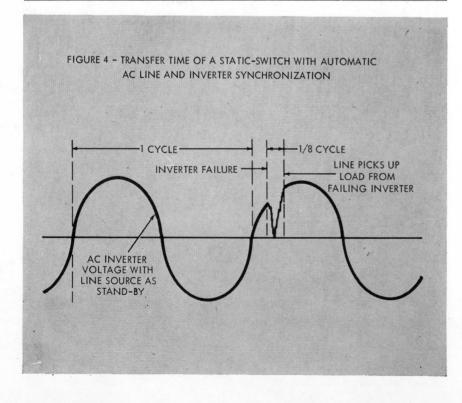

FIGURE 4 - TRANSFER TIME OF A STATIC-SWITCH WITH AUTOMATIC
AC LINE AND INVERTER SYNCHRONIZATION

able inverter current in its limiting state, a static switch can transfer the load to the line. With this arrangement, when the output voltage of the inverter begins dropping, the static switch automatically transfers the critical load to the power line. The power line, a lower impedance source, starts feeding and quickly clears the fault while maintaining the bus voltage.

After a preset timing period—about 2 to 3 sec—the static switch automatically retransfers the load from the power line to the inverter.

It is important that the static switch is limited in the amount of current it can safely carry. Therefore, it is mandatory to coordinate the rating of the static switch with the available short-circuit current from the normal AC line.

So that the static switch, inverter, battery or rectifier charger can be removed for repairs or inspection, a synchronized make-before-break transfer switch is often used. This switch is electromechanic and has overlapping contacts which permit the transfer of power inverter output to the line source or vice-versa. The transfer is possible only when an in-phase condition is shown by a synchronizing indicating lamp. Then an operator can manipulate the bypass switch in a manner similar to that of paralleling alternators.

As shown in the first section of UPS systems (3.1) the basic nonredundant UPS consists of a rectifier, a battery and an inverter. The rectifier float-charges the battery while supplying full load to the inverter. In turn, the inverter powers the critical load, and the battery supplies the inverter, which supports the critical load during line power failures. Five-to 60-min battery support, in line failure is commonly used.

Its One Big Shortcoming

This nonredundant UPS system is lowest in cost and simplest in operation. However, it has one shortcoming: an internal failure of the inverter may cause the system to shut down. Inverters have proved to be reliable but not infallible. If the system is properly applied, according to statistical failure rates, it will fail once in five years.

To improve the reliability is to parallel the system components, or the UPS parallel-redundant system. These systems, with two or more paralleled rectifiers and inverters, are so designed that the full critical load can be carried with one inverter out of service. Figure 6 on this page shows a parallel-redundant UPS system made possible by using static transfer switches.

Although the static switch is optional for continuous nonredundant UPS systems, the static switch is obligatory for parallel-redundant systems. Simply operating the inverters in parallel without the static transfer switches would obviously result in a poorer reliability than that achieved with one inverter. The failure of one inverter could cause the other one to feed into the faulted inverter and shut down all the system.

The solution is to make sure that the failure of a single inverter will not generate a malfunction of the critical load. This is possible only if the failing inverter is immediately isolated from the critical bus before the bus voltage drops below a specified value.

The method that has performed this task successfully used solid-state switches to isolate the faulted inverter from the critical bus in 2 millisec or even less.

Sometimes inverter failures result in short circuit through the inverter. If this happens, the critical load bus to which the inverter is connected also might short circuit. Unless the faulted inverter is removed from the critical bus, the bus voltage will collapse to zero, and the entire UPS system will fail to keep the critical load energized.

So parallel-redundant UPS that use static switches offer improved reliability over the nonredundant systems. This added reliability is made possible by the use of the static switch. The static switch by its very quick action keeps the bus energized even during the failure of one of the inverters by quickly switching over the load to the other inverter.

The solid-state transfer switch may clear load branch circuit faults on large circuits by transferring the load to the AC line and, after the faults are cleared, by retransferring the load to the inverter supply. It also transfers the load to the AC line source for UPS components inspection or repair.

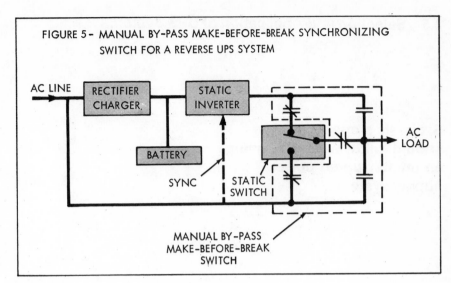

FIGURE 5 - MANUAL BY-PASS MAKE-BEFORE-BREAK SYNCHRONIZING SWITCH FOR A REVERSE UPS SYSTEM

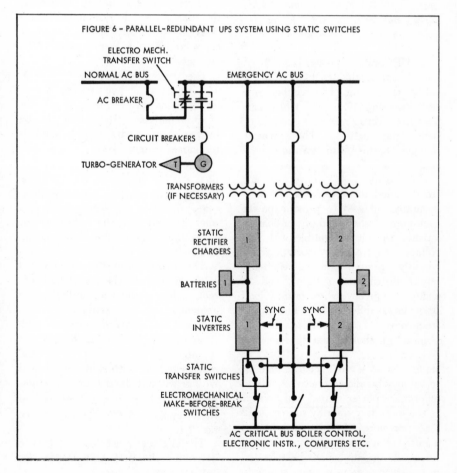

FIGURE 6 - PARALLEL-REDUNDANT UPS SYSTEM USING STATIC SWITCHES

3.5 Selection and Application of UPS Systems

Six basic steps an engineer should follow when designing an uninterrupted power supply system

The four previous sections discussed the theory and operation of uninterrupted power supply (UPS) systems, described their solid-state hardware—transistors, thyristors and diodes—and explained the operating theory of solid-state battery chargers, inverters and static switches. This section 3.5 discusses factors to consider in selecting and applying UPS systems.

A UPS system consists basically of a solid-state rectifier, a battery and a solid-state inverter. The rectifier converts incoming AC to DC, which supplies the inverter and also charges, or floats, the battery. The inverter changes DC to AC to run the critical load.

Uninterrupted AC power systems are designed to protect against power-supply outages, to provide power conditioning when load power characteristics are not compatible with line voltage and frequency variations inherently present on conventional power distribution systems, and to change frequency when critical load frequency is different from line supply frequency.

Based on the transfer time characteristics, there are two types of standby systems. In Type 1, a time interval may be allowed between failure of primary power source and transfer to the secondary standby source (4-12 cycles or more). In Type 2, load and major voltage interruptions or frequency transients cannot be tolerated in transferring from primary source to secondary standby source.

Type 2, which is the main point of discussion here, is extensively used for such critical loads as boiler flame-detectors, computers, electronic control instrumentation and critical communication complexes. In these critical loads, an outage of even a small fraction of a cycle cannot be tolerated.

From the viewpoint of reliability, the many possible system configurations may be categorized as either nonredundant or parallel-redundant systems.

The basic nonredundant system, which consists of one rectifier, a battery and one inverter, is fairly reliable at minimum cost. Reliability can be further improved by using a parallel-redundant system.

The parallel-redundant system protects against failures in the UPS system and thus provides maximum reliability. Inverters and rectifiers are parallel-operated, and the failure of one of the units will not shut down the entire system.

The main Type 2 nonredundant UPS systems are the *continuous system,* with or without a standby engine generator set and without a static switch; the *forward system,* with static switch and with or without standby engine-generator set; and the *reverse system,* with static switch and with or without standby engine-generator set. Block diagrams of each of these systems were shown in section 3.1.

The engineer must take six steps to determine the best UPS system for any application.

Step 1: Determine the allowable transfer time.

Transfer time is the time interval over which the load voltage is less than the acceptable value for proper load operation. If the system is required to protect only against power-line outages, the forward system is most appropriate. Its variations depend on the transfer time that can be tolerated if it fails, (shown in Fig. 1).

If the system is required to protect against power outages and also provide power conditioning, a continuous or a reverse UPS transfer system is applicable, as shown in Figures 2 and 3. In the reverse transfer system, the power conditioning is available only when the load is supplied from the inverter.

If the UPS system is required to provide all conditions (protection against power outages, voltage and frequency regulation, and frequency change), a continuous UPS system is applicable, as shown in Figure 4.

The type of critical load dictates the transfer time and the power supply conditioning as follows:

Types of loads that can withstand more than ¼ cycle of voltage loss:
Motors
Emergency lighting systems (incandescent or fluorescent) in which absolute continuity is not important
Heating elements.

Types of loads that can withstand ¼-cycle loss of voltage without appreciable effect:
Electronic-process control instruments
Flame-control systems
Most relays and contactors
Data process and process computers
Communication equipment (including digital data systems)

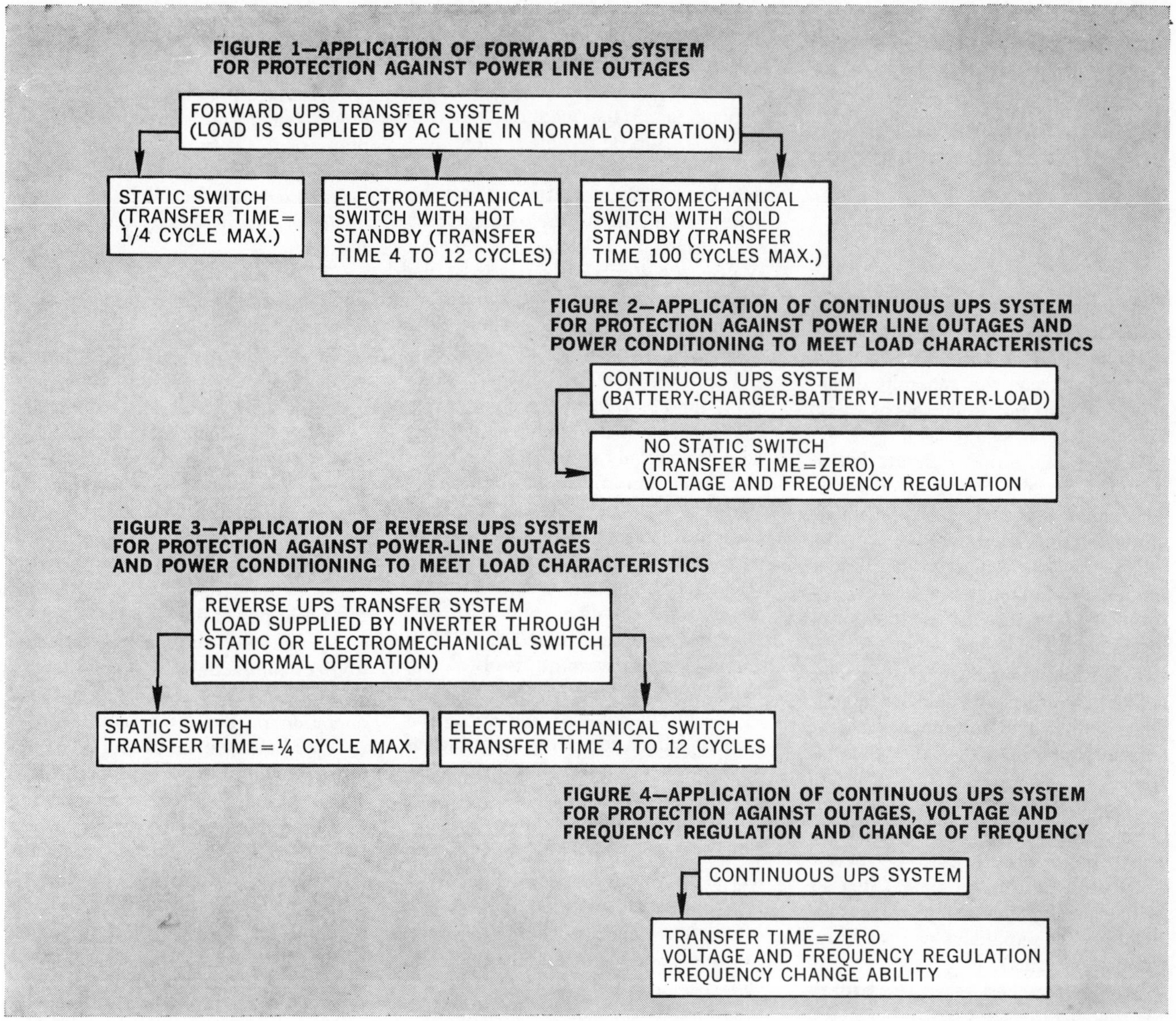

FIGURE 1—APPLICATION OF FORWARD UPS SYSTEM FOR PROTECTION AGAINST POWER LINE OUTAGES

FORWARD UPS TRANSFER SYSTEM
(LOAD IS SUPPLIED BY AC LINE IN NORMAL OPERATION)

STATIC SWITCH (TRANSFER TIME = 1/4 CYCLE MAX.)

ELECTROMECHANICAL SWITCH WITH HOT STANDBY (TRANSFER TIME 4 TO 12 CYCLES)

ELECTROMECHANICAL SWITCH WITH COLD STANDBY (TRANSFER TIME 100 CYCLES MAX.)

FIGURE 2—APPLICATION OF CONTINUOUS UPS SYSTEM FOR PROTECTION AGAINST POWER LINE OUTAGES AND POWER CONDITIONING TO MEET LOAD CHARACTERISTICS

CONTINUOUS UPS SYSTEM
(BATTERY-CHARGER-BATTERY—INVERTER-LOAD)

NO STATIC SWITCH
(TRANSFER TIME = ZERO)
VOLTAGE AND FREQUENCY REGULATION

FIGURE 3—APPLICATION OF REVERSE UPS SYSTEM FOR PROTECTION AGAINST POWER-LINE OUTAGES AND POWER CONDITIONING TO MEET LOAD CHARACTERISTICS

REVERSE UPS TRANSFER SYSTEM
(LOAD SUPPLIED BY INVERTER THROUGH STATIC OR ELECTROMECHANICAL SWITCH IN NORMAL OPERATION)

STATIC SWITCH
TRANSFER TIME = 1/4 CYCLE MAX.

ELECTROMECHANICAL SWITCH
TRANSFER TIME 4 TO 12 CYCLES

FIGURE 4—APPLICATION OF CONTINUOUS UPS SYSTEM FOR PROTECTION AGAINST OUTAGES, VOLTAGE AND FREQUENCY REGULATION AND CHANGE OF FREQUENCY

CONTINUOUS UPS SYSTEM

TRANSFER TIME = ZERO
VOLTAGE AND FREQUENCY REGULATION
FREQUENCY CHANGE ABILITY

Lighting systems in which continuity of light is important (fluorescent and mercury-vapor)

Constant-voltage transformers.

Types of loads that can withstand no interruptions:

High-speed communication networks in which loss of power implies loss of intelligibility

Electronic data process systems in which lost microseconds mean lost digits or loss of memory

Nuclear reactor control systems

Missile tracking and launching systems

Air-traffic control systems for high-speed aircraft direction

Microwave repeater systems.

Types of loads that cannot withstand frequency fluctuations:

Digital computers

Critical timing circuits

Tuned circuits

Frequency discriminators.

Step 2: Determine the AC load by tabulating all critical loads with their respective power factors and maximum inrush currents.

These data will determine the size of the required inverter, usually rated in kva at a given power factor. The power factor of an AC load is the ratio of watts (useful power) output to volt-ampere output. The relationship between power factor, watts, volt-amperes and the respective formulas necessary for Step 2 are shown graphically in Figure 5.

The power factor is unity for purely resistive loads and less than unity for all other loads. To determine the kva and power factor for a critical load, measure AC voltage with a voltmeter, AC current with an ammeter and AC power with a wattmeter. Compute kva by using Formula 1; compute power factor with Formula 3.

When different critial loads have different power factors, do this:

a) Determine kva for each load using Formulas 1 or 4 or both.

b) Determine kw by Formula 2.

c) Determine kvar by Formula 6.

d) Add all kvar for all lagging (inductive) power factors, assigning a negative sign.

e) Add all kvar for all leading (capacitive) power factors, assigning a positive sign.

f) Add d and e to obtain net kvar.

g) Determine total kva by using Formula 5.

h) Obtain total power factor by Formula 3.

An example of this procedure is shown in the tabulation on page 77.

If the load is not available or cannot be metered, the total kva can be found from the nameplates on the equipment, where the power factor and current data are usually indicated. When the voltage requirements for different loads are dissimilar, step-up or step-down transformers can be used.

Another important factor to consider in determining inverter capacity is the motor inrush currents. The in-

UPS systems are used for such critical loads as boiler flame-detectors, computers, electronic control instrumentation and critical communication complexes.

rush current can be measured with an ammeter at the instant the critical equipment is energized. Knowing the type of load, one can generally determine what the inrush current is going to be for a given steady load.

Where large inrush currents (more than 125 percent of the inverter rating) are considered, current-limiting protection may be required.

The size of the inverter can be determined from manufacturers' catalogs based on the calculated total kva, total power factor and inrush current.

Other important factors to consider are single- or 3-phase, sine- or square-wave output and maximum ambient temperature where the inverter is installed.

Step 3: Select the UPS system.

Selecting the most suitable UPS system—continuous, forward or reverse—is based on transfer time (Step 1) load characteristics (Step 2), and reliability (nonredundant or parallel-redundant systems).

Step 4: Size and select the battery for the inverter load and other eventual DC loads for the time period of possible power failure.

The inverter is supplied with DC from the battery during a power outage; so are any other DC critical loads. The time the UPS system will operate during a power outage is determined by the amp-hr capacity of the battery supplying the inverter and by any eventual DC loads.

Battery-support times of from 5 to 60 min are commonly encountered. Depending on the magnitude of the critical load to be powered, there may be a break-even point at which a standby engine-generator set can be bought with a short-time battery. This may result in a lower cost than a long-time battery. An analysis of the magnitude of the load and specific requirements can show where the break-even point is.

The lead-calcium battery, extensively used in UPS systems, employs a lead-calcium plate alloy and offers long life at only a 10 to 15 percent cost premium over the antimony lead-acid type of battery. The lead-calcium battery does not require equalized charging; it is nongasing (which is important where batteries are in a self-contained unit with battery chargers and inverters). Most manufacturers warrant lead-calcium batteries for 20 years.

The nickel-cadmium battery is not recommended for UPS applications because of its high cost. Moreover, it requires equalized charging and must be discharged and recharged periodically to stay at full capacity. This battery's main advantages: it does not lose capacity at low temperatures and can deliver high discharge currents for short periods (measured in seconds).

The lead-acid battery voltage during discharge varies between 2- and 1.75-v/cell. Inverter DC input varies with battery voltage. The average voltage and current drawn from a lead-acid battery can be calculated by using the curves in Figure 6.

To determine battery size and selection, proceed as follows:

a) Determine DC input to the inverter with battery voltage at the discharge condition of 1.75 v/cell.

b) Select protection time for a power outage of between 30 and 60 min.

c) The discharge current is the maximum value for 1 hr or less. For longer discharge periods, use curves in Figure 6.

d) Multiply current of *a* by factor determined in *c* and obtain the average current.

The DC input to a fully-loaded inverter under a discharged battery condition of 1.75 v/cell can be obtained from any UPS manufacturer's catalog. The battery has to be selected for a specific hour rate (protection time) of average amps to a final 1.75 v/cell at 77 F.

The following example applies for a 120-v battery that must operate during a 2-hr power outage:

Assume that the inverter selected from a manufacturer's catalog shows a DC input of 172 amp for a full-load operation of the inverter under discharged battery conditions. (105 v corresponds to a 60-cell battery at 1.75 v/cell.) From Figure 6, corresponding to 2-hr operation, the average current factor is 0.95. The average amperage is found by multiplying 172 amp by 0.95, equaling 161.7 amp. This calls for a 60-cell, lead-acid battery having a 2-hr rate of 162 amp, or 324 amp-hr to a final voltage of 1.75 v/cell at 77 F. It can now be selected accordingly from any manufacturer's catalog. (The normal application temperature is 77 F and higher; for temperatures appreciably below 77 F, larger batteries are required.)

Step 5: Size and select the battery charger.

The battery charger must be prop-

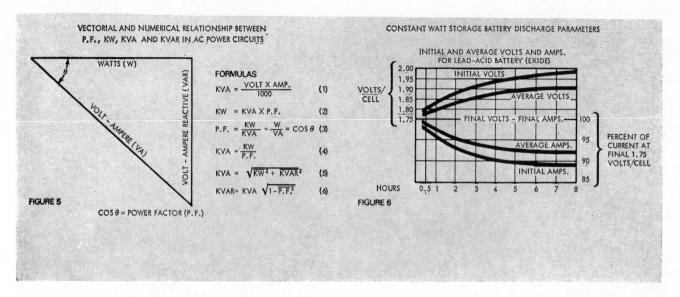

FIGURE 5 — VECTORIAL AND NUMERICAL RELATIONSHIP BETWEEN P.F., KW, KVA AND KVAR IN AC POWER CIRCUITS

FORMULAS

$$KVA = \frac{VOLT \times AMP.}{1000} \quad (1)$$

$$KW = KVA \times P.F. \quad (2)$$

$$P.F. = \frac{KW}{KVA} = \frac{W}{VA} = COS\,\theta \quad (3)$$

$$KVA = \frac{KW}{P.F.} \quad (4)$$

$$KVA = \sqrt{KW^2 + KVAR^2} \quad (5)$$

$$KVAR = KVA\sqrt{1 - P.F.^2} \quad (6)$$

$COS\,\theta = POWER\ FACTOR\ (P.F.)$

FIGURE 6 — CONSTANT WATT STORAGE BATTERY DISCHARGE PARAMETERS

TABULATION OF CRITICAL LOADS

LOAD	SIZE	P.F.	KVA (Formula 4)	KW (Formula 2)	KVAR (Formula 6)
Motor	2 kw 0.8	lagging	$\frac{2}{0.8} = 2.5$	(given) 2.0	$-2.5 \times \sqrt{1-(0.8)^2} = -1.5$
Lights	1 kw 1.0		$\frac{1}{1} = 1.0$	(given) 1.0	$1 \times \sqrt{1-1^2} = 0$
Instruments	5 kva 0.9	lagging	given = 5.0	$5 \times 0.9 = 4.5$	$-5 \times \sqrt{1-(0.9)^2} = -2.17$
Controls	3 kva 0.8	leading	given = 3.0	$3 \times 0.8 = 2.4$	$3 \times \sqrt{1-(0.8)^2} = +1.80$
				TOTALS kw = 9.9	kvar = −1.87

Using Formula 5, total kva = $(9.9)^2 + (-1.87)^2 = 10.08$.

Using Formula 3, total P.F. = $\frac{9.9}{10.8} = 0.98$ lagging.

erly sized and selected to supply the inverter and all eventual additional DC critical-load requirements and to satisfy the desired battery-recharge time (usually 8 hr).

Step 6: Select accessories as required.

Several other features such as current-limiting provisions, audio filters, inverter synchronizing circuits and transfer switches, have to be considered. Which will be needed depends on the critical load and the degree of protection required.

Current-limiting circuits. These protect the inverter against overloads and short circuits at the output. Large solenoids or motors draw heavy inrush current when energized. The inrush current can be limited to a safe value without tripping the inverter off the load if the inverter rating is determined by the inrush current rather than by normal operating current.

Audio filters. Where voice-commu-

nication equipment that is sensitive to battery ripple is connected at the bus with the inverter, audio input filters are required. They isolate inverter audio noises from the bus.

Inverter synchronizing circuits. These are used to make the inverter output phase and frequency the same as the power frequency signal applied to the synchronizing terminals of the inverter. The circuit is normally used to synchronize the inverter with the line or with any power frequency source. It is also used with the synchronizing bypass switch arrangement.

Transfer switches. Not all inverters are suited for use with static transfer switches because of the operation requirement at unity or the leading power factor at the static-switch load terminal. The required inverter should be selected, along with the transfer switch, from a manufacturer's catalog.

Manual bypass switches. These are

used to isolate the static switch or the inverter and take them out of service without interrupting the load. The switch is usually make-before-break and is often mounted in the inverter enclosure.

AC line regulator. An automatic magnetic voltage regulator with ±3 percent total harmonic distortion, the unit regulates AC line voltage within ±2 percent.

Undervoltage trip. This device shuts down the inverter if battery voltage drops below the discharged value.

By following the six steps closely, any UPS system can be tailored to satisfy the specific requirements of the critical loads.

The design engineer must analyze his system and determine the extent of the damage that may occur from a power failure. He must then select the most inexpensive UPS system that will provide suitable power to the critical load within the minimum allowable time. After the three main elements and necessary additional accessories have been selected, a specification form must be filled out.

3.6 Solid-State Automatic AC Bus Transfer Switch; Specifications for UPS Systems

An automatic transfer switch transfers power loads from a preferred source to an emergency standby source almost instantly when the preferred source is lost. The ¼-cycle maximum total interruption, because of the use of solid-state components, makes applying the transfer switches to critical loads possible where fast operation is imperative. In addition, the switches are maintenance-free because they are completely static.

During normal operation, the load is supplied by the preferred AC power source through the SCR units, as shown in Figure 1. The preferred AC source may be through an inverter or direct from an AC power line. Each switch pole is provided with two silicon-controlled rectifiers (thyristors) connected back to back so that the current can flow.

The static switch monitors the AC line voltage. If the preferred-source voltage drops below a preset undervoltage point, which is adjustable from 60 percent to 100 percent of normal-source voltage, the conducting SCRs are turned on, automatically

transferring the load to the standby source.

Transfer Time: Two Seconds
When the preferred-source voltage has been re-established above an adjustable preset value for a return to the normal source and after 2 sec have elapsed, the load is automatically retransferred. The 2-sec interval ensures stability by allowing the automatic synchronizing equipment on either source to operate before retransfer.

Two adjustments at the control module are necessary: the setting of the desired undervoltage transfer point to the emergency source and the setting for retransfer to the normal source.

The components can be easily removed from the cabinet shown on page 112. Terminals are also provided for manual transfer to either source for testing.

Transfer switches are manufactured in many sizes and shapes, for single- or 3-phase, ranging from 100 va to 400 kva. Their overload capability is about 125 percent for 2 min and the

line voltage transient tolerance ranges from 120 percent for synchronized sources to 200 percent for unsynchronized sources.

For loads that can stand an interruption of more than 4 to 12 cycles, the less expensive electromechanical transfer switches can be used. But for critical loads that cannot stand more than ¼ cycle of power loss, such as boiler-flame controls, computers, electronic-process controls and microwave equipment, only solid-state automatic transfer switches are applicable.

Writing The Specs
Specifications for UPS systems are extremely important. Here are the main points to include when specifying UPS system components:

A. BATTERY CHARGER

Input data shall indicate the following:

1. *Source voltage.* (The input voltage defines the required equipment. The range of input voltage variation should be indicated if possible. Known source transients not included in the source voltage variation, such

as line voltage dips due to motor starting, should also be shown. Switching other loads on the source supplying the UPS equipment can be dangerous. The equipment must be designed to suppress transients and be capable of carrying 20 percent transients safely for up to 6 cycles without damaging the power supply.)

2. *Phase and frequency of power source line* (single or 3-phase, 60, 50 cycles).

3. *Protection of supply line* (breakers or fuses).

4. *Power failure alarm relay* (optional item).

Output data shall indicate:

1. *DC voltage* (125, 48, 24, etc., DC volts).

2. *Voltage regulation* (0.5 percent when the input AC voltage variation is within ± 10 percent and the input frequency variation is within ± 5 percent).

3. *Battery recharge rate capability* (usually 8 hr, together with inverter supply).

4. *Protection* (breakers or fuses).

5. *Ground detector with indicating light or alarm* (optional).

6. *Instruments* (ammeter and/or voltmeter, float equalizing switch if required, low DC voltage relay to detect loss of power to charger [optional]).

7. *Mounting* (wall or floor).

B. BATTERY AND RACK

1. *Type of battery* (lead calcium, nickel-cadmium or lead-plate; the nongasing lead-calcium battery is preferable).

2. *Voltage* (125, 48, 24, etc., volts DC).

3. *Amp-hr capacity of the battery at 8-hr discharge rate* (satisfactory operation of the inverter for the period of time outage specified without detrimental drop in voltage at the battery terminal shall be guaranteed).

4. *Steel rack for battery* (shall be as compact as possible and consist of one or two steps, one or two lengths, as dictated by space and manufacturers' standards).

5. *Intercell and inter-row connections, cable lugs, electrolite and standard accessories.*

6. *Duration of power supply capacity from battery in a power failure* (this time varies between 15 and 60 min, depending on the availability of a standby source after the support time of the battery has elapsed; 60 min is often used).

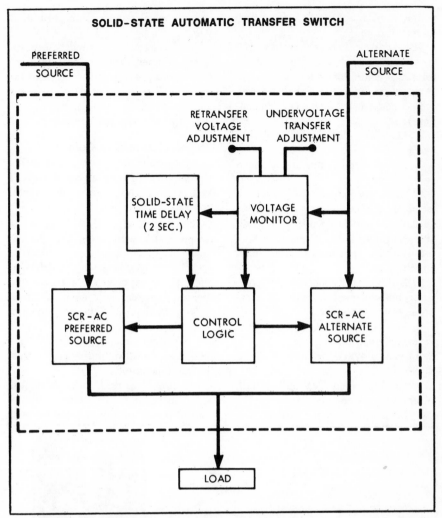

SOLID-STATE AUTOMATIC TRANSFER SWITCH

Block diagram for solid-state automatic transfer switch from preferred normal to standby source and retransfer to preferred source.

7. *Control timer* (to control the equalizing charge of the battery, if necessary).

C. INVERTER

Input data shall indicate:

1. *Voltage* (120, 48, 24, etc., DC volts).

2. *Ampere* (at the selected voltage and at full load).

3. *Protection* (breakers or fuses).

Output data shall indicate:

1. *Voltage* (480, 240, 120 AC volts).

2. *Phases* (single or 3-phase).

3. *Cycles* (25, 50, 60 cycles at ± 1 percent).

4. *Wave shape* (sine or square).

5. *Harmonic distortion* (maximum ± 5 percent).

6. *Output voltage regulation* (usually within ± 3 percent at 1.0 power factor).

7. *Frequency regulation.* (Automatic synchronizing to control output phase within ± 10 percent of the normal AC power line, provided the power line frequency is maintained within ± 2 percent of the nominal frequency. Upon power line failure, the inverter must maintain output frequency within ± 1 percent of nominal, until normal power returns. The inverter must then automatically resynchronize to the power line).

8. *Current limit.* (Automatic current limit is provided to protect the inverter against overloads or short circuits [optional]. It enables the inverter to continue operating normally after a short-circuit is removed. As long as the overload exists, the current limit keeps output current at 150 percent, a value that will not damage the inverter).

9. *Synchronizer bypass switch* (optional, but if specified should have make-before-break contacts for servicing or inspecting the inverter).

10. *Protection* (fuses or breakers —indicate type to suit critical load conditions).

11. *Instruments* (ammeter and/or

voltmeter AC and/or DC, frequency meter [optional]).

12. *Ambient temperature* (0 to 100 F; forced air cooling can be specified for 120 F continuous operation).

D. CRITICAL LOAD DATA shall indicate

1. *Steady-state load* (in voltampere).

2. *Over-all power factor of critical loads.*

3. *Inrush load* (starting load in va).

4. *Time for which load must be supplied without charger operating* (usually 30 min, depending on available rotating standby source).

5. *Voltage* (percent of variation admissible).

6. *Nature of critical loads* (computer, boiler flame failure device, electronic instruments, etc.).

7. *Special conditions of operation for critical load.*

E. GENERAL SPECIFICATIONS shall include:

1. Self-contained UPS unit or individual separate components.

2. Provision for space heaters.

3. Tropicalized or fungus-proofed unit.

4. Manufacturer shall indicate types, outlines, weights, clearances required and provide connection and interconnection diagrams with operating and maintenance instructions.

5. List of spare parts required.

Manufacturers Can Help

A worthwhile procedure is requesting the supplier to send a manufacturer's engineer to be on hand for the inverter startup.

The specification should define the scope of the installation and the nature of circuit protection.

Where a large capacity or extended outages are expected, rotating generation equipment should back up the inverter, so that the inverter may provide the uninterrupted power supply for a certain time, say 30 to 60 min, and the standby source can supply power indefinitely.

As use of critical loads is continually increasing, the static uninterrupted power supply systems become

more important. Computers and electronic control instrumentation need reliable buffer systems that isolate the voltage-sensitive critical loads from the inherent power system disturbances.

UPS systems offer the ideal solution to the problem by their fast transient response, stable frequency, low maintenance and high efficiency. The growing technology of solid-state devices promises continuous improved performances at decreasing cost for UPS systems.

The task of the application engineer is to carefully analyze all aspects of the problem, determine the extent of damage that may occur from a power failure and consequently select the best and most inexpensive UPS system that will ensure emergency power within the minimum allowable time.

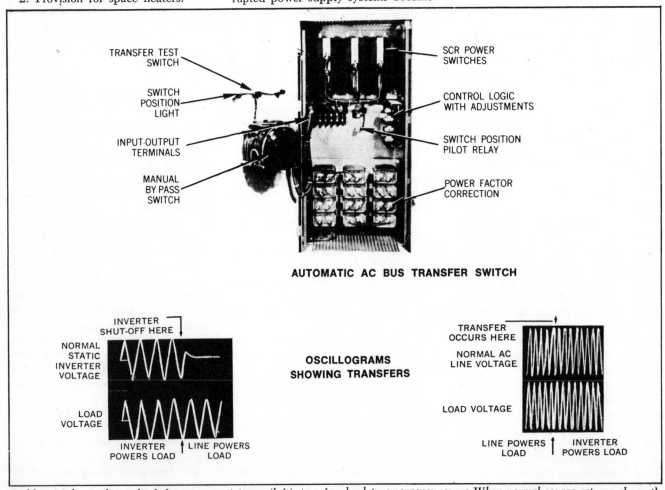

AUTOMATIC AC BUS TRANSFER SWITCH

OSCILLOGRAMS SHOWING TRANSFERS

Sudden AC line voltage dip below preset minimum (left), transfers load to emergency source. When normal source returns above the preset transfer voltage and remains for two seconds, retransfer to normal supply load occurs (right).

4

Coordinating Protection for Electrical Systems in Plants

4.1 Design Considerations for a Properly Coordinated Protective System

A frequently overlooked part of industrial power system design is the proper selection and coordination of protective devices. Proper protective device coordination prevents equipment damage, costly downtime and personnel injury. Breakdowns in electrical distribution systems can cause loss of power to machines, computers, laboratories and many other services, resulting in a loss of production time.

This section 4.1 will discuss the procedures to determine the short-circuit currents that may occur, the time and current settings for adjustable protective devices, as well as the selection of nonadjustable ones, to achieve equipment coordination.

Well-designed electrical systems must assure a continuous supply of energy at a reasonable cost. Failures caused by faults are undesirable but often unavoidable. Since a total fault-proof system is infeasible, a certain number of faults must be tolerated during the life of a system, and the likelihood of fault frequency increases with the age of the system.

The main types of faults on 3-phase systems are 3-phase, phase-to-phase, 2-phase to ground, single-phase to ground and arcing. When a fault occurs, the flow of current to the faulted part of the system must be interrupted immediately without removing the service to other areas. This is accomplished by fault-detecting and disconnecting devices that have sensing and switching functions. The basic protective devices are protective relays, the direct-acting trips used with circuit breakers, and fuses. A protective system consists of an arrangement of these detecting and switching devices (both adjustable and nonadjustable), coordinated to be selective with each other in operation.

The time-current characteristics of all adjustable protective devices must be set in the field so that they are coordinated with each other and with the fixed nonadjustable time-current characteristics. The protective device closest to the fault on the power source side should operate first. If this protective device fails to operate, the next device toward the power source must take over and open the circuit.

To meet this need protective devices must be adjusted to operate on minimum currents. This will permit them to distinguish between true fault currents and permissible load-current peaks. Operations must occur in the least time possible while maintaining system selectivity. In this way, the protective devices will activate only the minimum number of breakers and fuses connecting the defective element to the system. Proper protective selectivity ensures that the various relays and breakers in the system are adjusted to the desired degree of coordination with each other and with nonadjustable devices in the system. This coordination is necessary because though relays are the brains of the power system, they must be told what to do, in the form of time and current settings.

System changes and additions

Protective devices are assumed to be properly coordinated when the electrical system is built. They do not remain coordinated, however, when additions or system changes are made. The system supply capacity (kva), voltage, connected motor types and loads, and the cable and transformer impedances determine the magnitude of the fault current. These determinants are specific quantitative factors used to calculate protective settings. A change in any of these factors can upset the coordination of the system's protective devices. Additions, deletions or changes of supply power transformers, feeders, cables or motors alter system impedance and affect the magnitude of the fault current to be cleared. Consequently, protective device timing must be reset. Any change in the utility system capacity, or ties between parts of the system, also changes the device settings. Periodic studies of protective device settings, therefore, are often necessary.

An overcurrent protective system is composed of a variety of coordinated devices such as fuses, direct-acting trips, adjustable breakers, protective relays, interrupters, load-break switches, disconnect switches, contactors, etc. An understanding of these devices and their characteristics is necessary to assure proper selection and coordination of protective devices.

Disconnects are considered in coordination studies when they are to be specified for the main incoming line or principal feeder—but only if they are motor-operated. Such disconnects operate in a prescribed sequencing manner, for example, Breaker X must be opened before motor-operated Disconnect Y opens. Key-type sequential interlocking is important in a coordinated system. Disconnects are often operated to restore power to a lost production line. During these times, improper switching operations may occur, but such errors can be avoided by properly designed interlocking.

Fuses are simple and widely used for circuit protection. They frequently are combined with switches on a common base (usually in a metal enclosure) and designated as fused switches. A fuse clears the flow of current to a fault or overload section of the distribution system by means of its link or internal element (the link melts and opens the circuit when excessive current flows).

The two basic types of fuses are current limiting and noncurrent limiting. Both have interrupting ratings expressed in symmetrical amperes and are capable of interrupting asymmetrical fault currents 1.6 times the symmetrical rating values. Noncurrent limiting fuses are usually the refill type and have limited interrupting ratings. Current-limiting fuses have higher interrupting capacities and operate extremely fast, acting in less than a quarter cycle. Noncurrent-limiting fuses can operate in one or two cycles, depending on the level of fault-current.

Fuses are represented for coordination purposes by two time-current curves, minimum melting and maximum clearing, plotted against the current that can flow through the fuse. Figure 1 shows minimum melting and Figure 2 maximum clearing curves against current and time. There are a variety of fuses and fused devices for circuits of 2.4 kv and higher, such as power fuses for indoor or outdoor use, oil fuse cutouts and distribution cutouts for outdoor use. The main application for fused switches is for disconnecting means combined with overcurrent and short-circuit protection.

Circuit breakers are of many different types. For systems above 600 v, oil circuit breakers can be equipped with direct-acting internal current transformers and trip coils or indirect tripping devices in the form of overcurrent or voltage relays operating from the secondaries of current transformers installed in the circuit. Time vs. current-log-log curve data must be obtained for all the protective relays types used in the system. The curves must be carefully considered in the selective coordination study with respect to the time tripping as it relates to various fault currents in the system. Breakers have clearing times in the order of 5 to 8 cycles, depending on their size and design. Oil circuit breakers can be either the static-oil or forced-oil insulated type.

Large power air circuit breakers are specified for low-voltage systems and for high voltage systems from 600 v to 15 kv. In the direct-acting type, the overcurrent or fault current flows directly through heavy current coils. The direct-acting trip mechanisms provide an instantaneous magnetic trip function reflected in the corresponding tripping curves. These curves show additional trip-vs.-overcurrent time relationships that should be considered in the coordination study.

Air circuit breakers for systems less than 600 v usually are equipped with adjustable trip devices, such as long time, short time and instantaneous, which are the static type.

Power circuit breakers above 600 v are usually provided with current transformers, operating overcurrent or voltage-relay trip devices. These devices' characteristic time-vs.-current curves allow the engineer to match the rest of the protective devices for selective coordination. The interrupting speed of power circuit breakers above 600 v is approximately 5 cycles, and for air circuit breakers of 600 v and below, about 2 to 4 cycles. Figure 3 shows time-current curves for air circuit breaker coordination in a 1,000-kva substation.

Molded case breakers are manufactured for systems of 600 v and less. They have built-in thermal or magnetic trips, or both. The magnetic trips act instantaneously (within approximately 1 to 4 cycles). Some are adjustable. The time-current characteristics of these breakers must be considered when coordinating the selective devices.

FIGURE 1 TYPICAL MINIMUM MELTING TIME-CURRENT
CHARACTERISTICS FOR HIGH-VOLTAGE CURRENT-LIMITING POWER FUSES

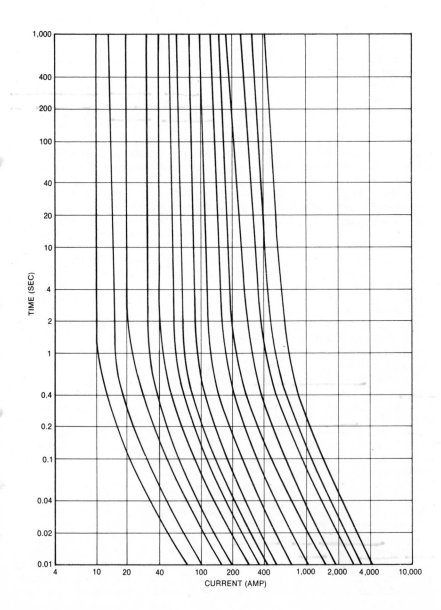

Current-limiting, fused molded-case breakers (limiter breakers) combine the high interrupting capacity of current-limiting fuses with the general advantages of breakers. The breaker automatically trips when any fuse blows, thus avoiding single phasing. Recently introduced molded-case breakers are provided with adjustable static trip devices. Future breakers may be completely solid-state and have instantaneous tripping speeds.

Basically, the *protective relay* consists of an operating element and a set of contacts. The operating element takes the information from the instrument transformers in the form of currents and voltages, performs a measuring operation and translates the result into contact motion. When the contacts close, they actuate a warning signal or trip the current breaker, isolating the faulty element by interrupting the current flow.

Relays can be actuated by current only or by current and voltage. When the relay is actuated by the two quantities, the characteristics may be shown in terms of the magnitude of one quantity and the phase angle between the two quantities, the relative magnitudes of the two quantities, or the relative magnitudes and phase angles of the two quantities.

Overcurrent relays are the most common type of protective relays. They trip the breaker when more than the proper amount of current flows into a particular portion of a power system. The characteristics of overcurrent relays are shown graphically by a family of time-current curves for various multiples of pickup current and for various time-dial settings.

Overcurrent relays have adjustment provisions for current pickup. If the current operates the relay without intentional time delay, the protection is called "instantaneous." If the overcurrent is transient in nature, it is undesirable to open the breaker. This is the reason why most relays are equipped with a time-delay mechanism that permits a current several times greater than the relay setting to persist for a limited period of time. If a relay operates faster as the current increases, it is said to have an iinverse-time characteristic. Adjustments for a given current are made by means of a time-lever or time-dial.

The three most commonly used shapes of inverse-time overcurrent characteristics are inverse, very inverse and extremely inverse (see Figure 4). They differ by the rate at which the time operation of the relay decreases as the current increases.

Voltage relays have similar characteristics and use voltage as the actuating quantity in the operating element. They may be the undervoltage or overvoltage type, or a combination of the two.

Directional relays are used in applications where it is desirable to allow tripping for current flow in one direction only. These relays are the current-voltage type. One winding may be energized by the circuit voltage to "polarize" the unit—i.e., to predetermine the direction of current flow for which the unit should operate—and the other winding is energized by the desired current.

Differential relays, used mainly for transformers, generators, motors and bus protection, have a current-balance characteristic causing relay operation if the current entering the protected section is not balanced by the current

FIGURE 2 TYPICAL TOTAL CLEARING TIME-CURRENT
CHARACTERISTICS FOR HIGH-VOLTAGE CURRENT-LIMITING POWER FUSES

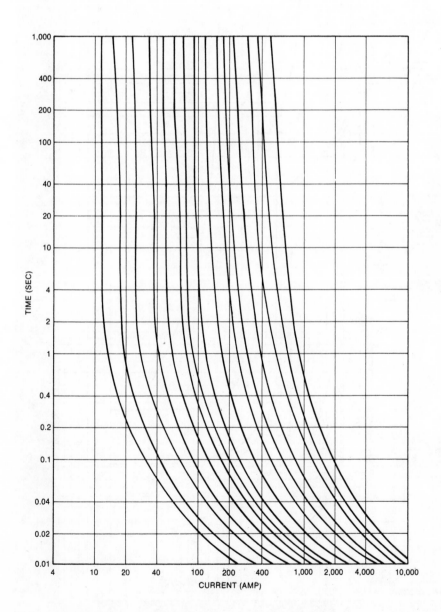

leaving the protected section. Under external fault conditions, these currents are in balance and the relay will not trip the breaker. For internal faults, however, the current will no longer be in balance, and the relay will trip the breaker at the line terminal. Percentage-differential relays permit more sensitive protection.

Distance relays respond to a ratio of voltage to current and, consequently, to impedance—the measure of distance along a transmission line that the relays protect.

Instantaneous relays operate without any intentional time delay. Ground relays receive only the zero-sequence current and are unaffected by load currents. They may be set to operate for single-phase-to-ground currents smaller than the full load currents. In general, ground relays have lower pickup current ranges.

Frequency relays operate when the system frequency either exceeds or falls below the value for which the relay is set. These relays are used to restore the balance between load and generation automatically.

In addition to these familiar relays, a

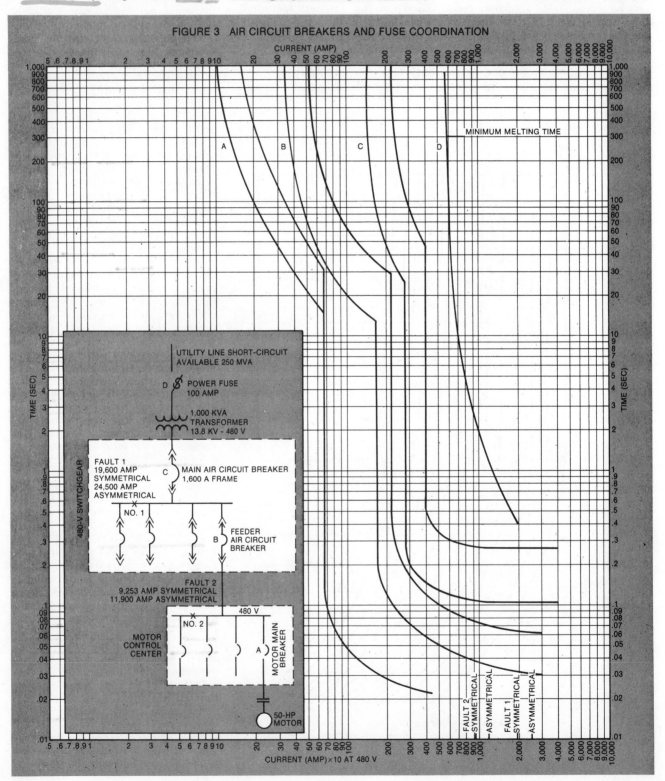

FIGURE 3   AIR CIRCUIT BREAKERS AND FUSE COORDINATION

series of other types are used for special relaying applications.

Electromagnetic relays are the plunger, hinged-armature, induction-disc, or induction-cup type. The first two types are based on the magnetic attraction principle; the latter two are based on the magnetic induction principle by which torque is developed in a metallic disc rotating between the pole faces of an electromagnet.

Static relays utilize static semiconductor devices, such as transistors and thyristors. Because there are no moving parts, the static relays operate very fast and have response times as low as a quarter of a cycle. In addition they deliver a high degree of reliability, provide close coordination, finer protection and require less maintenance than their movable counterparts.

All relays must fulfill three basic application requirements—sensitivity, selectivity and speed.

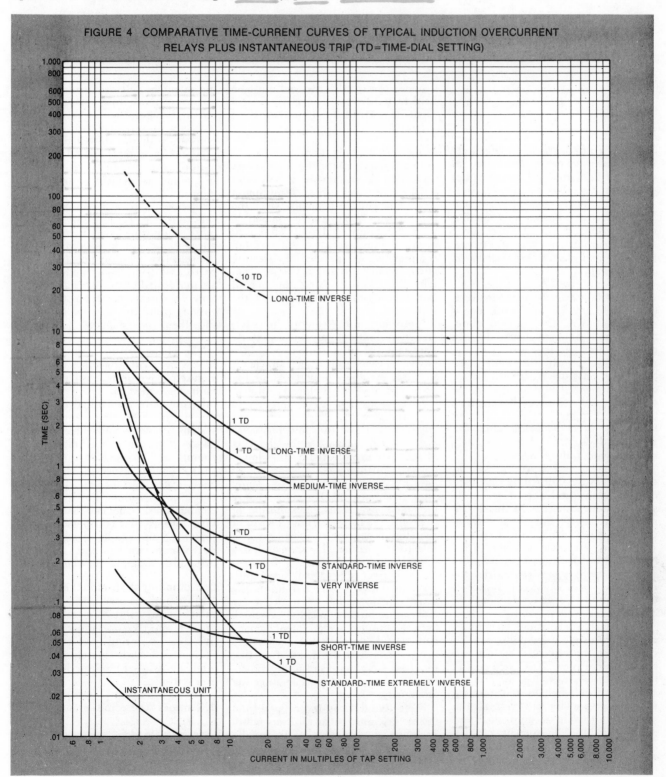

FIGURE 4   COMPARATIVE TIME-CURRENT CURVES OF TYPICAL INDUCTION OVERCURRENT RELAYS PLUS INSTANTANEOUS TRIP (TD=TIME-DIAL SETTING)

4.2 Short Circuits and Data Required for Selective Coordination of Protective Devices

Section 4.1 discussed the nature of selective coordination of protective devices and described the characteristics of various protective devices. This section deals with the general philosophy of selective coordination, relationship with short-circuits, and data required for a coordination study. Figures, formulas and tables are numbered consecutively.

Industrial power systems should be designed to provide the electric energy needed to power equipment in a safe, reliable and economical way. If only normal operation is considered, the installation would be inadequate because of possible equipment failure or human error. The primary purpose of good selection and selective tripping of protective devices is to minimize system damage and limit the extent and duration of service interruption when failures occur.

The degree and extent of system protection is determined by economic considerations and the selection of system components. At least the minimum safety and reliability requirements should be met to assure satisfactory electrical system performance. Modifying an inadequate system is more expensive than designing desired features into the system in the beginning of the selection and coordination process.

Selective coordination techniques require philosophic and policy considerations of the electrical system and the particular plant. The main goal is to isolate the affected portion of the system quickly while maintaining normal service for the rest of the system. If this is accomplished, arc damage to the equipment directly involved with the fault is minimized. At the same time, the other parts of the system not directly involved must be held in until other protective devices clear the trouble. This is called *selectivity*.

Protection vs. selection

The initial planning of system protection is to ensure a safe and reliable electrical supply at minimum cost. The engineer should keep the final design simple and compatible with the safety, reliability and economic considerations. Any added complexity may prove self-defeating and actually reduce the system reliability while raising the overall initial cost and maintenance of the system.

Protection and selectivity, however, are often contradictory in objectives. Fast removal of a faulted part in a power system can trigger nuisance tripping in adjacent portions of the system. Conversely, slowing protective devices (to meet selectivity objectives with other devices in adjacent parts of the power system) may result in damage to the elements of the system protected by the slower device. Furthermore, a short-circuit within a switchgear is interrupted only after the main breaker relay timing interval elapses. This interval is longer in a selective system. Thus, the risk of switchgear damage is increased in a selective coordinated system unless a proper setting is chosen.

The correct approach is a compromise in which protection limits the extent of a power failure in such a way that an economic balance is struck between the cost of equipment damage and added expense to meet safety needs. It is a tradeoff situation that requires weighing conflicting objectives and making good engineering judgments.

Protective devices are shipped from the factory, preset at an arbitrary point. A time-overcurrent relay is usually shipped with its tap preset at 5 amp, its time dial at 0 or 1, and its instantaneous element usually at the minimum.* A low-voltage power circuit breaker often is shipped with its long time delay preset at 100 percent and its instantaneous trip element at maximum. Usually a molded-case circuit breaker has its instantaneous element preset at maximum.

Obviously, to achieve the desired selectivity, it is necessary to make on-site adjustments of the protective element settings in accordance with the selective coordination study. Most protective device coordination studies are performed by comparing operating time vs. current characteristics of the various protective devices and drawing them on standard logarithmic curve sheets, as shown in Figure 5.

The characteristics and settings of the overcurrent protective devices in Figure 5 have been selected so that a fault anywhere in the system will interrupt only the faulted element of the circuit. For a large and complex system, drawing time-current coordination curves might be laborious and complicated. Closed-loop or network system layouts, especially, may be too complicated for manual drawing of curve coordination. For such cases, computers can calculate relay settings, fuse ratings, device operating times (based on the results of a previously performed short-circuit study and principles of device coordination).

Coordinating short-circuit devices

Minimum as well as maximum short-circuit values are required to predict selective operation of protective devices during fault currents. A short-circuit study, therefore, is absolutely necessary for selective coordination settings.

The subtransient reactance (X''_d) determines the short-circuit current

---

* The usual available range of time-overcurrent relays are: tap: 0.5 to 2 amp or 1.5 to 6 amp or 4 to 16 amp; time-dial: from 0.5 to 10; instantaneous: 2 to 8 amp or 4 to 16 amp or 10 to 40 amp.

FIGURE 5 TIME-CURRENT CURVE SELECTIVE COORDINATION FOR TYPICAL INDUSTRIAL POWER SYSTEM

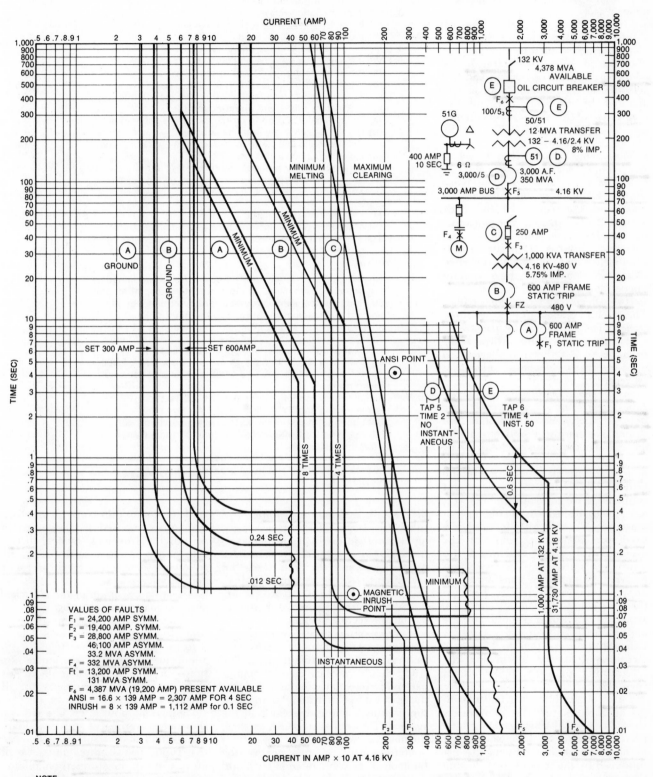

NOTE:
Breakers A and B are provided with static trips.
For breakers without static trips, see curves on Figure 3, Section 4-1.

immediately after the fault inception. The subtransient reactance lasts for the first few cycles and in approximately 0.1 sec increases to the next value—the transient reactance (X'_d), which determines the short-circuit current magnitude (I'_d). This second period lasts for about 2 sec.

Afterward, the final value of short-circuit (I_d) reaches a steady-state condition determined by the synchronous reactance (X_d). The setting of the adjustable protective devices and the selection of the nonadjustable ones is affected by the duration and the magnitude of the short-circuit currents determined by the X''_d, X'_d and X_d reactances as follows:

Time-delay relays and direct-acting trips. These devices are too slow in operation to be affected by the very short duration of the subtransient reactance X''_d values of the fault current I''_d. For this kind of protective device, therefore, the initial value symmetrical current (I'_d) corresponding to the value of transient reactance (X'_d), can be used as the maximum operating current.

High-speed induction-type relays. These relays operate in less than three cycles. The initial fault current (I''_d) corresponding to the subtransient reactances (X''_d), therefore, have to be used as their maximum operating current.

Instantaneous induction or plunger-type relays and circuit-breaker trip coils. All these devices are fast and are responsive to direct and alternating current. They operate on the first half cycle of the fault current. Their operating current, therefore, is the initial asymmetrical total rms current contributed by all rotating equipment, calculated on the basis of subtransient reactance X''_d. A multiplier of 1.6 is used to obtain the value of the asymmetrical offset current. A 1.5 multiplier is used, however, when 2.4- to 5-kv systems have transformers or appreciable line resistance between the source and the point of fault. The same 1.5 multiplier should also be applied to systems of 600 v and less, although it differs from the 1.25 offset factor applied for calculating the interrupting duty for 600-v circuit breakers.

Fuses. Fuses have inherent nonadjustable characteristics. Engineers should be careful when selecting these protective devices. Fuse elements melt because of heat created by the RI^2 loss produced by the fault current flowing through the fuse. The DC and AC components of the initial asymmetrical current I''_d, corresponding to the subtransient reactance X''_d, affects the

TABLE 1

Protective devices	Short-circuit current
1 Medium- and long-time induction relays	I'_d
2 Standard-time induction relays	I'_d
3 Short-time induction relays:	
(a) Equal to or less than two time dial setting	I''_d
(b) More than 2 time dial setting	I'_d
4 Long-time mechanism trips on 600-v air circuit breakers	I'_d
5 Short-time mechanism trips on 600-v air circuit breakers:	
(a) When operating on 0.1 sec or more	I'_d
(b) When operating in less than 0.1 sec	$I''_d \times 1.5$
6 Instantaneous and short-time (less than 0.1 sec) plunger or hinged-armature relays and direct-acting trips:	
(a) On systems 2,300 v and more with direct generation	$I''_d \times 1.6$
(b) On 2,300- to 5,000-v systems supplied by transformers	$I''_d \times 1.5$
(c) On systems 5,000 v and more supplied by transformers	$I''_d \times 1.6$
(d) On systems 600 v and less	$I''_d \times 1.5$
7 Time-delay plunger or hinged-armature relays and direct-acting trips on power circuit breakers (over 600 v) taking 1 sec or more	I'_d
8 Fuses:	
(a) Fast melting (less than 0.1 sec)	Same as 6a, b, c
(b) More than 0.1 sec melting time on sustained fault	I'_d
9 Generator, transformer and bus differential, power-line-current balance and wire pilot relays	I''_d

Where:

$I_d =$ Symmetrical steady-state short-circuit current determined by synchronous reactance of the system to the point of fault.

$I'_d =$ Initial symmetrical short-circuit current determined by the transient reactance of the system to the point of fault.

$I''_d =$ Initial symmetrical short-circuit current determined by the subtransient reactance of the system to the point of fault.

$1.6 =$ Multiplier allowing for DC component of offset (asymmetrical) short-circuit current wave on systems 2,400 v or more, except when 2400- to 5,000-v faults come through transformers.

$1.5 =$ Multiplier allowing for DC component of offset (asymmetrical) short-circuit current for relays and direct-acting trip operation on low-voltage systems, 600 v and less. Also for 2,400- to 5,000-v fault currents coming through transformers.
(1.5 multiplier should not be confused with 1.25 multiplier used for low-voltage air circuit breaker interrupting duty calculations.)

fuse's fast melting-time zone. The subtransient current decreases very quickly as fuse melting time increases. A multiplying factor of 1.6 is usually used to obtain the value of the asymmetrical offset current. Table 1 shows the kind of short-circuit operating currents used for setting various protective devices.

A coordination study is necessary to determine the characteristics and settings of all protective devices. The study should indicate the best combination of protection, thus assuring that the least load is interrupted in the least time while clearing any fault in the system. To localize the disturbance, the devices should be selective in their operation—e.g., the one nearest the fault on its power source side should operate first. If this device does not operate, the next device in the chain toward the power source, must take over and open the circuit.

Since an overcurrent protection system is composed of a large variety of individual devices, such as direct-acting trips, relays and fuses, the following data are necessary for a coordination study:

A one line diagram of the electrical distribution system showing:

• Location and function of each protective device in the system: relays, direct-acting trips, fuses, etc.

• Type designation, current rating, range or adjustment, manufacturer's style and catalog number, for all protective devices.

• Apparent power, voltage ratings, impedance, primary and secondary connections of all transformers.

• Type, manufacturer and ratio of all instrument transformers energizing each relay.

• Nameplate ratings of all motors and generators with their subtransient reactances. Transient reactances of synchronous motors and generators and synchronous reactances of all generators.

• Sources of short-circuit currents such as utility ties, generators, synchronous motors and induction motors.

• All significant circuit elements such as transformers, cables, breakers, fuses, reactors, and so on.

• Emergency as well as normal switching conditions.

• The time-current setting of existing adjustable relays and direct-acting trips should be included, if applicable.

An impedance diagram showing:

• Power supply, available mva or impedance, from the utility company.

• Local generated capacity impedance.

• Bus impedance.

• Transformer and/or reactor impedances.

• Cable impedances.

• System voltages.

• Grounding scheme (resistance grounding, solidly grounding or no grounding).

A complete short-circuit study of the system including first cycles and interrupting duty values. This shows the maximum and minimum total rms values of short-circuit currents expected to flow through each protective device whose performance is to be studied under all possible operating conditions, as well as maximum and minimum ground-fault currents. (The procedure for a short-circuit study applied to selective coordination purposes will be discussed in the following sections.

Any special overcurrent protective requirements stipulated by the National Electrical Code, dictated by the load characteristics or imposed by the utility supplying the industrial plant.

Short-time, maximum or emergency load currents that can be expected on each feeder. Motor circuits should include full-load, and locked-rotor current, allowable locked-rotor time and starting time for all medium-voltage motors.

Type of breakers, type of trip unit and trip settings for each 480-v transformer main and secondary circuits.

Time-current characteristics of all adjustable and nonadjustable protective devices involved in the study.

Desired coordinating time interval between settings of adjacent overcurrent relays and selected fuses.

max. total RMS $= I_{sc}$ @ X_d'' ~~with~~ multiplied with $1.6 =$
$=$ Total asymetrical sc currents contributed by all rotating machinery. use X_d'' for all rotating machinery

Min. $I_{sc} =$ Interrupting duty I_{sc}'. use X_d'' for generators & X_d' for synchronous motors. ~~No induction motor included~~. &induction

The previous section 4.1 reviewed the basic considerations in the design of a properly coordinated protective system. Section 4.2 discussed the general philosophy of selective coordination for protective devices and the data required for a coordination study. Figures are numbered consecutively.

☐ Protective devices for electrical distribution systems, such as circuit breakers, protective relays and fuses, provide adequate protection and isolate trouble properly only if they are able to operate at the correct short-circuit current values and are set to operate at those values. The system design engineer can determine proper short-circuit values by carefully considering the ratings of the protected equipment and the relationship of the various protective devices in the distribution system.

To determine the best selection and setting of protective devices, the engineer must calculate the maximum magnitude of short-circuit current and carefully examine the tripping characteristics of protective devices under fault conditions. Coordination may require minimum as well as maximum short-circuit values.

Fault current varies in time, from the fault inception to the moment when the protective device operates. Protective devices interrupting in several cycles after fault initiation allow the fault current to decay from its maximum asymmetrical value. The protector and all series devices, however, must withstand the maximum short-circuit current. On the other hand, protective devices that interrupt in a fraction of a cycle reduce the short-circuit withstandability requirements of the series devices.

Inadequate short-circuit protection is often the source of failures that result in unnecessary damage, power interruption, injury to personnel and expensive production shutdowns. Oversized or overrated protective devices, however, constitute a waste in unnecessary costly equipment and may not operate at low enough values to protect properly. Consequently, exact determination of short-circuit conditions for the electric power system is of great importance.

Interrupting capacity represents the maximum short-circuit current that a power system causes to flow through a breaker or fuse when a fault occurs in the circuit. Noninterrupting devices, such as cables, bus ducts and disconnect switches, must withstand the thermal and mechanical stresses of the high short-circuit currents. A thorough knowledge of the maximum values of short-circuit currents is necessary not only to select and set protective devices but also to select and apply breakers on the basis of safe operation, such as interrupting capacity and momentary duty. Besides the normal continuous current that breakers and fuses have to carry, they must also withstand the maximum short-circuit that may flow through them.

The magnitude of the power system supplying the load dictates the amount of maximum short-circuit current. Under normal operation, the load draws a current proportional to the applied voltage and the line and load impedance. When a short-circuit occurs, the voltage is applied across a low impedance of only the conductors and transformer, from the source of voltage to the point of short-circuit. It no longer is opposed by the normal load impedance. Breakers, which are selected on the basis of the normal continuous current they carry, must also be capable of withstanding and interrupting the high short-circuit currents that may occur. Obviously then, the load current is determined by the normal load the breaker carries and has no relationship to the size of the system supplying the load.

The magnitude of the short-circuit current through the breaker, however, depends on the size of the supplying system and is independent of the normal load. For example, consider a source of infinite capacity and a single-phase 50-kva transformer supplying a 10-hp motor, as shown in Figure 6. Assume that the transformer has a secondary voltage of 240 v and an impedance of Zt = 1.4%. For simplicity, neglect the line impedance between the fault location at Point F and the transformer.

Under normal conditions, the motor will draw 50 amp, the current perceived by the protective breaker. Assuming a bolted short-circuit fault at Point F, the maximum short-circuit current that the protective breaker will pick up, considering the transformer impedance, is calculated:

$$\text{Isc max} = \frac{\text{Ifl sec}}{\% \ Zt/100} =$$

$$\frac{100 \times \text{Ifl sec}}{\% \ Zt}$$

Where:

Isc max = the maximum short-circuit current.

Ifl sec = the transformer secondary full-load current.

% Zt = the transformer's percent impedance.

The transformer secondary full load is:

$$\frac{50 \ \text{kva} \times 1,000}{240 \ \text{v}} \cong 208 \ \text{amp}$$

Substituting in the short-circuit formula:

$$\text{Isc max} = \frac{100 \times 208 \ \text{v}}{1.4 \ \text{imp}} =$$

14,857 amp symmetrical

The breaker protecting the feeder and the motor, therefore, must not only be able to carry the normal load of 50 amp but must also be able to withstand the maximum short-circuit that may occur, which is 7,429 amp. (For simplicity, the resistance and reactance of the circuit between the transformer and Point F have been neglected. In reality, short-circuit currents are higher in value, depend-

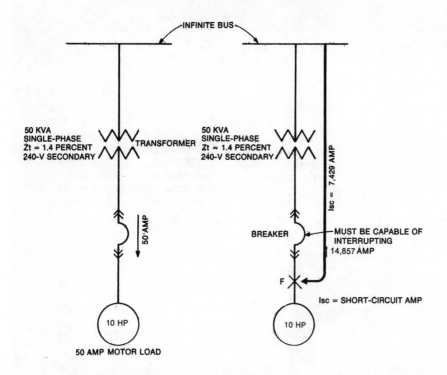

FIGURE 6 CIRCUIT BREAKER SEES 100-AMP MOTOR CURRENT, BUT MUST BE ABLE TO INTERRUPT 7,429 AMP

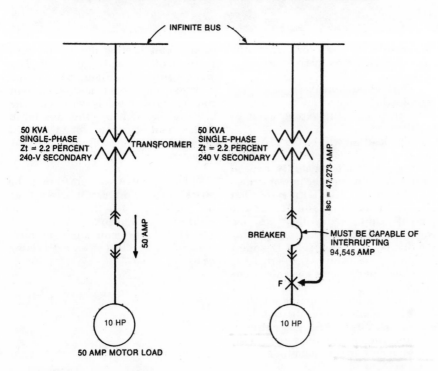

FIGURE 7 WHEN LARGER TRANSFORMER SERVES SAME LOAD, BREAKER MUST WITHSTAND 47,273 AMP SHORT CIRCUIT

ing on the ratio of the reactance to the resistance X/R of the circuit considered. This point will be discussed later).

Assume now that instead of the previously selected 50-kva transformer, there is a 500-kva transformer with an impedance of 2.2 percent supplying the same 10-hp motor, as shown in Figure 7.

The transformer secondary full load is:

$$\frac{500 \text{ kva} \times 1,000}{240 \text{ v}} = 2,080 \text{ amp}$$

If the same fault occurs at Point F, the short-circuit current through the same breaker will be:

$$\text{Isc max} = \frac{100 \times 2,080 \text{ amp}}{2.2 \text{ imp}} =$$

94,545 amp

instead of the previous 14,857 amp short-circuit symmetrical for the 50-kva transformer.

This example proves that the magnitude of the short-circuit through the breaker depends on the size of the supplying power system. It also proves that the short-circuit availability in a system dictates the proper selection of the breaker or fuse sizes. Those selected must withstand the mechanical stresses and interrupt the maximum short-circuit current delivered by the system into the bolted short without destroying the interrupting devices.

A mechanical analogy

A short-circuit-proof interrupting device can be compared with an explosion-proof device used in hazardous areas. The device must perform a certain funtion even if there is an explosion within it. The device must be strong enough, mechanically, to confine the explosion and withstand the thermal and mechanical stresses accompanying the explosion.

Besides its normal operation, the device must also be explosion-proof in the same way an interrupting device must carry the normal load and also withstand the thermal and mechanical stress of a possible short-circuit current. In other words, it must be short-circuit-proof to avoid destruction of the device and possible spread of thermal and mechanical effects.

Another well-known analogy is the comparison of normal loads and short-circuit currents with the water flow in hydroelectric generating plants. The normal load of the turbines determines the flow of water for normal conditions of operation and has no bearing on the magnitude of the water reservoir behind the dam. If the dam breaks, the quantity of water that

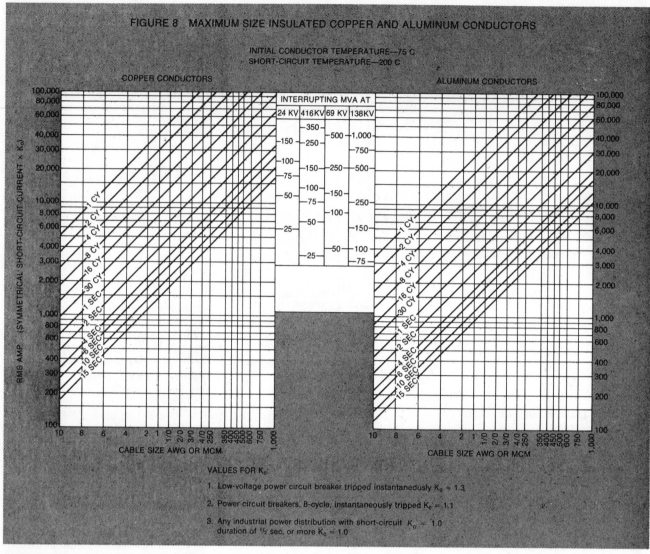

FIGURE 8 MAXIMUM SIZE INSULATED COPPER AND ALUMINUM CONDUCTORS

INITIAL CONDUCTOR TEMPERATURE—75 C
SHORT-CIRCUIT TEMPERATURE—200 C

VALUES FOR K_o:

1. Low-voltage power circuit breaker tripped instantaneously $K_o = 1.3$

2. Power circuit breakers, 8-cycle, instantaneously tripped $K_o = 1.1$

3. Any industrial power distribution with short-circuit $K_o = 1.0$ duration of $^1/_2$ sec. or more $K_o = 1.0$

flows depends on the magnitude of the reservoir, which bears no relationship to the normal load of the turbines. The normal flow of water can be compared with the normal flow of the electrical current. If the dam breaks, this flow of water can be compared to the flow of short-circuit current when a short-circuit occurs.

The interrupting (protecting) devices prevent unwanted mishaps by containing a corresponding short-circuit capability. Coordinated selective protection in modern industrial power systems assures effective isolation of faulted sections allowing the rest of the system to operate normally.

Seven steps to proper protection

To ensure adequate short-circuit protection, the following points must be observed:

• Available short-circuit currents must be accurately determined and protective devices carefully selected and set. Until the magnitude of short-circuit currents is known it is impossible to be sure that the short-circuit protective devices are adequate.

• Only circuit breakers, fuses and combination motor starters of known adequate interrupting rating should be installed.

• The load growth of the plant and the fact that interrupting devices in their short-circuit capability depend on the magnitude of the power system must be kept in mind. If the system has circuit breakers adequate for the present requirements, they will become too small, from an interrupting standpoint, when capacity is added. Failure to consider the effect of increased short-circuit currents is one of the most common causes of. many older installations becoming unsafe.

• All circuit stresses in bus bars, etc., have to be checked. These stresses are proportional with the square of the short-circuit current magnitude.

• Cable sizes, besides their normal current-carrying capabilities, must be checked for their ability to withstand short-circuit heating due to the high short-circuit currents to which they may be subjected. Figure 8 shows the selection of copper and aluminum conductors that safely withstand the heating caused by the available short-circuit currents for a certain duration expressed in seconds or cycles, or both.

• The power system must be checked for short-circuit safety from the supply point to the last motor or utilization equipment.

• The short-circuit study problem must be approached on an engineering basis.

4.4 Sources of Short-Circuit Currents, How They Behave, and Ways to Detect Them

The previous section 4.3 discussed the importance of knowing the exact magnitude of short circuits and the steps to take to ensure adequate short-circuit protection and coordination. This part examines sources, behavior and characteristic reactances of short-circuit currents, circuit components, limiting magnitudes of fault-current values, short-circuit waves and their asymmetry, decrement X/R ratio, and interrupting and momentary duty of breakers. Figures and tables are numbered consecutively.

Magnitudes of short-circuit currents depend on the various sources generating them, on their reactances and on the system reactances from these sources up to the fault's location. The main sources of short-circuit current are utility systems, generators, synchronous and induction motors, as shown in Figure 9. (Utilities provide information about the available magnitude of short-circuit currents.)

Generally, utility systems supply power through stepdown power transformers at the user's desired voltage level. Transformers are sometimes erroneously considered sources of short-circuit current. This is not strictly correct, since transformers change but do not generate voltage and current magnitudes. The amount of short-circuit current delivered through a transformer depends on its secondary voltage rating and percent impedance. It also depends on the reactance of the generators and the system down to the transformer terminals, and on the reactance of the circuit between the transformer and the fault location.

The percent impedance of a transformer is the percent of rated primary voltage applied to the transformer to produce the normal rated full-load current in its short-circuited secondary. Based on this definition, percent impedance is a percent voltage measure rather than an impedance:

$$\% \, Z = \frac{EZ \times 100}{EN} \text{ single-phase}$$

(For 3-phase, multiply by $\sqrt{3}$)

Where: % Z = percent impedance; EN = normal rating of primary voltage; EZ = applied primary voltage to produce normal rated current when secondary is short-circuited.

Because utility systems are much larger than industrial plant systems, any decrease in symmetrical short-circuit current during a fault is noticeable (see Figure 10). Short-circuit currents concern measurements of the root-mean-square (rms), or the effective value of the sinusoidal wave. The effective value of an alternating current is the square root of the average of the squares of the instantaneous values of currents:

$$I = \sqrt{\text{mean value of i}^2}.$$

These sinusoidal current waves (Figure 11) can be symmetrical or asymmetrical. A symmetrical sinusoidal current wave is an alternating current balanced around the zero line, which in this case, is the wave axis. The sinusoid may decrease in magnitude. An asymmetrical sinusoidal current wave (Figure 12) is an alternating current not balanced around the zero line, which in this case does not coincide with the wave axis. The "envelope" in Figure 12 defines the peak values of the wave about its own axis.

Generator-produced short-circuits

Prime movers such as steam and gas turbines, diesel engines or water turbines may drive generators. If a short-circuit occurs, the generator continues to generate voltage, since by rotating at normal speed it maintains a field excitation. The generated voltage produces a short-circuit of large current magnitude that flows to the fault point. This flow is limited only by reactance of the generator and impedance of the circuit between generator and fault location. The generator's reactance magnitude changes after the fault inception moment and is formed by the following values:

X''_d = subtransient reactance

This value determines the short-circuit current immediately after fault inception. The value lasts for the first few cycles after the fault occurs and in about .1 sec increases to the next value:

X'_d = transient reactance

This value lasts for about 2 sec, while increasing to the final value:

X_d = synchronous reactance

This value determines the current flow after a steady-state condition is reached. The steady-state condition is effective in several seconds after the fault inception.

A generator has a variable reactance that gains magnitude with time. Consequently, short-circuit current decreases exponentially in time from an initial high value to a lower steady-state level.

The decay rate, of course, depends on generator constants. The machine manufacturers' values X''_d and X'_d are usually the lowest, and their use results in the available short-circuit current.

Motor-induced faults

Synchronous motors perform much like synchronous generators. If a fault occurs, system voltage dips to a low value and the synchronous motor stops taking power and quickly slows down. When this happens, inertia acts as a prime mover, and with excitation maintained, the motor acts as a generator supplying short-circuit current for several cycles after a fault occurs. Designations for the variable reactances of synchronous motors are the same as those for generators, but the values of X''_d, X'_d and X_d are different.

The magnitude of short-circuit

FIGURE 9 SHORT-CIRCUIT CURRENT SOURCES

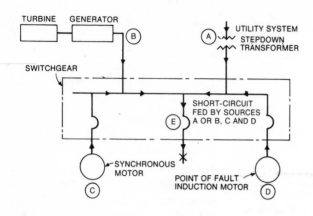

FIGURE 11 SYMMETRICAL SINUSOIDAL WAVE

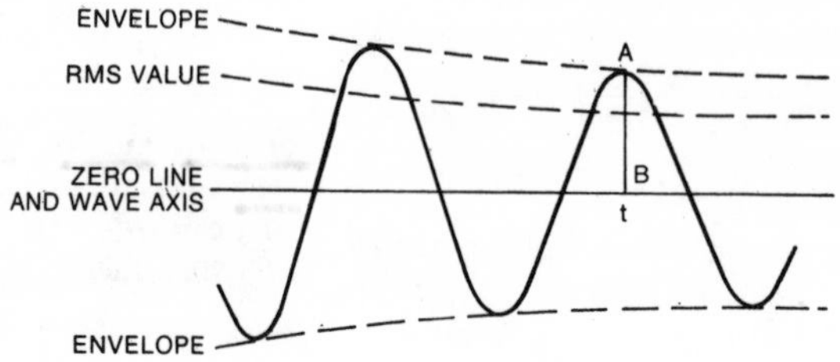

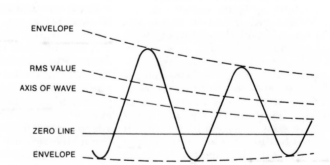

$$\text{RMS AT T TIME} = \frac{\text{PEAK VALUE AT T}}{1.414} \qquad \text{AB} = \text{PEAK VALUE AT T TIME}$$

FIGURE 10 SHORT-CIRCUIT CURRENTS

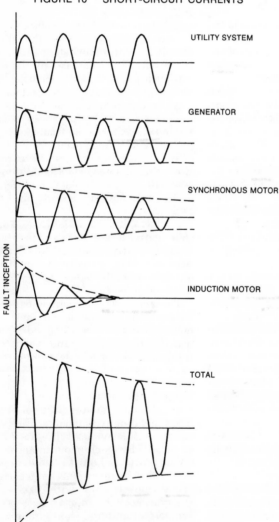

TIME, CYCLES

The total symmetrical short-circuit current is a
summation of the fault currents contributed by
several sources, each source behaving in a
characteristic way

FIGURE 12 ASYMMETRICAL SINUSOIDAL WAVE

current caused by synchronous motors depends on the hp, voltage rating and reactance of the motor, plus the system reactance to the point of fault.

Induction motors also contribute short-circuit current caused by the generator action produced by the load inertia and rotor driving the motor after the fault occurs. A major difference exists between the short-circuit current contributions of induction and synchronous motors. The field flux of an induction motor comes from stator induction rather than a direct-current field winding. Since the flux decays rapidly on removal of source voltage after a fault occurs, the induction motor contribution drops quickly and ceases after a few cycles.

Without field excitation, the induction motor does not contribute steady-state fault current and, consequently, has only a subtransient value of reactance, X''_d. This value is nearly equal to the locked-rotor reactance. It follows that the initial symmetrical value of short-circuit current is almost equal to the full-voltage starting current of the induction motor, about 600-900 percent of the normal load current. The magnitude of the short-circuit current from the induction motor, like that of the generator and synchronous motor, depends on the hp, voltage rating, motor reactance and system reactance to the fault point.

The total symmetrical short-circuit is a combination of all short-circuit current sources. The rotating machine flux decays with time after the fault inception, and the fault-current contribution consequently also decays. The resulting total short-circuit current also decays, as shown in Figure 10. The current magnitude is highest during the first half-cycle and decreases in value after a few cycles. After one or two cycles the induction-motor contribution disappears.

Limiting short-current value

Only the symmetrical components of short-circuit current contributions have been discussed so far. But, in fact, the short-circuit current magnitude is further increased during the first few cycles by the so-called DC component. Since short-circuit current magnitude varies with time, any short-circuit calculation procedure must determine the current magnitude at various times after fault inception.

Components limiting short-circuit current values are transformer imped-ances, reactors, cables, buses, current-limiting fuses and any other circuit impedances.

Transformers, because of their impedance, reduce the magnitude of short-circuit currents produced by the sources to which the transformers connect.

Reactors limit short-circuit current values by intentionally introducing a reactance into the circuit. Reactors have some pronounced disadvantages, however. They produce a voltage drop that can cause system voltage dips at the fault occurrence or at the starting of large motors. They may adversely affect voltage regulation and even trip undervoltage devices. They also are energy consumers. The engineer must consider these shortcomings when deciding whether to specify reactors, circuit breakers with greater interrupting capacity, or current-limiting fuses.

Cables and busways form part of the link between short-circuit sources and the point of fault. Their impedance limits the short-circuit current value by varying amounts, depending on the size, nature and length of cable. Some busways are designed to introduce impedance in the system circuit. Values of resistance, reactance and impedance for cables and busways appear in manufacturers' catalogs.

Current-limiting fuses open the circuit before the short-circuit current has risen to peak value, as shown in Figure 13. They clear both symmetrical and asymmetrical faults usually in the first quarter-cycle. The total clearing time consists of a melting period as heat increases in the fuse element and an arcing period after the element melts and the fuse's filler components cool gaseous arc products. The arc introduces an impedance that limits the current, reducing it finally to zero. The current-limiting fuse has a low impedance until a very high current starts to flow through it. It is both a current-limiting and a short-circuit-interrupting device. Typical fuses and circuit breakers are interrupting devices only.

Three major classes of components participate in a short-circuit—sources with time-variable reactances that produce short-circuit currents; circuit components with fixed reactances that limit short-circuit current magnitudes, and breakers and fuses that interrupt short-circuit currents. The first step in a short-circuit calculation determines the reactances of these three compo-nent classes for a specific fault.

The subtransient reactances X''_d determine the short-circuit current in the first half-cycle. These determine the momentary duties of breakers and fuses, which constitute the highest stress that they must withstand.

Short-circuit waves in industrial plants are mainly of the sine-wave shape (Figures 11 and 12). Depending on the circuit voltage, typical power-circuit resistance is usually negligible compared to reactance. In addition, when a short-circuit occurs, much resistance shorts out and a highly reactive circuit remains.

If a fault occurs in such a circuit at the instant of voltage-wave peak, the short-circuit current starts at almost zero, and its sine-wave, which must be 90 deg out of phase with the voltage, is totally symmetrical about the zero axis (see Figure 14). If the short-circuit occurs at the voltage-wave zero-point, the current—again starting at zero—cannot increase with the voltage and remains in phase with it. The current wave must lag the voltage by 90 deg; therefore, it is displaced from the zero axis. As the voltage reaches its peak, the current wave continues to increase until voltage becomes zero, thus producing a totally asymmetrical short-circuit current, as shown in Figure 15. The total asymmetrical current can be visualized as a symmetrical current having a direct-current component superimposed on it (see Figure 16).

The DC component represents sine-wave displacement from the zero axis. In reality, a short-circuit current is likely to occur anywhere between zero and peak voltage, so the offset of the current wave will fall somewhere between the two extremes (Figure 17). Any real circuit has some resistance, and this causes the DC component to decay to zero in several cycles after the fault inception. The effect is a change from an initial asymmetrical current to a symmetrical one. The DC component, assumed to be generated in the AC system rather than any external source, will have its energy dissipated at a RI^2 loss in the circuit resistance (Figure 18). The X/R factor is the reactance-to-resistance ratio of the circuit considered. The DC component decay, also called decrement, depends on the X/R ratio, X and R being the reactance and resistance of all circuit components between the source and fault. If R = 0, the ratio is infinity and

FIGURE 13
HOW CURRENT-LIMITING FUSES CLEAR A FAULT

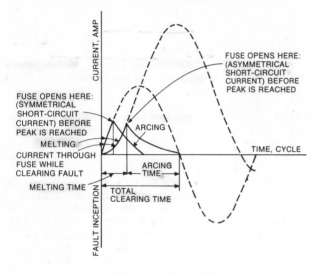

FIGURE 14

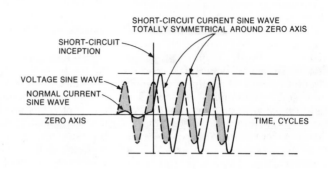

When short-circuit occurs at the instant of a voltage peak, and the short-circuit is totally reactive, short-circuit wave is symmetrical about zero axis.

FIGURE 15

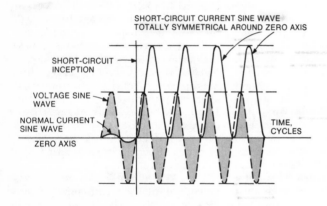

When short-circuit occurs at a voltage zero and the short-circuit is totally reactive, the short-circuit wave has no symmetry with respect to zero axis.

FIGURE 16

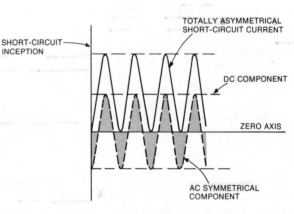

The asymmetrical short-circuit current can be visualized as a summation of a symmetrical alternating current with a DC component superimposed on it.

FIGURE 17

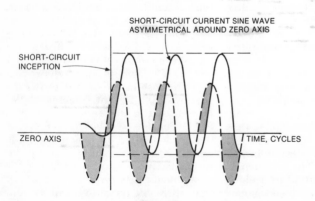

In a real circuit, the short-circuit most often occurs at some point between the peak and zero values of the voltage wave. Circuit shown is totally reactive.

FIGURE 18

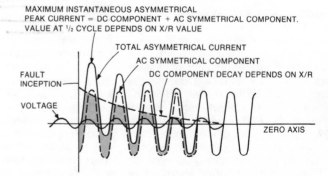

The DC component in an actual circuit decays with time due to presence of some resistance. Initial asymmetrical current changes into symmetrical current.

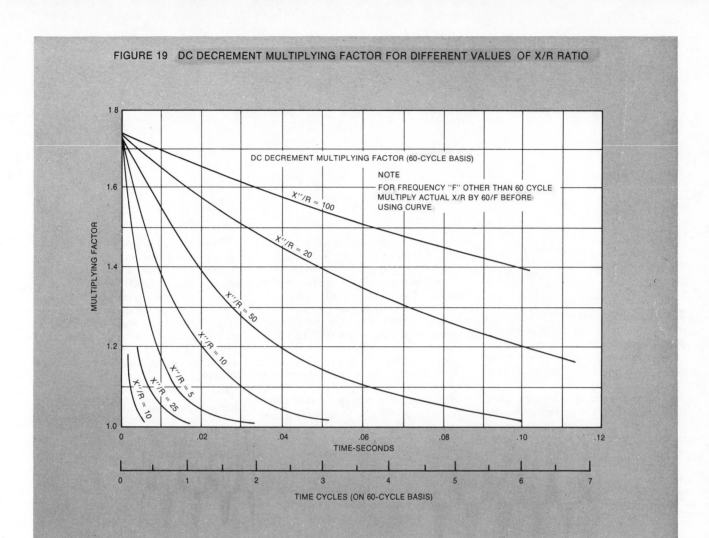

FIGURE 19 DC DECREMENT MULTIPLYING FACTOR FOR DIFFERENT VALUES OF X/R RATIO

DC DECREMENT MULTIPLYING FACTOR (60-CYCLE BASIS)

NOTE
FOR FREQUENCY "F" OTHER THAN 60 CYCLE
MULTIPLY ACTUAL X/R BY 60/F BEFORE
USING CURVE

the DC component will never decay. If X = 0, the ratio is zero and the DC component decays instantly. Otherwise, the DC component decays in time to zero, the time depending on the particular X/R ratio: the greater the reactance over the resistance, the longer component will take to decay.

An exact calculation of rms asymmetrical current at different times after fault inception is too involved. It would require knowledge of accurate factors for rate of change in apparent generator reactances and decrement factors for DC components. Simplified methods account for the DC components with an accepted multiplier, which converts the calculated symmetrical rms amperes into asymmetrical rms amperes (including the DC component).

New practices

Traditionally, the determination of short-circuit current asymmetrical values was accomplished by applying multipliers to the calculated values of symmetrical short-circuit currents. The recent trend is to rate protective devices based on symmetrical values (see ANSI C37.010-1972 and later revisions), the asymmetry being accounted by various formulas according to equipment class. These application formulas are in the "American National Standards for Power Circuit Breaker Application" published in *IEEE Transactions on Industry and General Applications*, Vol. IGA-5, September/October, 1969, and as in ANSI C37.5 1969.

The application of breakers and fuses considers only maximum DC components for the momentary duty. Thus, the applied protective device must withstand the maximum short-circuit that may occur in the system. For momentary duty the engineer must consider all subtransient reactances at the first half-cycle of the symmetrical short-circuit current before applying the multiplier. Practical calculations generally use a multiplier of 1.5 to 1.6 for medium- and high-voltage circuits and approximately 1.25 for low-voltage circuits. Figure 19 shows multiplying factors for various X/R values and periods up to seven cycles

after fault inception.

The magnitude of short-circuit current when circuit breaker contacts separate or the fuse blows determines the interrupting duty. Circuit breakers interrupt after three, five or eight cycles, depending on breaker type. After eight cycles, the induction motor contribution vanishes and the synchronous motor reactance changes from subtransient to transient. This explains why the interruption duty of breakers above 600 v requires the generator subtransient reactance and the synchronous motor transient reactance, neglecting the induction motors. The DC component almost disappears after eight cycles, so these breakers, used generally in industrial plants, take a multiplier of 1.

4.5 Formulas for Short-Circuit Calculations and Basic Characteristics of Breakers and Fuses

The previous section 4.4 discussed sources, behavior and characteristics of short-circuit currents, components limiting fault-current values, short-circuit waves and their asymmetry, decrement, and X/R ratio.

The following part discusses multiplying factors for asymmetrical short-circuit current values, the per-unit method and formulas for short-circuit calculation, and characteristics of power and low-voltage breakers and fuses. Figures and tables are numbered consecutively.

The first step in a selective coordination study of protective devices is the short-circuit calculation. Its purpose is to determine the minimum and maximum fault-current values required in a selective coordination of time-current curves for the various protective devices.

Section 4.4 discussed two factors that cause the initial fault current to be greater than the steady-state fault current. One factor is the variable reactance of the rotating machines, which is accounted for by using their initial subtransient reactances. The second factor, the initial asymmetry caused by the decaying DC component, is practically accounted for by using simple multiplying factors applied to the calculated symmetrical fault-current values.

Formerly, these multipliers were applied to obtain the asymmetrical fault-current values in the selection of equipment with asymmetrical current capability ratings. The recent trend eliminates asymmetrical equipment ratings. Table 2 shows asymmetrical multiplying factors for obtaining the rms asymmetrical values for applying protective devices.

Determination of short-circuit cur-

rent values depends on all reactances from the sources of fault to the fault point. Basically, the determination of these reactances is the main problem in short-circuit calculations. The reactances of all circuit elements must be determined and then combined in series or parallel, or both. The three main systems used to express reactances of the circuit elements are in ohms, percent, or in per-unit on a chosen base value.

The per-unit system is used extensively, especially in systems that have various voltage levels. The per-unit system on a chosen base allows the combination of reactances without regard for the transformer turns-ratio in systems utilizing several voltage levels. No conversion is necessary from one level to another.

The per-unit (or percent) method used in IEEE publications expresses numbers in a form allowing them to be easily compared. In fact, the per-unit value is a ratio based on a preselected number: per-unit=a number÷chosen base number.

The base kva number might be any round number, such as 1,000 or 10,000 kva, but it usually is the kva of the system's largest transformer. Reactances for circuit elements—buses, cables, lines, current transformers, air circuit breakers, etc.—usually are in ohms, and it is necessary to convert these values by the following formulas:

$$\text{Per-unit reactance}=\frac{\text{percent reactance}}{100} \tag{1}$$

$$\text{Per-unit reactance}=\frac{\text{ohms} \times \text{kva base}}{1{,}000 \times \text{kv}^2} \tag{2}$$

$$\text{Per-unit reactance}=\frac{\text{ohms} \times \text{mva base}}{\text{kv}^2} \tag{3}$$

$$\text{Percent reactance}=\frac{\text{ohms} \times \text{kva base}}{10 \times \text{kv}^2} \tag{4}$$

$$\text{Percent reactance}=\frac{\text{ohms} \times \text{mva base}}{\text{kv}^2} \times 100 \tag{5}$$

Where: ohms = line to neutral value (single conductor); kva base = 3-phase chosen kva base; kv = line-to-line voltage; mva = 1,000 kva.

Some system elements, such as transformers, generators, motors, etc., usually have their reactances expressed in percent on their own kva ratings. These reactances must be converted to the chosen kva base as follows:

$$\text{Per-unit reactance} = \text{per unit reactance} \times \frac{\text{base kva}}{\text{rating}} \tag{6}$$

To convert the available symmetrical short-circuit kva at the utility service to per-unit reactance, use:

$$\text{Per-unit reactance} = \frac{\text{base kva}}{\text{available s-c kva}} \tag{7}$$

In low-voltage systems, the utility company may express available short-circuit in amperes. The system design engineer must determine if this value is symmetrical or asymmetrical and learn the X/R value at the service entrance. If the short-circuit current is in asymmetrical amperes, the appropriate multipler for the given X/R value can be found in Figure 19 and this formula applied to convert asymmetrical to symmetrical amperes:

$$\text{Amp rms symm} = \frac{\text{amp asymm}}{\text{multiplier}} \tag{8}$$

Then convert symmetrical rms amperes to per-unit reactance:

$$\text{Per-unit reactance} = \frac{\text{Base kva}}{\text{amp symm} \times \text{kv} \times \sqrt{3}} \tag{9}$$

After all the reactances are converted to per-unit values on the chosen kva base, they must be combined in series and parallel to arrive at the total equivalent per-unit reactance. This is done by using Formulas 10 through 14, shown in Figure 20. Finally, Formula 15 is used to obtain the symmetrical short-circuit kva value from the total per-unit reactance:

$$\text{Symmetrical short-circuit kva} = \frac{\text{base kva}}{\text{total per-unit reactance}} \tag{15}$$

FIGURE 20   FORMULAS FOR COMBINING SERIES AND PARALLEL REACTANCES, AS WELL AS WYE TO DELTA OR DELTA TO WYE CONVERSION

FORMULA 11—COMBINING SERIES BRANCHES

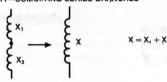

$$X = X_1 + X_2$$

FORMULA 14—TRANSFORMING WYE TO DELTA

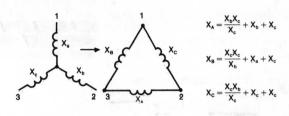

$$X_A = \frac{X_b X_c}{X_c} + X_b + X_c$$

$$X_B = \frac{X_c X_c}{X_b} + X_a + X_c$$

$$X_C = \frac{X_c X_b}{X_c} + X_c + X_c$$

FORMULA 12—COMBINING TWO PARALLEL BRANCHES

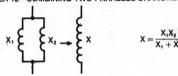

$$X = \frac{X_1 X_2}{X_1 + X_2}$$

FORMULA 15—TRANSFORMING DELTA TO WYE

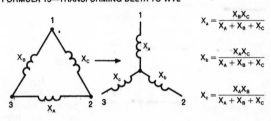

$$X_a = \frac{X_B X_C}{X_A + X_B + X_C}$$

$$X_b = \frac{X_A X_C}{X_A + X_B + X_C}$$

$$X_c = \frac{X_A X_B}{X_A + X_B + X_C}$$

FORMULA 13—COMBINING SEVERAL PARALLEL BRANCHES

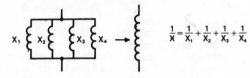

$$\frac{1}{X} = \frac{1}{X_1} + \frac{1}{X_2} + \frac{1}{X_3} + \frac{1}{X_4}$$

TABLE 2   MACHINE REACTANCES AND MULTIPLYING FACTORS USED IN SIMPLIFIED CALCULATIONS OF SHORT-CIRCUIT DUTY

Type of short- circuit duty and kind of equipment	Machine reactances to use			Multiplying factors to be applied to calculated symmetrical value[1]	
	Synchronous generators	Synchronous motors	Induction motors	General case[2]	Special case[2]
Interrupting duty or power circuit breakers with rated interrupting times of					
8 cycles	Subtransient	Transient	Neglect	1.0	1.1
5 cycles	Subtransient	Transient	Neglect	1.1	1.2
3 cycles	Subtransient	Transient	Neglect	1.2	1.3
2 cycles	Subtransient	Transient	Neglect	1.4	1.5
Momentary duty for				General case[3]	Special case[3]
power circuit breakers	Subtransient	Subtransient	Subtransient	1.6	1.5
Interrupting duty for L-V power circuit breakers	Subtransient	Subtransient	Subtransient		1.0
Interrupting duty for molded-case circuit breakers	Subtransient	Subtransient	Subtransient		1.0
Interrupting duty for				General case[4]	Special case[4]
fuses and fused cutouts (above 1,500 v)	Subtransient	Subtransient	Subtransient	1.6	1.2
Interrupting duty for LV fuses (600 v and below)	Subtransient	Subtransient	Subtransient		1.0[5]
Interrupting duty for L-V motor controllers (incorporating fuses or molded-case circuit breakers)	Subtransient	Subtransient	Subtransient		1.25

[1] The calculated symmetrical value to which the multiplier is applied should be in rms amperes, kva, or mva depending on the terms in which the rated capability of the particular equipment is expressed.
[2] Use special-case multiplier only if the calculated symmetrical duty exceeds 500 mva and the circuit is principally fed direct from generators or entirely through current-limiting reactors; otherwise use general-case multiplier.
[3] Use special-case multiplier only if operating voltage is 5,000 or less and the circuit is not principally fed direct from generators or entirely through current-limiting reactors; otherwise use general-case multiplier.
[4] Use special-case multiplier only if the operating voltage is 15,000 or below, and the fuses are not of the current-limiting type, and the supply-circuit, X/R, is less than 4; otherwise use general-case multiplier.
[5] General Electric Type CLF fuses require the 1.0 multiplier as do LV fuses that meet current NEMA Standards.

If symmetrical short-circuit rms amperes are required, use:

$$\text{Symm s-c amp} = \frac{\text{base kva}}{\text{total per-unit reactance} \times \text{kv} \times \sqrt{3}}$$

(16)

The interrupting and momentary duties are obtained by applying the corresponding multipliers from Table 2 to the calculated symmetrical values.

Breaker and fuse characteristics

For coordination purposes, minimum and maximum values of possible short-circuits are required. As shown section 4.4 the fault current varies with time after fault inception. This is why the following times are recommended for calculating short-circuit current:

• At first cycle, maximum symmetrical values are required for low-voltage systems and fuses in general.

• Between 1.5 and 4 cycles, maximum values are required for the applications of high-voltage circuit breakers.

• At approximately 30 cycles ($\frac{1}{2}$ sec), the reduced values of fault currents are required for the performance of time-delay relays and noncurrent limiting fuses. These minimum values are necessary to be sure the protective device opens at a desired time delay. This time is the total necessary for the protective relay to close contacts, the breaker trip coil to release its operating mechanism, the breaker's contacts to part and the arc to be interrupted in the arc chamber. The highest mechanical stresses occur during the first half-cycle because of the DC component and the short-circuit current contribution from motors and generators.

From the inception of a short-circuit until the breaker contacts part, the current decreases by the value of the DC component and by the change in motor reactance values. Consequently, the value of the current the breaker must interrupt at 4, 5 or 8 cycles after the fault is less than the maximum value during the first half-cycle.

Therefore, two bases of short-circuit ratings must be considered for power circuit breakers (above 600 v): the momentary rating accounting for the breaker's ability to close against and withstand the mechanical and thermal stresses of the maximum short-circuit current of the first half-cycle; and the interrupting duty rating, accounting for the breaker's ability to interrupt the flow of short-circuit current within its interrupting element after 4, 5 or 8 cycles, according to the breaker type.

Power-circuit breaker ratings are fied on a symmetrical rating basis

by ANSI C37.06 and recommended by IEEE. They are classified according to type of breaker, voltage, current and interrupting capacity.

Table 3 shows characteristics of medium-voltage power-circuit breakers. Each of the 15 columns has a specific rating for a selected breaker. Five limits never to be exceeded in power-circuit breaker selection are: rated maximum voltage (Column 4, Table 3); momentary closing and latching (Column 15); maximum symmetrical interrupting capability (Column 13); nominal 3-phase mva (Column 3); and rated continuous current (Column 8).

For a 4,160-v, 250-mva power breaker, the most important ratings are operating voltage, momentary current, interrupting mva nad maximum interrupting rating.

TABLE 3 POWER CIRCUIT BREAKER CHARACTERISTICS

1	2	3	4	5	6	7	8
	Identification						Rated values
			Voltage		Insulation level		Current
Line No.	Nominal voltage class kv, rms	Nominal 3-phase mva class	Rated maximum voltage[1] kv, rms	K Rated voltage range factor k_2	Rated withstand test voltage — Low frequency kv, rms	Impulse kv, crest	Rated Continuous current at 60 Hz amp, rms
1	4.16	75	4.76	1.36	19	60	1,200
3	4.16	250	4.76	1.24	19	60	1,200
4	4.16	250	4.76	1.24	19	60	2,000
4A	4.16	350	4.76	1.19	19	60	1,200
4B	4.16	350	4.76	1.19	19	60	3,000
4D	7.2	500	8.25	1.25	36	95	1,200
4E	7.2	500	8.25	1.25	36	95	2,000
6	13.8	500	15	1.30	36	95	1,200
7A	13.8	750	15	1.30	36	95	1,200
7B	13.8	750	15	1.30	36	95	2,000
8	13.8	1,000	15	1.30	36	95	1,200
9	13.8	1,000	15	1.30	36	95	3,000
							NONSTANDARD BREAKERS—
10	4.16	250	4.76	1.24	19	60	1,200 2,000
11	13.8	500	15	1.30	36	95	1,200 2,000
12	13.8	750	15	1.30	36	95	1,200 2,000

handwritten annotations: "interrupting upper limit mva", "of rated operating voltage range", "K"

[1] *Maximum voltage for which the breaker is designed and the upper limit for operation.*
[2] *K is the ratio of rated maximum voltage to the lower limit of the range of operating voltage in which the required symmetrical and asymmetrical interrupting capabilities vary in inverse proportion to the operating voltage.*
[3] *To obtain the required symmetrical interrupting capability of a circuit breaker at an operating voltage between 1/K times rated maximum voltage and rated maximum voltage, the following formula shall be used:*

Required symmetrical interrupting capability = rated short-circuit current x

$$\frac{\text{(Rated max. voltage)}}{\text{(Operating voltage)}}$$

For operating voltages below 1/K times rated maximum voltage, the required symmetrical interrupting capability of the circuit breaker shall be equal to K times rated short-

Operating voltage, listed as rated maximum voltage 4.76 kv rms (Column 4), is the highest rms voltage at rated frequency for which the breaker is designed.

Momentary current (Column 15) is 58,000 amp. It is the maximum rms asymmetrical current the breaker will withstand, including short-circuit currents, from all sources and the DC component. Momentary current accounts for the maximum current during the first cycle after fault inception. It defines the breaker's ability to close and latch against mechanical stresses produced by the largest offset of the short-circuit current. This value is very important because mechanical stresses are proportional with the square of the current. A power circuit breaker is proportioned so that its momentary rating is about 1.6 or more times the maximum interrupting rating in amperes.

Interrupting mva is 250, listed as the nominal 3-phase mva (Column 3). This is the product of the maximum kv at which the breaker operates, rated short-circuit current in kilo-amperes and the square root of 3.

Maximum interrupting rating (Column 13) is 36,000 amp, the highest rms current the circuit breaker will interrupt regardless of voltage. Where no short-circuit contribution from motors occurs, only an interrupting duty (mva) check is necessary. If this value does not exceed the value in Column 13, the maximum short-circuit current, including the DC component, will be within the breaker's momentary rating. When a substantial motor load contributes to the short-circuit, both momentary and interrupting duty should be checked.

The maximum momentary duty of the power circuit breaker is found by determining the current at the first half-cycle. The short-circuit current during this time includes all sources of short-circuit current contributed by generators, synchronous and induction motors, and utility supply connection.

Subtransient reactances of generators and synchronous and induction motors must all be accounted for in the total reactance diagram. The DC component, which is maximum in the first half-cycle, must also be accounted for by a multiplier in the general case (in Table 2, the multiplier is 1.6). In the special case where the calculated symmetrical duty exceeds 500 mva and generators or current-limiting reactors directly feed the circuit, the multipler is 1.5.

A power circuit breaker's interrupting duty is checked by determining the short-circuit current at the moment the breaker's contacts part. With fewer cycles required for the contacts to part, the current to be interrupted will be proportionately greater. Accordingly, power circuit breakers are classed according to the breaker's operating speed. There are 8-, 5- and 3-cycle breakers. Instead of accounting for the time at which the short-circuit current has to be calculated, a multiplier (Table 2) is used to account for the generator and motor reactances at that time.

In industrial and power plants, 8-cycle breakers are generally specified. Normally, the induction motor contribution has disappeared, and the reactance of synchronous motors has changed from subtransient to transient values even before the contacts part. Consequently, generator subtransient reactances and synchronous motor

(SYMMETRICAL RATING BASIS ANSI C37.06 1969)

Momentary current →

Lower Limit of the range of operating voltage →

9	10	11	12	13	14	15
			Related required capabilities			
				Current values		
Rated short-circuit current at rated max. kv[3,4] ka, rms	Rated interrupting time cycle	Rated permissible tripping delay, Y sec	Rated maximum voltage divided by K kv rms	Maximum symmetrical interrupting capability[5] K times rated short-circuit current ka, rms	3 sec short-time current carrying capability K times rated short-circuit current ka, rms	Closing and latching capability 1.6 K times rated short circuit current ka/rms
8.8	5	2	3.5	12	12	19
29	5	2	3.85	36	36	58
29	5	2	3.85	36	36	58
41	5	2	4.0	49	49	78
41	5	2	4.0	49	49	78
33	5	2	6.6	41	41	66
33	5	2	6.6	41	41	66
18	5	2	11.5	23	23	37
28	5	2	11.5	36	36	58
28	5	2	11.5	36	36	58
37	5	2	11.5	48	48	77
37	5	2	11.5	48	48	77

HIGH CLOSE AND LATCH CAPABILITY

9	10	11	12	13	14	15
29	5	2	3.85	36	36	78
18	5	2	11.5	23	23	58
28	5	2	11.5	36	36	77

circuit current.
[4] With the limitation stated in 04-4.5 of ANSI C37.04-1969, all values apply for polyphase and line-to-line faults. For single phase-to-ground faults, the specific conditions stated in 04-4.5.2.3 of ANSI C37.04-1969 apply.
[5] Current values in this column are not to be exceeded even for operating voltages below 1/K times rated maximum voltage. For voltages between rated maximum voltage and 1/K times rated maximum voltage, follow [3] above.
ANSI-C37.06 symmetrical rating basis is supplementary to ANSI-C37.6 (total current rating basis) and does not replace it. When a changeover from the total current basis of rating to the symmetrical basis of rating is effected the older standards will be withdrawn.
In accordance with ANSI-C37.06, users should confer with the manufacturer on the status of the various circuit breaker ratings.

TABLE 4   RATINGS FOR LOW-VOLTAGE ALTERNATING-CURRENT POWER CIRCUIT BREAKERS WITH DIRECT-ACTING INSTANTANEOUS TRIP DEVICES

Line No.	Rated voltage (v)	Rated minimum voltage (v)	Insulation level, dielectric withstand (v)	3-phase[1] short-circuit rating (symmetrical amp)	Frame size (amp)	Continuous current ratings (amp) range of trip rating[2] dual overcurrent trip or instantaneous overcurrent trip
1	600	635	2,200	14,000	225	40-225
2	600	635	2,200	22,000	600	40-600
3	600	635	2,200	42,000	1,600	200-1,600
4	600	635	2,200	42,000	2,000	200-2,000
5	600	635	2,200	65,000	3,000	2,000-3,000
6	600	635	2,200	85,000	4,000	4,000
7	480	508	2,200	22,000	225	40-225
8	480	508	2,200	30.000	600	100-600
9	480	508	2,200	50,000	1,600	400-1,600
10	480	508	2,200	50,000	2,000	400-2,000
11	480	508	2,200	65,000	3,000	2,000-3,000
12	480	508	2,200	85,000	4,000	4,000
13	240	254	2,200	25,000	225	40-225
14	240	254	2.200	42,000	600	150-600
15	240	254	2.200	65,000	1,600	600-1,600
16	240	254	2,200	65,000	2,000	600-2,000
17	240	254	2,200	85,000	3,000	2,000-3,000
18	240	254	2,200	130,000	4,000	4,000

[1] Single-phase short-circuit-current ratings are 87 percent of these values.
[2] The continuous-current-carrying capability of some circuit-breaker—trip-device combinations may be higher than the trip device current rating.
From ANSI C37.16-1973. This table may also be found in IEEE JH 2112-1 [1]

TABLE 5   RATINGS FOR LOW-VOLTAGE ALTERNATING-CURRENT POWER CIRCUIT BREAKERS WITHOUT DIRECT-ACTING INSTANTANEOUS TRIP DEVICES

Line no.	Rated voltage (v)	Rated maximum voltage (v)	Insulation level dielectric withstand (v)	3-phase[1] short-circuit rating[3] or short-time rating (symmetrical amp)	Frame size (amp)	Minimum time band	Inter-mediate time band	Maximum time band
1	600	635	2,200	14,000	225	100-225	125-225	150-225
2	600	635	2,200	22,000	600	175-600	200-600	250-600
3	600	635	2,200	42,000	1,600	350-1,600	400-1,600	500-1,600
4	600	635	2.200	42,000	2,000	350-2,000	400-2,000	400-2,000
5	600	635	2,200	65,000	3,000	2,000-3,000	2,000-3,000	2,000-3,000
6	600	635	2,200	85,000	4,000	4,000	4,000	4,000
7	480	635	2,200	14,000	225	100-225	125-225	150-225
8	480	508	2,200	22,000	600	175-600	200-600	250-600
9	480	508	2,200	42,000	1,600	350-1,600	400-1,600	500-1,600
10	480	508	2,200	50,000	2,000	350-2,000	400-2,000	500-2,000
11	480	508	2,200	65,000	3,000	2,000-3,000	2,000-3,000	2,000-3,000
12	480	508	2,200	85,000	4,000	4,000	4,000	4,000
13	240	254	2,200	14,000	225	100-225	125-225	150-225
14	240	254	2,200	22,000	600	175-600	200-600	250-600
15	240	254	2,200	42,000	1,600	350-1,600	400-1,600	500-1,600
16	240	254	2,200	50,000	2,000	350-2,000	400-2,000	500-2,000
17	240	254	2,200	65,000	3,000	2,000-3,000	2,000-3,000	2,000-3,000
18	240	254	2,200	85,000	4,000	4,000	4,000	4,000

[1] Single-phase short-circuit-current ratings are 87 percent of these values.
[2] The continuous-current-carrying capability of some circuit breaker—trip-device combinations may be higher than the trip device current rating.
[3] Short-circuit-current ratings for circuit breakers without direct-acting trip devices, opened by a remote relay, are the same as those listed here.
From ANSI C37.16-1973. This table may also be found in IEEE JH 2112-1[1]

TABLE 6 TYPICAL INTERRUPTING CURRENT RATINGS FOR MOLDED-CASE CIRCUIT BREAKERS

Frame sizes (amp)	Rated continuous current (amp)	Single-pole alternating current 120 v 120/240 v		277 v		Two- and 3-pole Alternating current 120/240 v 240 v		Two- and 3-pole alternating current 600 v AC rated circuit breakers 240 v		480 v		480 v	
		Sym	Asym	Sym	Asym	Sym	Asym	Sym	Asym	Sym	Asym	Sym	Asym
100	0-100	5,000	5,000	—	—	5,000	5,000	—	—	—	—	—	—
100	0-100	7,500	7,500	10,000	10,000	7,500	7,500	18,000	20,000	14,000	15,000	14,000	15,000
100	0-100	—	—	—	—	—	—	65,000	75,000	25,000	30,000	18,000	20,000
100	0-100	—	—	—	—	—	—	100,000	—	100,000	—	100,000	—
200	125-200	—	—	—	—	10,000	10,000	—	—	—	—	—	—
225	125-225	—	—	—	—	10,000	10,000	22,000	25,000	18,000	20,000	14,000	15,000
225	70-225	—	—	—	—	—	—	25,000	30,000	22,000	25,000	22,000	25,000
225	70-225	—	—	—	—	—	—	65,000	75,000	35,000	40,000	25,000	30,000
225	70-225	—	—	—	—	—	—	100,000	—	100,000	—	100,000	—
225	70-225	—	—	—	—	—	—	35,000	40,000	25,000	30,000	22,000	25,000
400	200-400	—	—	—	—	—	—	65,000	75,000	35,000	40,000	25,000	30,000
400	200-400	—	—	—	—	—	—	100,000	—	100,000	—	100,000	—
400	200-400	—	—	—	—	—	—	42,000	50,000	30,000	35,000	22,000	25,000
600	300-600	—	—	—	—	—	—	—	—	—	—	—	—
600	300-600	—	—	—	—	—	—	100,000	—	100,000	—	100,000	—
800	300-800	—	—	—	—	—	—	42,000	50,000	30,000	35,000	22,000	25,000
800	300-800	—	—	—	—	—	—	65,000	75,000	35,000	40,000	25,000	30,000
800	600-800	—	—	—	—	—	—	100,000	—	100,000	—	100,000	—
1,000	600-1,000	—	—	—	—	—	—	42,000	50,000	30,000	35,000	22,000	25,000
1,200	700-1,200	—	—	—	—	—	—	42,000	50,000	30,000	35,000	22,000	25,000

From ANSI C37.16-1973. This table may also be found in IEEE JH 2112-1 [1]

reactances are used to calculate interrupting duty, and the induction motors are neglected.

When the contacts part (after 8 cycles), almost all the DC component has died, which explains the use of a multiplier of 1. In large power systems, where the symmetrical interrupting duty is greater than 500 mva and the circuit is fed mainly from generators or entirely through current-limiting reactors, special-case multipliers in Table 2 should be used. In this special case, some DC component may remain when the breaker contacts part.

High-voltage fuses are either current limiting, which open the circuit before the first current peak, or noncurrent limiting, which open the circuit in one or two cycles after fault inception.

Fuses are rated on the basis of maximum rms current flowing in the first cycle after the short-circuit occurs. They are rated in terms of available short-circuit current, determined by using the subtransient reactances of all generators, induction motors, synchronous motors and utility sources, and allowing for the maximum DC component by using a 1.6 multiplier. In special cases, where the operating voltage is 15 kv or less, the fuses noncurrent limiting, and the supply circuit ratio X/R less than 4, the multiplier is 1.2. The interrupting rating of power fuses in amperes is thus calculated the same way as the momentary rating of power circuit breakers.

Low-voltage circuit breakers (up to 600 v), unlike high-voltage breakers, operate almost instantaneously at currents close to their interrupting rating. The low-voltage breaker's contacts part during the first cycle of short-circuit current. Because of this fast operation, the momentary and interrupting duties are considered to be the same.

It follows that the short-circuit for low-voltage breakers is the current at the first half-cycle. Consequently, subtransient reactances of generators, induction motors and synchronous motors should be used, and the DC component accounted for. The multiplier is lower than that for high-voltage breakers because the lower X/R ratio in low-voltage circuits results in faster decay of the DC component.

In the past, low-voltage breaker interrupting ratings were based on the total asymmetrical rms current of the first half-cycle as an average of all three phases. NEMA and IEEE had a multiplier of 1.25 based on an X/R ratio of 11.72. The multiplier was applied to the symmetrical short-circuit current of the first half-cycle.

For several years, however, NEMA has used an asymmetrical current-interrupting basis. Breakers are tested under maximum asymmetrical conditions with a test circuit X/R no less than 6.6, which corresponds to an average multiplier of 1.17. This multiplier accounts for most low-voltage systems supplied by oil-filled transformers. For dry-type transformers, the X/R ratio can be more than 6.6, and the breakers must be selected by their asymmetrical medium-voltage ratings.

Tables 4 and 5 show ratings for low-voltage AC power-circuit breakers with and without instantaneous-trip devices. Table 6 shows typical interrupting current ratings in amperes for molded-case circuit breakers.

4.6 Numerical Example of Short-Circuit Calculation

Sections 4.4 and 4.5 discussed the basic principles of fault calculation and protective device application. This section (4.6) describes applying a simplified method of short-circuit calculation that is a safe and reliable basis for selecting interrupting devices. This method can replace other complicated methods involving decrement curves. Figures and tables are numbered consecutively.

A short-circuit study requires seven steps. The formulas referred to are in section 4.5.

Step 1: Prepare a one-line diagram of the plant's distribution system showing all short-circuit current sources and impedance elements. The diagram should include utility supplies, generators, induction and synchronous motors as well as significant impedance elements, such as transformers, reactors, cables, buses and circuit breakers.

Step 2: Select a convenient kva to serve as a common base for all voltage levels. Use a round number, such as 1,000, 10,000 or 100,000. Each nominal voltage level calls for a separate base voltage. Usually transformer voltages are selected as base values.

Step 3: Get proper reactance values, preferably from manufacturers' data. Tables 7, 8, 9, 10, 11 and 12 show typical reactance values.

The reactance of an AC rotating machine is not a fixed value as is the case with transformers, buses or cable reactances. The rotating machine reactance varies within the short time period after fault inception. For example, a short-circuit applied to the generator terminals starts out at a high value and decays to a steady state after a time. The field excitation voltage and speed are substantially constant within the short interval considered; so an assumption that the reactance has changed will explain the change in current value.

For simplicity, three values of reactances are assigned for this variable reactance in time: subtransient X''_d, transient X'_d and synchronous X_d.

X''_d, subtransient reactance, is the apparent reactance of the stator winding at the instant the short-circuit occurs. It determines the short-circuit current value I''_d flowing during the first few cycles after short-circuit inception.

X'_d, transient reactance, is the apparent reactance of the stator winding, if the effect of amortisseur windings is ignored and only the field winding is considered. This reactance determines the short-circuit current I'_d following the period when subtransient reactance is the controlling value. It is effective up to $1/2$ sec or longer, depending on machine design.

X_d, synchronous reactance, is the apparent reactance determining the current flow I_d when a steady-state condition is reached. It is effective several seconds after fault inception,

TABLE 7   EQUIVALENT CENTER-TO-CENTER SPACING OF CONDUCTORS

(CALCULATED INDUCTIVE REACTANCE FOR PARALLEL CONDUCTORS WITH STANDARD STRANDING WHERE VALUES ARE PER CONDUCTOR FOR TWO-WIRE, SINGLE-PHASE CIRCUITS AND LINE-TO-MEUTRAL FOR 3-PHASE CIRCUITS)

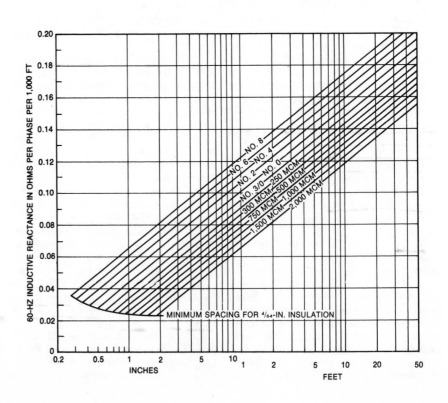

and so it has no value in short-circuit calculations for the selection of circuit breakers, fuses or contactors; but it is useful for relay setting and coordination studies.

Synchronous motors have the same kind of reactances as AC generators but of different values. Induction motors have no field coils, but their rotor bars have the effect of amortisseur winding in a generator. Induction motors, therefore, are considered to have a subtransient reactance only.

The assignment of three reactance values to a rotating machine is merely a simplified way to determine short-circuit values delivered at three selected specific times after fault inception. The values are used to calculate the short-circuit duty of circuit breakers, fused switches, etc., and to determine proper protective relay settings. (Previous sections have covered the selection of subtransient and transient reactances for rotating equipment contributing short-circuit current. Table 2 section 4.5 and Tables 7 through 12 in this one are guides for correct reactance selection.)

Reactances of different types of equipment are expressed in different ways. Transformers in the one-line diagram are in percent reactance on their own kva base, while cables and bus reactances must be calculated from tables as so many ohms per 1,000 ft, depending on conductor size and space configuration. Reactances of the rotating machinery are expressed in per-unit values on the machine's own base. The selected reactance values are then introduced into a reactance

TABLE 8   GENERATOR SUBTRANSIENT REACTANCE, APPROXIMATE PER UNIT REACTANCE ON KVA RATING

Salient pole with damper winding	12 poles or less	0.18
	14 poles or more	0.24
Salient pole without damper winding	12 poles or less	0.25
	14 poles or more	0.35
Distributed pole		
625 to 9,375 kva	2 poles	0.09
12,500 kva and more	2 poles	0.10
12,500 kva and more	4 poles	0.14

TABLE 9   MORE REACTANCES, APPROXIMATE PER UNIT REACTANCE ON KVA RATING

	Subtransient	Transient
Synchronous, individual		
large motor 6 poles	0.10	0.15
8 to 14 poles	0.15	0.24
Synchronous groups		
600 v or less	0.25	0.33
more than 600 v	0.15	0.25
Induction, individual large	0.25	—
Induction groups,		
600 v or less	0.25	—
more than 600 v	0.20	—

TABLE 10   TRANSFORMER REACTANCES, PER UNIT REACTANCE ON TRANSFORMER KVA BASE

3-phase load centers, primary 13.8 kv or less, low voltage secondary

300 to 500 kva	0.050
750 to 2,500 kva	0.055

Single-phase distribution transformers

kva	5 kv and below	5.1 to 15 kv
3 to 5	0.020	0.023
10 to 15	0.020	0.020
25 to 50	0.025	0.024
75 to 167	0.033	0.037
250 to 500	0.047	0.051

3-phase power transformers, secondary more than 2.4 kv, more than 500 kva

Primary kv	Per unit reactance on kva base
11.23	0.055
34.5	0.060
46	0.065
69	0.070

Single-phase power transformers, secondary more than 2.4 kv, more than 500 kva

Primary kv	Per unit reactance on kva base
2.2 to 25	0.055
25.1 to 34.5	0.060
34.6 to 46	0.065
46.1 to 69	0.070

TABLE 11   CABLE AND BUSWAY, OHMS PER 1,000 FT, LINE TO NEUTRAL

A	R	X	Z	X/R
Plug-in busway, copper bus bars				
225	0.0836	0.0800	0.1157	
400	0.0437	0.0232	0.0495	
600	0.0350	0.0179	0.0393	
800	0.0218	0.0136	0.0257	
1,000	0.0143	0.0135	0.0198	
Plug-in busway, aluminum bus bars				
225	0.1090	0.0720	0.1313	
400	0.0550	0.0222	0.0592	
600	0.0304	0.0121	0.0327	
800	0.0243	0.0154	0.0288	
Low-impedance feeder busway				
800	0.0219	0.0085	0.0235	
1,000	0.0190	0.0050	0.0196	
1,350	0.0126	0.0044	0.0134	
1,600	0.0116	0.0035	0.0121	
2,000	0.0075	0.0031	0.0081	
2,500	0.0057	0.0025	0.0062	
3,000	0.0055	0.0017	0.0053	
4,000	0.0037	0.0016	0.0040	
Current-limiting busway				
1,000	0.013	0.063	0.064	4.85
1,350	0.012	0.061	0.062	5.08
1,600	0.009	0.056	0.057	6.22
2,000	0.007	0.052	0.052	7.45
2,500	0.006	0.049	0.049	8.15
3,000	0.005	0.046	0.046	9.20
4,000	0.004	0.042	0.042	10.50

TABLE 12 APPROXIMATE 60-HZ RESISTANCE, REACTANCE, IMPEDANCE OF COPPER CONDUCTOR CABLE PER 1,000 FT*

AWG or MCM	In magnetic duct † 600-v, 5-kv nonshielded			5-kv shielded and 15 kv			In nonmagnetic duct ** 600-v and 5-kv nonshielded			5-kv shielded and 15 kv		
	R	X	Z	R	X	Z	R	X	Z	R	X	Z
Three-conductor cable												
8	.811	.0577	.813	.811	.0658	.814	.811	.0503	.812	.811	.0574	.813
8 (solid)	.786	.0577	.788	.786	.0658	.789	.786	.0503	.787	.786	.0574	.788
6	.510	.0525	.513	.510	.0610	.514	.510	.0457	.512	.510	.0531	.513
6 (solid)	.496	.0525	.499	.496	.0610	.500	.496	.0457	.498	.496	.0531	.499
4	.321	.0483	.325	.321	.0568	.326	.321	.0422	.324	.321	.0495	.325
4 (solid)	.312	.0483	.316	.312	.0508	.317	.312	.0422	.315	.312	.0495	.316
2	.202	.0448	.207	.202	.0524	.209	.202	.0390	.206	.202	.0457	.207
1	.160	.0436	.166	.160	.0516	.168	.160	.0380	.164	.160	.0450	.166
1/0	.128	.0414	.135	.128	.0486	.137	.127	.0360	.132	.128	.0423	.135
2/0	.102	.0407	.110	.103	.0482	.114	.101	.0355	.107	.102	.0420	.110
3/0	.0805	.0397	.0898	.0814	.0463	.0936	.0766	.0346	.0841	.0805	.0403	.090
4/0	.0640	.0381	.0745	.0650	.0446	.0788	.0633	.0332	.0715	.0640	.0389	.0749
250	.0522	.0379	.0670	.0577	.0436	.0707	.0541	.0330	.0634	.0547	.0380	.0666
300	.0464	.0377	.0598	.0473	.0431	.0640	.0451	.0329	.0559	.0460	.0376	.0596
350	.0378	.0373	.0539	.0386	.0427	.0576	.0368	.0328	.0492	.0375	.0375	.0530
400	.0356	.0371	.0514	.0362	.0415	.0551	.0342	.0327	.0475	.0348	.0366	.0505
450	.0322	.0361	.0484	.0328	.0404	.0520	.0304	.0320	.0441	.0312	.0359	.0476
500	.0294	.0349	.0456	.0300	.0394	.0495	.0276	.0311	.0416	.0284	.0351	.0453
600	.0257	.0343	.0429	.0264	.0382	.0464	.0237	.0309	.0389	.0246	.0344	.0422
750	.0216	.0326	.0391	.0223	.0364	.0427	.0197	.0297	.0355	.0203	.0332	.0389
Three single-conductor cable												
8	.811	.0754	.814	.811	.0860	.816	.811	.0603	.813	.811	.0688	.814
8 (solid)	.786	.0754	.790	.786	.0860	.791	.786	.0603	.788	.786	.0688	.789
6	.510	.0685	.515	.510	.0796	.516	.510	.0548	.513	.510	.0636	.514
6 (solid)	.496	.0685	.501	.496	.0796	.502	.496	.0548	.499	.496	.0636	.500
4	.321	.0632	.327	.321	.0742	.329	.321	.0506	.325	.321	.0594	.326
4 (solid)	.312	.0632	.318	.312	.0742	.321	.312	.0506	.316	.312	.0594	.318
2	.202	.0585	.210	.202	.0685	.214	.202	.0467	.207	.202	.0547	.209
1	.160	.0570	.170	.160	.0675	.174	.160	.0456	.166	.160	.0540	.169
1/0	.128	.0540	.139	.128	.0635	.143	.127	.0432	.134	.128	.0507	.138
2/0	.102	.0533	.115	.103	.0630	.121	.101	.0426	.110	.102	.0504	.114
3/0	.0805	.0519	.0958	.0814	.0605	.101	.0766	.0415	.0871	.0805	.0484	.0939
4/0	.0640	.0497	.0810	.0650	.0583	.0929	.0633	.0398	.0748	.0640	.0466	.0792
250	.0552	.0495	.0742	.0557	.0570	.0797	.0541	.0396	.0670	.0547	.0456	.0712
300	.0464	.0493	.0677	.0473	.0564	.0736	.0451	.0394	.0599	.0460	.0451	.0644
350	.0378	.0491	.0617	.0386	.0562	.0681	.0368	.0393	.0536	.0375	.0450	.0586
400	.0356	.0490	.0606	.0362	.0548	.0657	.0342	.0392	.0520	.0348	.0438	.0559
450	.0322	.0480	.0578	.0328	.0538	.0630	.0304	.0384	.0490	.0312	.0430	.0531
500	.0294	.0466	.0551	.0300	.0526	.0605	.0276	.0373	.0464	.0284	.0421	.0508
600	.0257	.0463	.0530	.0264	.0516	.0580	.0237	.0371	.0440	.0246	.0412	.0479
750	.0216	.0445	.0495	.0223	.0497	.0545	.0194	.0356	.0405	.0203	.0396	.0445

*Resistance based on tinned copper at 60 Hz per 1,000 ft at 75 C. Sometimes impedance calculations are based on operation at 25 C because faults can occur on lightly loaded lines as well as those that are fully loaded—at 25 C resistance values are lower and calculations are more conservative.
Reactance of 600-v and 5-kv nonshielded cable based on General Electric 5-kv varnished-cambric braided cable.
Reactance of 5-kv shielded and 15-kv cable based on 5-kv shielded Super Coronol-Geoprene cable.
† Also applies to steel interlocked armor used on 3/c cables.
** Also applies to aluminum interlocked armor used on 3/c cables.
NOTE: Since aluminum has 61 percent of the conductivity of copper (or 1.64 times the resistivity of copper) the above tables for copper can also be used for aluminum cable. The following formulas should be applied:
$R_{Al} = 1.64 R_{Cu}$
$X_{Al} = X_{Cu}$

diagram on the chosen base kva. (See section 4.5.)

Step 4: Make a reactance diagram by converting the one-line diagram to per-unit values on a chosen base. This diagram should include all significant reactances and resistances. Use of reactances will be favored, because use of impedances would require vector calculation to combine resistances with reactances. Usually the resistance of most system parts is a small percentage of the corresponding reactance, and a negligible error on the safe side results from ignoring resistance. This is the rule for circuits of more than 600 v. At 600 v and less, the resistance of feeders and branch circuits might be significant and should not be overlooked.

Typical reactance and one-line diagrams are shown in Figure 21. The reactance diagram is a drawing of a zero-reactance bus (the source bus) to which all short-circuit current sources connect. The addition of all significant reactances provides a complete reactance diagram that reflects all reactances to the fault point.

Step 5: Use Formulas 11-15, which appeared in section 4.5 to combine all reactances between the zero-reactance bus and the fault point into a single equivalent reactance. The resulting total equivalent reactance in per-unit on a chosen base is used to determine the short-circuit current and kva at different fault points. Each fault must be treated separately. Because of the location and type of protective devices, both momentary ($\frac{1}{2}$- to 1-cycle) and interrupting (8-cycle) values must be found. That is, calculations must be made using X''_d and also X'_d, depending on the protectors' location and type.

Step 6: Determine the symmetrical value of the short-circuit or kva with Formula 17 from section 4.5.

$$\text{Symmetrical short-circuit amp} = \frac{\text{base kva}}{\text{total per-unit reactance} \times \text{kv} \times \sqrt{3}}$$

For the symmetrical kva use Formula 16:

$$\text{Symmetrical short-circuit kva} = \frac{\text{base kva}}{\text{total per-unit reactance}}$$

Step 7: Find the asymmetrical value of the short-circuit current or kva by applying appropriate offset multipliers. Table 2 in section 4.5 gives the proper multipliers for various applications. Figure 19 in section 4.4 provides multipliers for the rms asymmetrical current required for a given short time after fault inception and for various X/R ratios.

Numerical example

A numerical example of short-circuit calculation for a medium- and low-voltage industrial power system can now be calculated. (Later, the calculated values of short-circuit currents at different system locations will be used to determine the selection and coordination of all protective devices in the plant.)

Step 1: The one-line diagram of an industrial plant power system, Figure 22, shows two 132-kv utility lines supplying (through respective oil circuit breakers) two 10-mva, 132-4.16-kv transformers. The double-ended 4.16-kv substation has two main breakers and one normally open tie

FIGURE 21
TYPICAL REACTANCE AND ONE-LINE DIAGRAMS

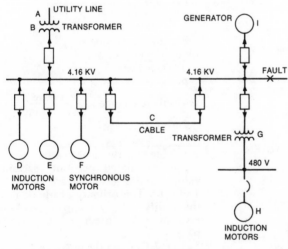

1. THE ONE-LINE DIAGRAM SHOWS ALL SHORT-CIRCUIT SOURCES AND IMPEDANCE ELEMENTS

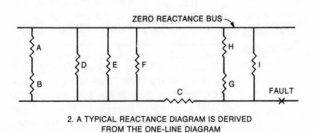

2. A TYPICAL REACTANCE DIAGRAM IS DERIVED FROM THE ONE-LINE DIAGRAM

FIGURE 22
ONE-LINE DIAGRAM OF AN INDUSTRIAL POWER SYSTEM

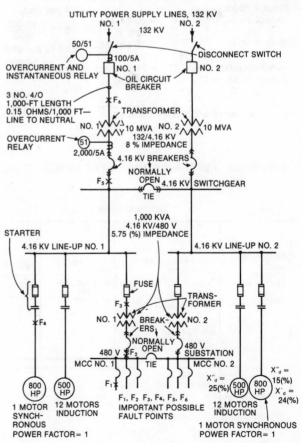

breaker. The 4.16-kv substation supplies two 4.16-kv motor starter lineups and a double-ended 480-v substation via two 1,000-kva, 4.16-kv,480-v transformers. Each side of the two 4.16-kv starter lineups supplies 12 500-hp induction motors and one 800-hp synchronous motor.

The double-ended 480-v substation has two main breakers and one normally open tie breaker. The secondary feeder breakers of the double-ended 480-v substation protect the feeders to different motor control centers in the plant. The 10-mva and 1,000-kva transformers are not supposed to be paralleled. Normally, all transformers operate at approximately half-load with the 4.16-kv and 480-v tie breakers open. If one of the 10-mva transformers fails or is in repair, the other can carry the plant's entire load by opening the faulted transformer secondary breaker and closing the tie breaker. The same applies for the 1,000-kva transformers.

The maximum short-circuit will be calculated assuming that one 10-mva transformer is out, since this is the case when maximum short-circuit current from rotating machinery flows toward the fault point.

The impedance of the 10-mva transformers is 8 percent, and that of the 1,000-kva transformers is 5.75 percent. The induction motors fed through the 1,000-kva transformer are assumed equal to the substation kva with 25 percent subtransient reactance (X''_d) on the substation rating base. The transmission line from the 132-kv oil circuit breakers to the 10-mva transformers is 1,000 ft long and consists of three No. 4/0 wires on poles, with 12 ft between wires and a resistance of .15 ohm/1,000 ft. The ratings and reactances of the rest of the equipment is shown on the one-line diagram, Figure 22.

Step 2: Select the base kva. In our example system, 10 mva is a convenient number. The high-voltage base is 132 kv, the medium-voltage base, 4.16 kv, and the low-voltage base, 480 v.

Step 3: Convert the various reactance values in the one-line diagram to per-unit values on the chosen 10-mva base. The following formulas from section 4.5 are repeated for convenience:

$$\text{Per-unit reactance} = \frac{\text{percent reactance}}{100} \quad (2)$$

$$\text{Per-unit reactance} = \frac{\text{ohm} \times \text{kva base}}{1,000 \times \text{kv}^2} \quad (3)$$

$$\text{Per-unit reactance} = \text{per-unit reactance} \times \frac{\text{kva base}}{\text{kva rating}} \quad (7)$$

$$\text{Per-unit reactance} = \frac{\text{kva base}}{\text{available short-circuit kva}} \quad (8)$$

The calculated per-unit reactance values for the example are shown in Table 13. The primary available from the utility supply company is 4,387 mva rms symmetrical and the selected base is 10 mva.

Step 4: Convert the one-line diagram into a reactance diagram (see Figure 23).

Steps 5, 6 and 7: Combine the reactances into a single equivalent value, using Formulas 11 through 15. Find the symmetrical and asymmetrical values of short circuit with Formulas 16 and 17 and Table 2.

Calculate the interrupting and momentary duty at fault location F_1 for 480-v feeder breakers. Low-voltage circuit breakers differ from medium- and high-voltage power circuit breakers in that their operation is practically

TABLE 13   REACTANCE CONVERSION CALCULATION

Circuit element	Reactance on element's own rating base	Per-unit reactance on chosen kva base	Formula
Utility line	4,387 mva available	$\frac{10,000 \text{ kva}}{4,387,000 \text{ kva}} =$ 0.00228 per unit	8
Main transformer	8 percent	$\frac{8}{100} = 0.08$ per unit	2
1,000-ft transmission line, No. 4/0 ACSR—12-ft distance, 0.15 ohms/1,000 ft line to neutral	(See Table 7)	$\frac{0.15 \times 10,000 \text{ kva}}{1,000 \times (132 \text{ kv})^2} =$ 0.000086 per unit	3
10,000-kva substation transformer	5.75 percent	$0.0575 \times \frac{10,000 \text{ kva}}{1,000 \text{ kva}} =$ 0.575 per unit	7
500-hp 4.16-kv induction motor	$X''_d = 20$ percent (See Table 9)	$0.2 \times \frac{10,000 \text{ kva}}{500} \text{ (approximately)} =$ 4 per unit	7
800-hp 4.16-kv	$X''_d = 15$ percent	$0.15 \times \frac{10,000}{800} =$ 1.875 per unit	7
synchronous motor— Power factor = 1	$X'_d = 24$ percent (See Table 9)	$0.24 \times \frac{10,000}{800} = 3$ per unit	7
1,000 kva of induction motors	$X''_d = 25$ percent (See Table 9)	$0.25 \times \frac{10,000}{1,000} = 2.5$ per unit	7

FIGURE 23   REACTANCE DIAGRAM OF AN INDUSTRIAL POWER SYSTEM

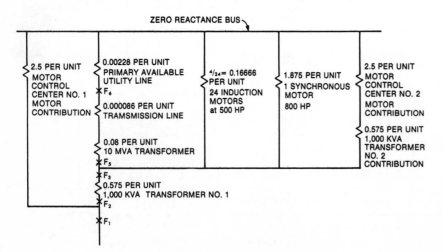

ZERO REACTANCE BUS

2.5 PER UNIT MOTOR CONTROL CENTER NO. 1 MOTOR CONTRIBUTION

0.00228 PER UNIT PRIMARY AVAILABLE UTILITY LINE
$\times F_6$

0.000086 PER UNIT TRAMSMISSION LINE

0.08 PER UNIT 10 MVA TRANSFORMER
$\times F_5$

$\times F_3$

0.575 PER UNIT 1,000 KVA TRANSFORMER NO. 1
$\times F_2$

$\times F_1$

4/24 = 0.16666 PER UNIT 24 INDUCTION MOTORS at 500 HP

1.875 PER UNIT 1 SYNCHRONOUS MOTOR 800 HP

2.5 PER UNIT MOTOR CONTROL CENTER NO. 2 MOTOR CONTRIBUTION

0.575 PER UNIT 1,000 KVA TRANSFORMER NO. 2 CONTRIBUTION

FIGURE 24 SYMMETRICAL AND ASYMMETRICAL SHORT-CIRCUIT VALUES AT FAULT POINT F₁

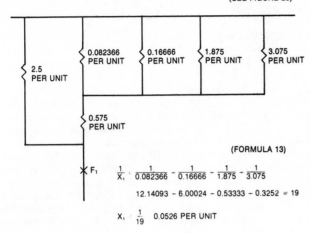

(SEE FIGURE 23)

(FORMULA 13)

$$\frac{1}{X_1} = \frac{1}{0.082366} - \frac{1}{0.16666} - \frac{1}{1.875} - \frac{1}{3.075}$$

$$12.14093 - 6.00024 - 0.53333 - 0.3252 = 19$$

$$X_1 = \frac{1}{19} = 0.0526 \text{ PER UNIT}$$

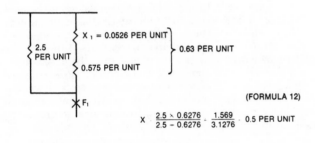

(FORMULA 12)

$$X = \frac{2.5 \times 0.6276}{2.5 - 0.6276} = \frac{1.569}{3.1276} = 0.5 \text{ PER UNIT}$$

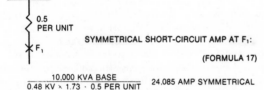

SYMMETRICAL SHORT-CIRCUIT AMP AT F₁:

(FORMULA 17)

$$\frac{10,000 \text{ KVA BASE}}{0.48 \text{ KV} \times 1.73 \times 0.5 \text{ PER UNIT}} = 24,085 \text{ AMP SYMMETRICAL}$$

(SAY 24,100 AMP SYMMETRICAL)

ASYMMETRICAL SHORT-CIRCUIT AMP AT F₁

$$1.25 \times 24,085 = 30,106 \text{ AMP ASYMMETRICAL}$$
(SEE TABLE 2, SECTION 4.5)

FIGURE 25 SHORT-CIRCUIT VALUES SEEN BY PROTECTIVE DEVICES AT VARIOUS FAULTPOINTS

FAULT F₂ AT TRANSFORMER SECONDARY MAIN 480 V BREAKER

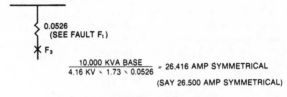

0.6276 PER UNIT
(SEE FAULT F₁)

F₂

$$\frac{10,000 \text{ KVA BASE}}{0.48 \text{ KV} \times 1.73 \times 0.6276 \text{ PER UNIT}}$$ 19.188 AMP (SAY 19,200 AMP) SHORT-CIRCUIT SYMMETRICAL

(FORMULA 17)

1.25 × 19,200 = 24,000 AMP ASYMMETRICAL

FAULT F₃ AT PRIMARY OF 1,000 KVA TRANSFORMER FUSE WILL SEE:

0.0526
(SEE FAULT F₁)

F₃

$$\frac{10,000 \text{ KVA BASE}}{4.16 \text{ KV} \times 1.73 \times 0.0526} = 26,416 \text{ AMP SYMMETRICAL}$$

(SAY 26,500 AMP SYMMETRICAL)

1.6 × 26,500 = 42,400 AMP ASYMMETRICAL

OR $$\frac{10,000}{0.0526} \times 1.6 = 304 \text{ MVA SYMMETRICAL}$$

FAULT F₄ AT 4.16 KV MOTOR STARTER SAME 304 MVA ASYMMETRICAL AS FAULT F₃

FAULT F₅ MAIN 4.16 KV BREAKER WILL SEE:

0.082366
(SEE FAULT F₁)

F₅ $$\frac{10,000 \text{ KVA}}{4.16 \text{ KV} \times 1.73 \times 0.082366} = 16,870 \text{ AMP SYMMETRICAL}$$

(SAY 16,900 AMP SYMMETRICAL)

OR $$\frac{10,000}{0.082366} = 122 \text{ MVA SYMMETRICAL}$$

FAULT F₆ PRIMARY OF 10-MVA TRANSFORMER, OIL-CIRCUIT BREAKER WILL SEE:

4,387 MVA AVAILABLE

$$\frac{4,387,000 \text{ KVA}}{132 \text{ KV} \times 1.73} = 19,200 \text{ AMP SYMMETRICAL}$$

Note: For Faults F₃ or F₄, if breakers were used instead of fuses, the interrupting duty would have to be calculated. The reactance diagram would contain transient reactances or synchronous motors and induction motor reactances would be removed—i.e., neglected.

---

instantaneous. Their contacts often part during the first cycle of current. Therefore, the short-circuit current determined should be for the first half-cycle and should be calculated on the same basis as that of checking momentary duty for medium- and high-voltage breakers—using the subtransient reactances of generators and induction and synchronous motors.

On this basis, the reactance diagram, the combined total per-unit reactance, and the interrupting and momentary values of short-circuit that the feeder breakers will see are calculated. They appear in Figure 24.

At fault location points F₂, F₃, F₄, F₅ and F₆, the reactance diagrams and short-circuit values that respective breakers and fuses will see are shown in Figure 25. The type of rotating machine reactances considered for the medium-voltage part of the short-circuit calculations are in Table 2 of Chapter 4.5.

For interrupting duty of 600 v and more, the contribution of induction motors is generally neglected and not shown in the reactance diagram. The synchronous motor is accounted for with a transient (X'_d) reactance value.

Based on the short-circuit calculations in this example, we will show how breakers and fuses are selected and properly coordinated to operate sequentially in a predetermined pattern. The breakers nearest the fault should trip first to isolate the troubled section from the rest of the system. The protective devices toward the power source should serve as a backup protection should the ones nearer the fault fail.

4.7 How to Use the Symmetrical Component Method to Calculate Short Circuits

Section 4.6 has discussed calculation of short-circuit values for an industrial plant example. It considered the 3-phase ungrounded fault because this kind of fault usually imposes the most severe duty on protective devices. The simplified method of calculation shown reflected such balanced faults. However, a 3-phase power system also may be subjected to phase-to-ground faults, phase-to-phase ungrounded faults, and phase-to-phase grounded faults.

A phase-to-ground fault may sometimes produce a larger short-circuit current than a 3-phase fault if unusual reactance values exist. Generally, a 3-phase short-circuit on a balanced 3-phase system produces a balanced 3-phase fault. Line-to-ground or line-to-line faults produce unbalanced 3-phase faults.

Determining unbalanced faults

Symmetrical component analysis is used for accurate determination of fault-current magnitudes with unbalanced loads resulting from line-to-ground and line-to-line faults. A balanced 3-phase system has three quantities (such as current and voltage) corresponding to the three phases in equal magnitude and 120 deg apart in phase. When a 3-phase fault occurs in such a system, the effects on currents and voltages can be visualized as shown in Figure 26. When a phase-to-phase or phase-to-ground fault occurs, it produces an unbalanced 3-phase system as shown in the last diagram in Figure 26.

The method of symmetrical components consists of reducing an unbalanced 3-phase system of vectors into three balanced systems, which are known as the positive, negative and zero-phase sequence components. Algebraic expressions for the components prove this, and were first published in 1918 by C. L. Fortescue

in his classic paper "Symmetrical Components."

The positive-sequence components consist of three vectors equal in magnitude, 120 deg out of phase and rotating in a direction so that they reach their positive maximum values in the sequence ABC. The negative-sequence components consist of three vectors equal in magnitude, displaced 120 deg apart and rotating in the sequence ACB. The zero-phase sequence components consist of three vectors equal in magnitude and in phase. (See Figure 27). Subscripts 1, 2 and 0 identify the positive, negative and zero sequence components, respectively.)

In balanced (symmetrical) power systems, voltages generated by rotating machinery are equal in magnitude and are 120 deg out of phase. In such systems the impedances in all phases are considered equal up to the point of fault. Positive-sequence currents produce only positive-sequence voltage drops, negative-sequence currents produce only negative-sequence voltage drops, and zero-sequence currents produce only zero-sequence voltage drops. This method assumes that no interaction exists between phase sequences.

Sequence reactances are designated as X_1, positive-sequence reactance; X_2, negative-sequence reactance; and X_0, zero-sequence reactance. These values represent the reactances of the system to the flow of positive-, negative- and zero-sequence currents.

Synchronous machinery has typical reactance values (X_d = synchronous, X'_d = transient, X''_d = subtransient), which are positive sequence reactances. The negative-sequence reactance (X_2) is in general equal to the subtransient, except for waterwheel generators without damper windings. Zero-sequence reactance (X_0) usually is less than any of the others (Table 14).

Transformers have identical positive- and negative-sequence reactances. The zero-sequence reactance also has the same value, except for

3-phase core-type transformers with connections that block the zero-sequence current. Zero-sequence currents will not flow if the transformer neutral is ungrounded. When zero-sequence current cannot flow, X_0 is considered infinite. In most cases where zero-sequence currents can flow, X_0 is the same as the positive-sequence reactance.

In a wye-delta-connected transformer, the zero-sequence current can flow through the neutral connection of the wye if the neutral is grounded. No zero-sequence currents flow in the delta-side connection. In a wye-wye-connected transformer, zero-sequence currents flow in both the primary and the secondary if there are enough connections from neutral to ground to give current paths.

The resistance of the transformer windings is usually negligible in short-circuit calculations. For transmission lines and cables, the positive and negative reactances are considered the same. In transmission lines, the zero-sequence reactance is different because the zero-sequence current is returning via the earth or overhead ground wire. The zero-sequence reactance is usually larger than the positive and negative sequences.

For cables, the zero-sequence reactance of a 3-phase cable is larger than the positive- and negative-sequence reactances because the spacing between outgoing and return conductors is larger in the zero-sequence circuit than in the positive or negative ones. The return path through a sheath or a distributed earth conductor may carry all the zero-sequence currents. This introduces a voltage drop three times larger than that produced if the return path carried the current of only one outgoing conductor. The return path in the zero-sequence circuit is given an impedance three times its actual impedance.

An exact determination of zero-sequence reactances of cables and transmission lines would be complex. For fair estimates, ratios of X_0/X_1 give

FIGURE 26 TYPES OF FAULTS THAT MAY OCCUR IN A POWER SYSTEM

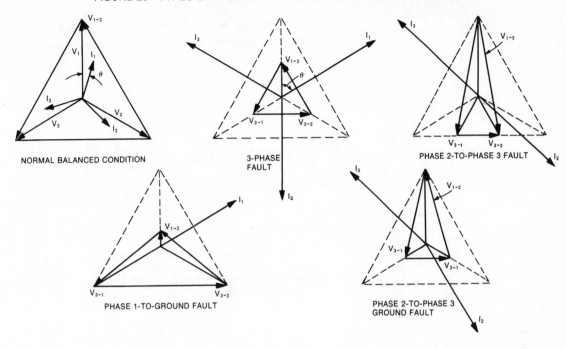

NORMAL BALANCED CONDITION

3-PHASE FAULT

PHASE 2-TO-PHASE 3 FAULT

PHASE 1-TO-GROUND FAULT

PHASE 2-TO-PHASE 3 GROUND FAULT

FIGURE 27 VECTOR RELATIONS FOR POSITIVE-, NEGATIVE- AND ZERO-SEQUENCE CURRENTS EQUIVALENT TO AN UNBALANCED 3-PHASE FAULT

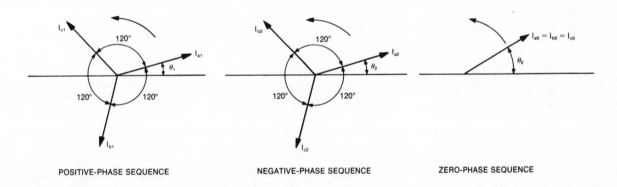

POSITIVE-PHASE SEQUENCE

NEGATIVE-PHASE SEQUENCE

ZERO-PHASE SEQUENCE

TABLE 14 APPROXIMATE REACTANCE VALUE OF 3-PHASE 60-CYCLE GENERATING EQUIPMENT

(Values in per unit stated kva base)

| | Positive Sequence | | | | | | | | | |
| | Synchronous X_d | | Transient X_d | | Subtransient X_d | | Negative sequence X_z | | Zero sequence X_0 | |
Apparatus	Avg.	Range	Avg.	Range	Avg.	Range	Avg.	Range	Avg.	Range
2-pole turbine generator (45 psig inner-cooled H₂)	1.65	1.22-1.91	.27	.20-.35	.21	.17-.25	.21	.17-.25	.093	.04-.14
2-pole turbine generator (30 psig H₂-cooled)	1.72	1.61-1.86	.23	.188-.303	.14	.116-.17	.14	.116-.17	.042	.03-.073
4-pole turbine generator (30 psig H₂-cooled)	1.49	1.36-1.67	.281	.265-.30	.19	.169-.208	.19	.169-.208	.106	.041-.1825
Salient pole generators and motors with dampers	1.25	.6-1.5	.3	.2-.5	.2	.13-.32	.2	.13-32	.18	.03-.23
Salient pole generators without dampers	1.25	.6-1.5	.3	.2-5	.3	.2-5	.48	.35-65	.19	.03-.24
Synchronous condensers air-cooled	1.85	1.25-2.20	.4	.3-.5	.27	.19-.3	.26	.18-.4	.12	.025-.15
Synchronous condensers (¹/₂ psig H₂-cooled)	2.2	1.5-2.65	.48	.36-6	.32	.23-.36	.31	.22-.48	.14	.03-.18

maximum practical values. For example, a 3-conductor cable with a nonmetallic sheath or conduit and an earth-return with distributed average conductivity will have an X_0/X_1 ratio from 3 to 5.

Sequence diagrams are developed for calculations as shown in Figures 28 and 29. Since the three sequence components are independent to the fault point, three network diagrams (phase-to-neutral of the power system) are necessary.

The positive-sequence network shows generator voltages, reactances of generators, transformers and lines. The negative-sequence network is usually a replica of the positive-sequence network except that no generator voltages are shown, since no synchronous generator operates with reverse phase order and negative-sequence reactance of synchronous machinery may occasionally differ from positive-sequence reactance.

The zero-sequence network usually is similar to the negative-sequence network except that special consideration is given to transformer connections. Wye-wye-grounded transformers allow zero-sequence current to flow from one side of the bank to the other. Wye-delta-connected banks allow current to flow in the grounded neutral but block passage of zero-sequence current from one side of the bank to the other. Also, resistors and reactors connected between machine or transformer neutrals and ground are shown at three times their normal value. Negative- or zero-sequence currents cannot flow in balanced systems because synchronous or induction machines generate only positive-sequence voltages.

When a fault occurs, it acts as a converter that changes positive-sequence voltages into negative- and zero-sequence voltages. The negative- and zero-sequence components are determined by setting up negative- and zero-sequence networks having a single source of voltage at the fault.

Figure 28 illustrates the calculation of unbalanced faults. The positive-sequence network includes the generated voltages E_s and E_u as well as the positive-sequence voltage E_{1f} at the fault point.

The negative- and zero-sequence networks include voltages E_{2f} and E_{0f}, respectively, produced by conversion at the fault. After reducing all reactances to an equivalent single reactance for the positive (X_1), negative (X_2) and zero (X_0) sequence network values, the following formulas (devel-

FIGURE 28   3-PHASE SYSTEM WITH A FAULT AT F
(Positive-, negative- and zero-sequence networks are shown)

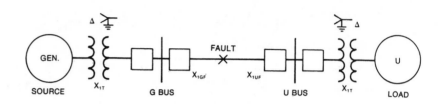

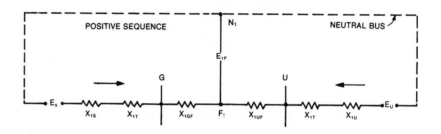

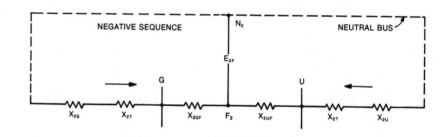

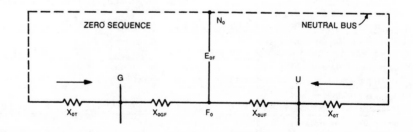

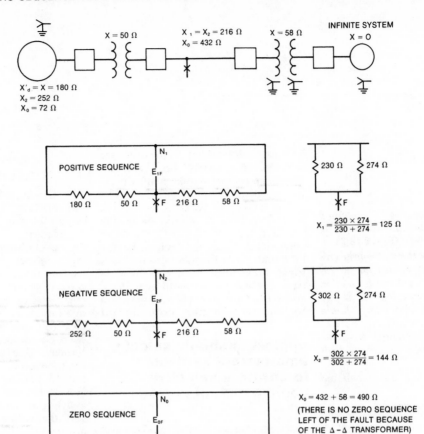

oped by Fortescue) are used to find the magnitudes of fault current:

Single line-to-ground fault:

$$I_F = \frac{3 \times E\phi - N}{X_1 + X_2 + X_0} \qquad (18)$$

Line-to-line fault:

$$I_F = \frac{E\phi - N \times \sqrt{3}}{X_1 + X_2} \qquad (19)$$

Double line-to-ground fault:

$$I_F = \frac{3 \times E\phi - N \times X_2}{X_1 \times X_2 + X_0(X_1 + X_2)} \qquad (20)$$

3-phase fault: $\quad I_1 \quad \dfrac{E\phi \quad N}{X_1} \qquad (21)$

Where: $E\phi$ N is the voltage phase-to-neutral and X_1, X_2 and X_0 are reactances expressed in ohms on the voltage base if the networks are set up in ohms on a voltage base.

These formulas will obtain the currents directly at the voltage base. Usually, reactances of machines and transformers are expressed in percent or per-unit values on their own kva rating. Since different units may be involved, it is necessary to reduce all of them to a chosen kva base. Formulas

for converting from one way of expressing reactances to another were given in section 4.5. It is desirable to be conversant with calculations, involving reactances expressed in all three methods—per-unit, percent or ohms.

A numerical example of a short-circuit calculation by the symmetrical components method is shown in Figure 29. The system consists of a generating station, a transmission line of 120 kv and an infinite system. The reactances are shown in ohms referred to 120-kv phase-to-phase chosen as a base. All resistances are considered negligible. The transmission line voltage to neutral is:

$$V\phi - N = \frac{120 \text{ kv}}{\sqrt{3}} = 69.3 \text{ kv}$$

Single line-to-ground fault:

$$I_F = \frac{3 \times E\phi - N}{X_1 + X_2 + X_0} = \frac{3 \times 60,300}{125 + 144 + 490}$$

$$= \frac{207,900}{759} = 274 \text{ amp} \qquad (18)$$

Line-to-line fault:

$$I_F = \frac{E\phi - N \times \sqrt{3}}{X_1 + X_2} = \frac{120,000}{125 + 144} =$$

446 amp
$\qquad\qquad (19)$

Double line-to-ground fault:

$$I_F = \frac{3 \times E\phi - N \times X_2}{X_1 X_2 + X_0(X_1 + X_2)} =$$

$$\frac{29,937,600}{149,810} = 200 \text{ amp} \qquad (20)$$

3-phase fault:

$$I_F = \frac{E\phi - N}{X_1} = \frac{69,300}{125} =$$

554 amp
$\qquad\qquad (21)$

REFERENCE
"Electrical Transmission and Distribution Reference Book," Westinghouse Electric Corp., East Pittsburgh, Pa.

4.8 Selection and Coordination of Breakers, Fuses, and Relays

The previous section (4.7) explained when and how to use the symmetrical component method for short-circuit calculations. Based on the previously calculated short-circuit values for an industrial power system example (section 4.6), the following section 4.8 shows how breakers, fuses and relays should be selected and then properly coordinated to assure a sequential, selective operation at the occurrence of any fault in the system.

Figures and tables are numbered consecutively.

The one-line diagram of the industrial power system example appears as Figure 30. The time-current characteristic curves for the protective devices (breakers, fuses, relays) selectively coordinated, as well as the short-circuit values for different points in the system, are shown in Figure 31. The procedure to arrive at this selection and coordination is as follows:

• *480-v switchgear feeder breakers.* The short-circuit value these breakers can "see" when a fault occurs at F1 (Figure 30) is 24,100 amp symmetrical. The proper selection is a 480-v, 600-amp frame breaker having 30,000-amp rms symmetrical interrupting capacity (see section 4.5, Table 4,) and provided with long-time instantaneous and ground-fault trips, preferably of the solid-state type.

• *480-v switchgear main breakers.* The short-circuit value these breakers can see if a fault occurs at F2 is 19,200 amp symmetrical. A 22,000-amp interrupting-capacity breaker would suffice, but the breaker must also carry the maximum secondary amperage of the 1,000-kva transformer, which, considering an operation at 65 F with fans, is 1,550 amp. Consequently, 480-v, 1,600-amp frame main and tie breakers with 50,000-amp rms sym-

metrical interrupting capacities are selected. (see section 4-5, Table 4). Maximum current requirements dictate the selection.

The selected transformer main secondary breaker should be of the selective type, equipped with series overcurrent tripping devices having long-time, short-time and ground-fault trips, preferably of the solid-state type. These devices should be selected and set to furnish overload protection for the transformer, ground-fault

Engineers should select time-current settings to ensure a selective coordination of curves

protection for the feeder breakers and to be selective with feeder breakers as well as with primary fuses.

To assure selective tripping between the primary fuse and the main secondary breaker, the total clearing time curve of the breaker must be below the fuse's minimum melting time for all values of current equal to or less than the maximum possible value of symmetrical fault current that may flow through the transformer for any secondary fault.

Complete selectivity with no overlapping of the characteristic curves between the primary fuses and the secondary main breaker is desirable but sometimes difficult to obtain because of differences in the shape of the curves.

Group feeder and feeder breakers of the main bus should be selected and set to assure complete selectivity with the transformer primary fuses.

• *1,000-kva transformer primary fuse, 4.16 kv.* In general, a fuse current rating of 140 to 150 percent of the transformer rated current, based on the self-cooled rating of the transformer will override the transformer magnetizing inrush current and provide adequate fault protection. The transformer rated primary current is

$$\frac{1,000 \text{ kva}}{(1.73)(4.16 \text{ kv})} = 139 \text{ amp}$$

A 4.16-kv, 200-amp fuse would be appropriate. The maximum short-circuit this fuse can see for a fault at F3 is 42,400 amp asymmetrical. A current-limiting fuse—such as CLE-1 200E, 50,000 rms symmetrical interrupting rating or a similar one—is the proper selection. The primary fuse characteristic band is made up of the minimum melting and maximum clearing curves. The fuse provides short-circuit protection for the transformer and arcing-fault protection for the transformer secondary. For proper transformer protection, the fuse must be selected so that the ANSI point lies above the maximum clearing curve and the inrush point is below the minimum melting curve of the fuse.

The ANSI point in amps for the 1,000-kva transformer with 5.75 percent impedance is found by this expression: .58 (1÷transformer per unit impedance) (transformer full load for 3.75 sec).

The inrush point in amps is found by this expression: 8 (transformer full load for 0.1 sec.).

The factor .58 takes into account the fact that a 100 percent line-to-ground fault in the secondary winding of a delta-wye transformer is reflected only with 58 percent $(1 \div \sqrt{3})$ in each of the two phases of the incoming to the primary of the same transformer. Consequently, the ANSI point must be decreased to 58 percent of the value used for 3-phase faults. The .58 factor does not apply to delta/delta transformers.

• *4.16-kv breakers.* The 4.16-kv main breakers must be able to interrupt fault F5 of 122-mva symmetrical and to carry a continuous current of 2,000 amps. Therefore, 4.16-kv main and tie breakers with 2,000-amp frames and 250-mva, 3-phase rms symmetrical interrupting capacities are selected (section 4.5, Table 3). The selection is dictated by the continuous maximum current requirements the

FIGURE 30   ONE-LINE DIAGRAM OF AN INDUSTRIAL POWER SYSTEM

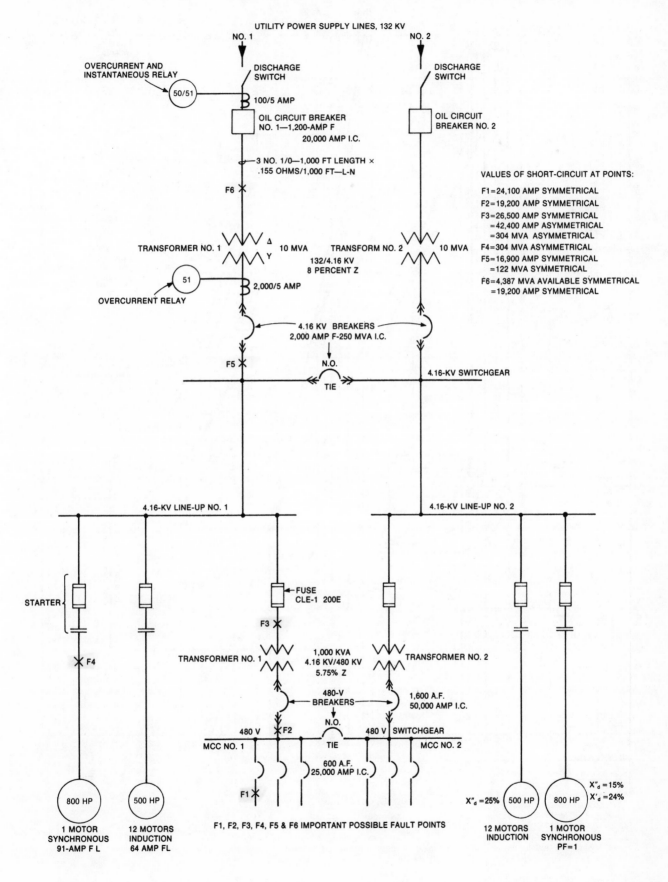

UTILITY POWER SUPPLY LINES, 132 KV

NO. 1   NO. 2

OVERCURRENT AND
INSTANTANEOUS RELAY   DISCHARGE
                                 SWITCH   DISCHARGE
                                                         SWITCH

50/51   100/5 AMP

OIL CIRCUIT BREAKER   OIL CIRCUIT
NO. 1—1,200-AMP F   BREAKER NO. 2
20,000 AMP I.C.

3 NO. 1/0—1,000 FT LENGTH ×
.155 OHMS/1,000 FT—L-N

F6   VALUES OF SHORT-CIRCUIT AT POINTS:

                                                         F1=24,100 AMP SYMMETRICAL
                                                         F2=19,200 AMP SYMMETRICAL
                                                         F3=26,500 AMP SYMMETRICAL
                                                           =42,400 AMP ASYMMETRICAL
                                                           =304 MVA ASYMMETRICAL
TRANSFORMER NO. 1   Δ   10 MVA   TRANSFORM NO. 2   10 MVA   F4=304 MVA ASYMMETRICAL
                        Y   132/4.16 KV   F5=16,900 AMP SYMMETRICAL
                                     8 PERCENT Z   =122 MVA SYMMETRICAL
51   F6=4,387 MVA AVAILABLE SYMMETRICAL
                        2,000/5 AMP   =19,200 AMP SYMMETRICAL
OVERCURRENT RELAY

                        4.16 KV BREAKERS
                        2,000 AMP F-250 MVA I.C.

F5   N.O.   4.16-KV SWITCHGEAR
                        TIE

4.16-KV LINE-UP NO. 1   4.16-KV LINE-UP NO. 2

STARTER   FUSE
                                     CLE-1 200E

                        F3

         F4   TRANSFORMER NO. 1   1,000 KVA   TRANSFORMER NO. 2
                                            4.16 KV/480 KV
                                            5.75% Z

                        480-V   1,600 A.F.
                        BREAKERS   50,000 AMP I.C.
                        N.O.
         480 V   F2   TIE   480 V SWITCHGEAR
         MCC NO. 1   MCC NO. 2

                        600 A.F.
                        25,000 AMP I.C.

         F1   X''d =15%
                                                                           X'd =24%

800 HP   500 HP   500 HP   800 HP
                                     X''d =25%
1 MOTOR   12 MOTORS   F1, F2, F3, F4, F5 & F6 IMPORTANT POSSIBLE FAULT POINTS   12 MOTORS   1 MOTOR
SYNCHRONOUS   INDUCTION   INDUCTION   SYNCHRONOUS
91-AMP F L   64 AMP FL   PF=1

115

FIGURE 31   TIME-CURRENT CHARACTERISTIC CURVES

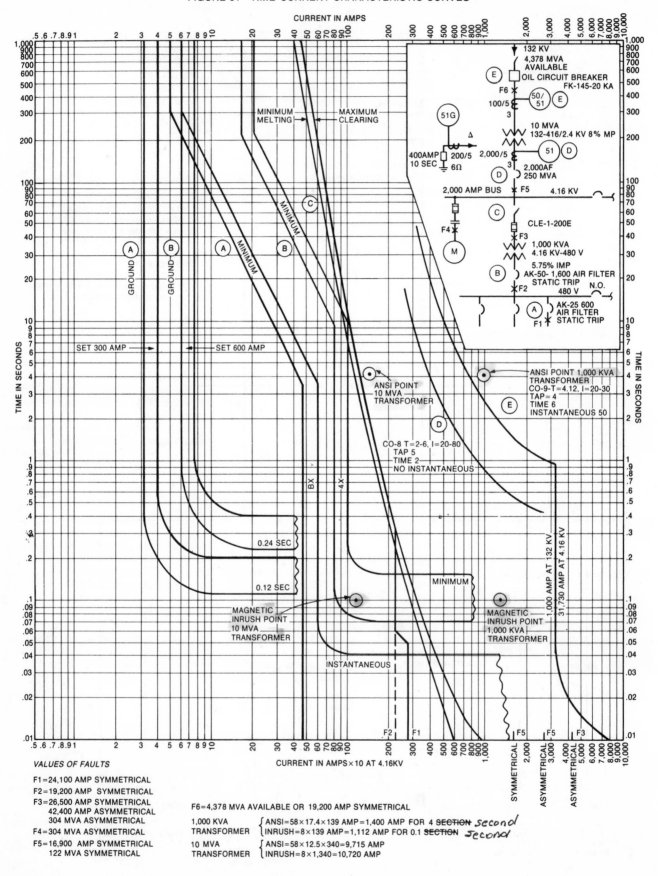

VALUES OF FAULTS

F1=24,100 AMP SYMMETRICAL
F2=19,200 AMP SYMMETRICAL
F3=26,500 AMP SYMMETRICAL
    42,400 AMP ASYMMETRICAL
    304 MVA ASYMMETRICAL
F4=304 MVA ASYMMETRICAL
F5=16,900 AMP SYMMETRICAL
    122 MVA SYMMETRICAL

F6=4,378 MVA AVAILABLE OR 19,200 AMP SYMMETRICAL

1,000 KVA   { ANSI=58×17.4×139 AMP=1,400 AMP FOR 4 SECTION second
TRANSFORMER   { INRUSH=8×139 AMP=1,112 AMP FOR 0.1 SECTION Second

10 MVA   { ANSI=58×12.5×340=9,715 AMP
TRANSFORMER   { INRUSH=8×1,340=10,720 AMP

breaker may carry:

$$\frac{14,000 \text{ kva}}{(1.73)(4.16 \text{ kv})} = 1,945 \text{ amp}$$

• *132-kv oil-circuit breaker.* The 132-kv oil-circuit breakers must be able to interrupt fault F6 of 19,200 amps; therefore, 145-kv oil circuit breakers with 1,200-amp frames and 20,000-amp symmetrical interrupting capacities are selected. The selection is dictated by the maximum possible interrupting capacity.

• *4.16-kv and 138-kv relay selection.* Different types of relays are available from various manufacturers. In general, the time-current characteristics of a given relay are the same for the main manufacturers. Table 15 lists the type designations of relays with equivalent time-current characteristics from several manufacturers.

The choices for the selected example, with a feeder that has a main incoming transformer serving a medium plant, are an *inverse type* relay (such as CO-8) for the secondary of the main 14-mva transformer and a *very inverse* type relay (such as CO-9) for the primary of the main 14-mva transformer.

Table 16 is a guide for proper selection of protective relay types related to the nature and extent of the electric power system.

Time-current settings

After selecting the appropriate types of breakers, fuses and relays, the engineer's next step is to select the time-current setting for the adjustable protective devices to ensure a selective coordination of their characteristic curves. This selection should start at the load end and work back toward the power source.

Current settings must be high enough to carry normal load swings, yet low enough to make sure the protective device operates on the minimum expected short-circuit current. Transformer feeders protected by current-limiting fuses should have the magnetizing inrush current point lower than instantaneous minimum melting time of the fuse.

Relay settings on incoming lines and feeders carrying miscellaneous loads should be just above the total of the starting current of the largest motor, plus full load of the remainders. In case more than one motor is started at the same time, the sum of the starting currents of all these motors must be added to the normal full load of the feeder.

Article 240 of the National Electrical Code covers requirements for proper

Complete selectivity is desirable but sometimes too difficult to obtain

overcurrent protection of conductors and is cross-referenced to related NEC articles defining protection requirements for motors, generators, transformers and other equipment. NEC Article 430 shows methods for protective device settings for motor branch circuits and motor feeder circuits. Article 450-3 includes requirements for primary overcurrent settings for transformers with or without secondary overcurrent protection.

Table 17 shows suggested settings of overcurrent relays and direct-acting trips for short-circuit protection purposes.

Transformer connections and faults

Wye/delta- or delta/wye-connected transformers cause a 30-deg shift in the relationship of the fault currents on opposite sides of the transformer. For 3-phase faults, this does not affect the overcurrent protective devices; the currents in the three phases on each side are still equal in magnitude. In the case of phase-to-phase faults, the currents on the opposite sides are in phase, but the current on the faulted phases is only .866 per unit of 3-phase fault current for that side of the transformer. The current on the unfaulted side is equal to 3-phase fault current on one phase, while only half that much flows in the other two phases.

For line-to-ground faults in the secondary of a delta/wye transformer, the current ratio will be 1 per unit in the faulted phase of the secondary and 0 current in the two remaining phases; but on the primary side of the transformer the current ratio will be .58 in two phases and 0 in the corresponding faulted phase. Table 18 shows the relationship between the transformer primary and secondary fault currents for secondary line-to-line and line-to-ground faults.

Plotting time-current curves

The engineer must plot the time-current curves for breakers, fuses and relays that are to operate selectively in series to make sure that there are no trouble spots due to overlapping or unnecessarily long operating time intervals between protective devices. It is best to use a current scale corresponding to the currents expected at the lowest voltage level of the devices when only two voltage levels are involved.

In the power system example where three voltages are involved—132 kv, 4.16 kv and 480 v—it is best to use the middle voltage 4.16-kv scale. This enables the engineer to plot all characteristic time-current curves on one sheet of log-log paper. For example, for fault-protective devices on 480 v, everything is plotted on a 4.16-kv scale by multiplying 480 v currents by 480 v ÷ 4,160 v. For fault protective devices on 132 kv, everything is plotted on a 4.16-kv scale by multiplying 132-kv currents by 132,000 v ÷ 4,160 v.

For proper coordination, minimum time margin of .35 sec is used between adjacent relays in series under maximum short-circuit condition. Assuming a circuit breaker having 8 cycles

TABLE 15 RELAY-TYPE DESIGNATIONS WITH EQUIVALENT TIME VS. CURRENT CHARACTERISTICS
FROM DIFFERENT MANUFACTURERS

Relay manufacturer	Short time	Long time	Definite time	Moderate inverse	Inverse	Very Inverse	Extreme inverse
Westinghouse	CO-2	CO-5	CO-6	CO-7	CO-8	CO-9	CO-11
General Electric	IAC-55	IAC-66		IAC-51		IAC-53	IAC-77
Federal Pacific		CDG12		CDG11, 21		CDG13, 23	CDG14, 24
I.T.E. Electric	ITE-51S	ITE-51L	ITE-51D		ITE-51I	ITE-51Y	ITE-51E

TABLE 16 GENERAL GUIDE FOR

(This table to be used in

Equipment to be protected	Type of relay	Tap range amps	Instantaneous range	Notes
1-Individual transformer with low-voltage switch-gear	Extreme inverse for phase	4-12 amp	40-160 amp	
	Very inverse for ground	0.5-25 amp	10-40 amp	For solidly grounded systems
			4-16 amp or 10-40 amp	For resistance grounded systems pending upon C.T. ratio and maximum ground-fault current
2-Transformer primary or switchgear incoming breaker a-relatively small plant feeders	Moderate inverse for phase	4-12 amp	1-Omit the instantaneous element	If relays are on incoming breakers and there is no supply transformer between relays and bus
b-Medium plant feeders	Very inverse for phase	4-12 amp		
c-Relatively large plant feeders	phase	4-12 amp	2-Use 10-40 amp Instantaneous for transformers with above 12% impedance Use 20-80 amp for transformers with 7-12% impedance Use 40-160 amp for transformers with impedance below 7%	If supply transformer is between relays and bus
	Very inverse for ground for cases a,b,c	0.5-2.5 amp	10-40 amp 4-16 amp or 10-40 amp	For solidly grounded systems For resistance grounded systems, pending upon maximum ground-fault current
3-Feeders serving several transformers each having individual primary fuses	Very inverse for phase	4-12 amp	None	
	Very inverse for ground	0.5-2.5 amp	4-16 amp or 10-40 amp	For resistance grounded systems pending upon C.T. ratio and maximum ground-fault current
			None	In solidly grounded systems

(.13 sec) opening time, a relay over-travel margin of .1 sec and a safety margin of .12 sec, we arrive at the minimum of .35 sec. A minimum of .25 sec may be used between a fuse and overcurrent relay when the fuse is located on the source side of the relay, because no relay over-travel is involved. When a combination of two current-tap and time-dial settings yield the desired operating time, the combination with the lower current and higher time-dial setting is preferred, since the relay with lower current-tap setting is more sensitive and faster acting on low-value fault currents.

The curves must be plotted on log-log transparent paper (e.g., Keuffel & Esser Co.'s time-current characteristic sheet No. 48-5258). In the upper right-hand corner of the sheet the engineer must draw a one-side diagram of the considered section. This diagram should show transformers, substations, motor control centers, motors and protective devices (such as

Equipment to be protected	Type of relay	Tap range amps	Instantaneous range	Notes
4-Feeders serving several transformers which do not have individual primary protection	Very inverse for phase	4-12 amp	40-160 amp	
	Very inverse for ground	0.5-2.5 amp	10-40 amp	For solidly grounded systems
			4-16 amp or 10-40 amp	For resistance grounded systems pending upon C.T. ratio and maximum ground-fault current
5-Feeder serving single fused medium-voltage Motor starter	Very inverse for phase	4-12 amp	None	
	Very inverse for ground	0.5-2.5 amp	None	For solidly grounded systems. Motor to have single phasing protection.
			4-16 amp or 10-40 amp	For resistance grounded systems pending upon C.T. ratio and maximum ground-fault current
6-Feeder serving several individually fused medium voltage motor starters	Same as 5	Same as 5	Same as 5	Same as 5 If feeder supplies small motors it may be possible to use moderate inverse phase relays
7-Individual motor protected by: a-Two relays for overload and short-circuit	Long time for phase	2- 6 amp	20-80 amp	
b-One relay for locked-rotor	Long time for phase	4-12 amp	20-80 amp Or none	
8-Feeder for relatively large motor controlled by own breaker and relays a-Motor without differential relays	Very inverse for ground	0.5-2.5 amp	None	
	Extreme inverse for phase	4-12 amp	None	
b-Motor with differential relays	Very inverse for phase	4-12 amp	None	
9-Transformer secondary breaker	Same as 2	Same as 2	Same as 2	Same as 2
10-Feeder serving long line having open conductors	Extreme inverse for phase	4-12 amp	4-160 amp	
	Very inverse for ground	0.5-2.5 amp	10-40 amp	For solidly grounded systems
			4-16 amp or 10-40 amp	For resistance grounded systems pending upon C.T. ratio and maximum ground-fault current

breakers, fuses and relays). In addition, it should indicate locations of assumed fault points and their respective calculated values. Finally, a tabulation should show current transformer ratio, type, range, tap, time and instantaneous settings of relays; type, long-time, short-time, ground-fault and instantaneous settings of breakers; and type and rating of fuses.

Setting the devices

A satisfactory selection, setting and coordination of protective devices is proved by plotting the time-current characteristic curves on log-log paper. This representation clearly indicates if any fault in the system will selectively trip breakers, blow fuses or actuate relays from the point of fault up to the source at predetermined selected interval times, and if there are no overlappings between curves of adjacent protective devices. In other words, the characteristic-curve plotting shows whether the protective devices will be selective in their

TABLE 17   SUGGESTED CURRENT SETTINGS OF OVERCURRENT RELAYS AND DIRECT-ACTING
TRIPS FOR SHORT-CIRCUIT PROTECTION

For time-delay devices on	Suggested current setting is
1. Incoming lines and miscellaneous feeders	Just above maximum permissible operating current, allowing for starting large motors
2. Individual motor feeders	Just above locked-rotor starting current
3. Transformer feeders to meet NEC requirement (a) If no transformer secondary breaker	2.5 per unit of transformer rating
(b) If there is a secondary breaker and the transformer reactance is between .06 and .10 per unit	4.0 per unit of transformer rating
(c) If there is a secondary breaker and transformer reactance is not over .06 per unit	6.0 per unit of transformer rating
4. Generator overcurrent relay with voltage restraint (IJCV) (a) Generators with voltage regulators (b) Generators without voltage regulators	2.0 to 2.5 per unit of generator rating 1.5 to 2.0 per unit of generator rating
5. Long-time induction relay (IAC66) for motor starting protection	A little above maximum running overload current
For instantaneous devices (relays and direct-acting trips) on	Suggested current setting is
1. Transformer feeders	Just above the primary current corresponding to maximum initial asymmetrical current for a secondary fault using 1.6 multiplier for the DC component on 5,000 v and above, and 1.5 below 5,000 v. This setting should be able to ride through transformer magnetizing current
2. Motor feeders	Just above the initial asymmetrical current that motors can contribute to a fault on some other current as determined by motor's subtransient reactance and a 1.6 multiplier for 2,300 v and above, and 1.5 multiplier for 600 v and below. If is not available, use locked rotor current plus 1.0 per unit motor current.

*From: General Electric Industrial Power System Data Book

operation with respect to each other.

If this condition is fulfilled, the effects of short-circuits on a system are kept to a minimum by disconnecting only the affected part of the system. Only the protective devices closest to the fault point should open, leaving the rest of the electric system intact and able to supply power to the rest of the system. When protective devices are selectively coordinated, and if for any reason the one closest to the fault does not operate, the next protective device toward the source must take over the tripping task.

• *Setting the 480-v air circuit breakers for the selected power system example.* Low-voltage air circuit breakers are equipped with solid-state trips that provide continuous wide-range adjustability. Current sensors provide energy and signals. Long delay, short delay, instantaneous and ground-fault protection are available

in any combination. These breakers come in frame ratings from 600 to 4,000 amp and have respective short-circuit ratings from 30,000- to 85,000-amp rms symmetrical.

Figures 32 and 33 show the time-current characteristics of typical 600-v air circuit breakers equipped with solid-state trips. The range of pickup and time settings for long time, short time, instantaneous and ground fault are indicated. They enable the proper setting for a selective coordination with other protective devices in series by plotting the curves without crossing each other.

Time-current characteristics are different in their shapes for different protective devices. Certain compromises are sometimes unavoidable when making the relay and series trip settings and fuse selections. Sometimes selectivity in a limited area may have to be sacrificed to keep the total

time within acceptable limits.

The engineer performs several trial coordination plottings before he arrives at the optimum protection coordination. The plots closest to the loads are used to proceed with the ones nearer the source.

The adjustable settings for the type of breakers selected earlier in this article's example are now chosen.

The selected switchgear feeder breaker was 480-v, 600-amp frame having 30,000-amp rms symmetrical interrupting capacity (also see part 5).

Set the long-time delay pickup at 80 percent:

$.8 \times 600$ amp = 480 amp at 480 v

$.8 \times 600$ amp $\times 480v \div 4,160v = 55$ amp at 4.16 kv

Set instantaneous at 8 × transformer tap setting.

Use minimum band curve.

Set ground relay at 300 amp and .12 sec.

TABLE 18 LINE CURRENT RATIOS FOR TRANSFORMER-SECONDARY PHASE AND GROUND FAULTS EXPRESSED IN PER-UNIT OF THE CURRENT THAT WOULD FLOW IN A 3-PHASE SECONDARY FAULT WITH SUSTAINED PRIMARY VOLTAGE

| TRANSFORMER CONNECTION | | PHASE | LINE-TO-LINE FAULT* | | LINE-TO-GROUND FAULT* | | |
PRIMARY (SOURCE)	SECONDARY CIRCUIT		PRIMARY	SECONDARY	PRIMARY	SECONDARY A	SECONDARY B
		1	1.0	.87	.58		1.0
		2	.5	.87	.58		0
		3	.5	0	0		0
		1	.87	.87	1.0		1.0
		2	.87	.87	0		0
		3	0	0	0		0
		1	.87	.87	.67		1.0
		2	.87	.87	.33		0
		3	0	0	.33		0
		1	.87	.87	.67	.67	1.0
		2	.87	.87	.33	.33	0
		3	0	0	.33	.33	0
		1	1.0	.87	.58	.67	1.0
		2	.5	.87	.58	.33	0
		3	.5	0	0	.33	0
		1	1.0	.87	.58	.67	1.0
		2	.5	.87	.58	.33	0
		3	.5	0	0	.33	0

*The same ratios between primary and secondary currents prevail even though system impedance or neutral resistor limited the fault currents to lower values. Load currents are not included.

From: General Electric Industrial Power System Data Book

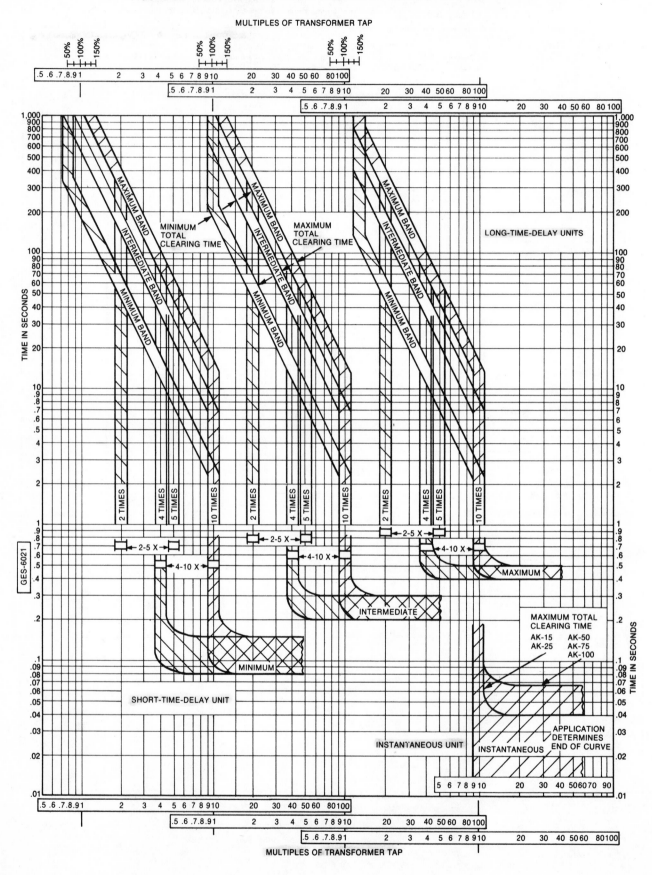

FIGURE 32   LONG-TIME AND SHORT-TIME DELAY CHARACTERISTICS

122

FIGURE 33 GROUND-FAULT PROTECTION CHARACTERISTIC CURVE

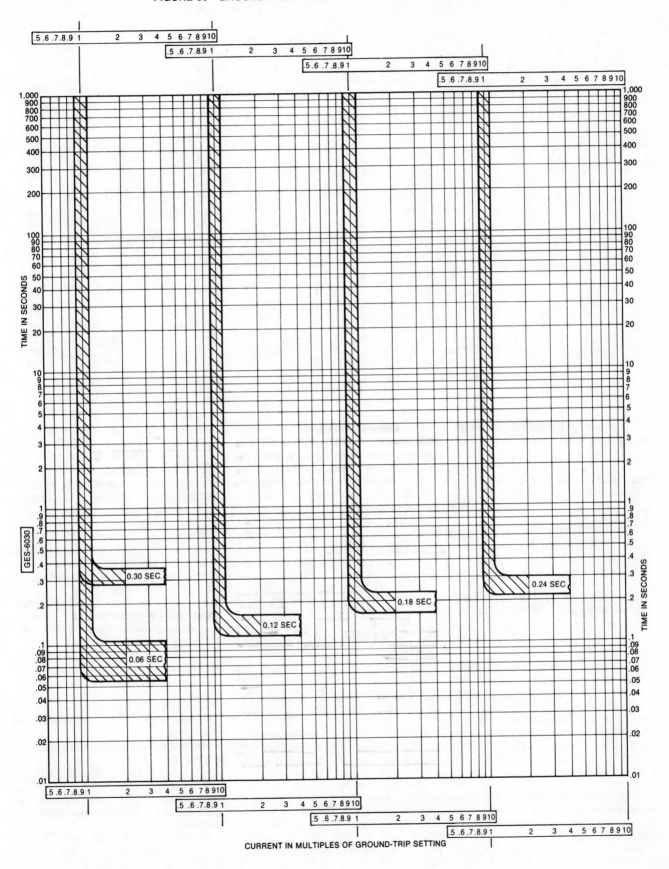

CURRENT IN MULTIPLES OF GROUND-TRIP SETTING

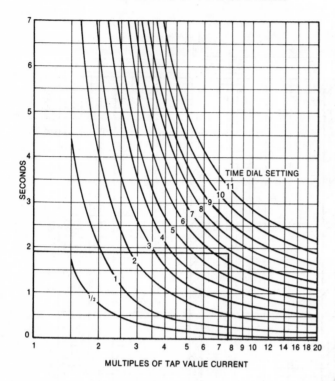

FIGURE 34

TYPICAL TIME CURVES OF TYPE CO-8 RELAY

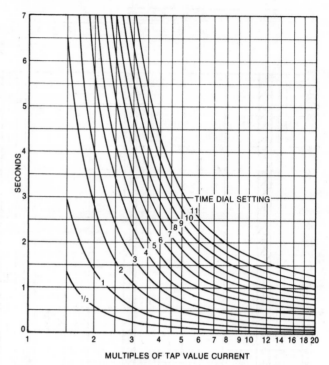

FIGURE 35

TYPICAL TIME CURVES OF TYPE CO-9 RELAY

The selected main switchgear feeder breaker type was 480 v, 1,600-amp frame having 50,000-amp rms symmetrical interrupting capacity. Set the long-time delay pickup at 100 percent—that is 1,600 amp at 480 v:

1,600 amp × 480 v ÷ 4,160 v = 185 amp at 4.16 kv

Set short-time delay pickup 4 × transformer tap setting.

Use minimum band curve.

Use minimum short-time delay curve.

Make instantaneous trip inoperative.

Set ground relay at 600 amp, .24 sec.

To set the 4.16-kv and 132-kv relays for the selected power system example, follow this procedure:

Once the short-circuit calculations for different values of minimum and maximum fault currents are established, the engineer can select and coordinate the time-current curves for the relays by using the manufacturer's characteristic time-current curves for the types of relays specified for the system. The engineer should check time and current settings for the adjustable devices with those of the nonadjustable ones in order to secure a combination that will operate in the sequence necessary to isolate any fault in a selective operation with minimum disturbance to the unfaulted part of the system.

The time-dial setting on a relay determines the length of time the unit requires to close its contacts when the current reaches a predetermined value. The contacts barely close when the dial is set at zero. When the dial is set at 10, the disc must travel the maximum amount to close the contacts; consequently, this is the maximum time setting. The primary adjustment for the operation time of the unit is made by means of time dial.

If selective action of more relays is required, the engineer must determine the maximum possible short-circuit current of the line and then choose a time value for each relay that differs sufficiently in order to ensure proper sequence in the operation of the several circuit breakers. He must allow for the time needed to open each breaker after the relay contacts close. Unless the circuit time of operation is known with accuracy, there should be a difference of about .5 seconds (at maximum current) between relays whose operation is to be selective.

The selection of time and current settings of the relays is exemplified in Figures 34 and 35, which show the time-current curves of overcurrent relays with inverse-time characteristics. Each time value shown represents the time required for the contacts to close according to particular time-dial settings when the current is a prescribed number of times the current tap setting. To secure any particular time-current settings in the figures requires that the removable plug be inserted in the proper tap receptacle and the time dial be adjusted to the proper position.

To illustrate the procedure of making a relay setting, assume a CO-8 relay is used for a circuit breaker that should trip on a sustained current of approximately 450 amp; also, the breaker should trip in 1.9 sec on a short-circuit of 3,750 amp. Assume that current transformers of 60/1 ratio are used:

450 amp = sustained current (minimum primary tripping current).

3,750 amp = short-circuit current (tripping time 1.9 sec).

60/1 = ratio of current transformer.

Current-tap setting = 450 amp ÷ 60 = 7.5 amp.

Since there is no 7.5-amp tap, use the 8-amp tap.

The proper time-dial setting to give 1.9 sec time delay at 3,750 amp is 3,750 amp ÷ 60 = 62.5 amp secondary current. This is 7.8 times the 8-amp tap setting.

By referring to the time-current curves of Figure 34, it can be seen that 7.8 times the minimum operating current yields 1.9 sec time delay when the relay is set to No. 7 time-dial setting.

The result can be checked by means of an accurate timing device. Slight readjustments of the dial can be made until the desired time is obtained.

The 4.16-kv relay at the secondary of the 10-mva transformer of the example (Relay D) protects the feeder to 24 500-hp induction motors, two 800-hp synchronous motors and two 1,000-kva transformers (see Figures 30 and 31).

The total maximum possible load is:

A. 2.5×87 amp (at start of 800-hp motor) = 218 amp at 4.16 kv

B. 24×59 amp (for 500-hp motors with 457 bhp) = 1,416 amp at 4.16 kv (one synchronous motor is a standby)

C. 1,200 amp (for two 1,000-kva transformers, one-half load on each) = 139 amp at 4.16 kv

Total: $A+B+C = 1,773$ amp at 4.16 kv

Therefore, select a 2,000-amp 4.16-kv breaker.

The relay settings are as follows:

• *Tap setting*—set pickup at 2,000 amps:

$2,000 \div 2,000/5^* = 5$

Set tap at 5.

• *Time setting*—for a fault at F3, Relay D sees F5 = 16,900 amp symmetrical:

16,960 amp $\div$ 2,000-amp trap = 8.4

$8 \times$ minimum pickup = 16,000 amp

Set time delay at 2 to assure tripping of Breaker D in .5 sec delay if fuse does not clear fault.

• *Instantaneous* —remove instantaneous setting of relay to allow fuses to clear fault before 4.16-kv main breaker trips.

Setting the 132-kv relay at the primary of the 10-mva transformer of the example (Relay E) is done this way:

• *Tap setting*—pickup of the secondary relay is 2,000 amp.

Relay E sees:

2,000 × 4.16 kv ÷ 132 kv = 63 amp at 132 kv

Select tap: 1.16×63 amps = 73 amps to coordinate with Relay D.

73 amps ÷ 100/5* = 3.65

Set Tap at 4.

$4 \times 20 = 80$ amp pickup at 132 kv.

• *Time setting*—80 amp (132 kv ÷ 4.16 kv) = 2,540 pickup at 4.16 kv.

Set time delay at 6 to coordinate with secondary Relay D.

• *Instantaneous setting*—the instantaneous trip is set at, or above, $1^{1/2}$ times the through fault current of the main transformer. The asymmetrical short-circuit current is 122,000 amp ÷ (1.73 × 132 kv) × 1.5 = 801 amp.

Set instantaneous pickup at 1,000 amp at 132 kv.

Set instantaneous at 1,000 ÷ 100/5* = 50 amp.

In conclusion

In concluding this Chapter 4 on selection and coordination of protective devices in industrial plants, it is appropriate to make the following general comments:

The selective coordination of fault protective devices encompasses the selection and application of circuit protectors that will assure safety and reliability under abnormal conditions for industrial plants. The range of fault currents varies between sustained overloads and the maximum possible short-circuits.

Because of the continual growth of electric industrial plants, there are at least three distinct periods in the life of an electrical installation when the adequacy of the protective devices must and should be reviewed.

The first obviously is when a new installation is designed. The second is when the power of the plant is increased. The third is when primary or network capacities of the power supply companies have increased to provide for the continually increased power demand.

In all three cases adequate data relating to new impedances of the circuit components, increases in loads as well as increases in short-circuits available at the source of power have to be obtained. On the basis of these new values, the engineer must calculate new expected short-circuit values and select adequate protective devices. These revised values, embodied in simple and permanent protective devices, assure safe interruption of faulted circuits and limit the effect of short-circuit currents to all the electric system during its lifespan, thus keeping pace with the safety requirements of modern, concentrated and ever-increasing power usage.

The short-circuit calculation method used in this Chapter 4, was the simplified method adopted by IEEE Standard 141 and by General Electric Publication EESG II-AP-1-1972. The simplified method was used because it yields short-circuit values on the conservative, safe side, and because of space limitations. Engineers interested in more detailed, complex and sophisticated methods of determining short-circuit currents at different times after fault inception and for X/R values exceeding 15 should refer to ANSI Publications C37.010-1972, C37-13-1973 and IEEE STD. 141-1976.

*C. T. Ratio

5

Making the Choice among Dry, Liquid, and Gas Transformers

5.1 Code Definitions and Characteristics of Different Types of Transformers

One of the most important aspects of electrical distribution system design is selecting the type of transformer that best suits technical and economic requirements. This section 5.1 gives basic definitions and characteristics of different types of transformers as reflected in the latest National Electrical Manufacturers' Assn. and American National Standards Institute standards as well as the National Electrical Code.

Electrical energy is transmitted economically over long distances by high voltages, but low voltages are necessary for distribution so that electric circuits may be safely handled. The transformer is the electrical device that allows electrical energy to be received at one voltage and delivered at another (higher or lower) voltage by electromagnetic induction.

A transformer consists basically of two separate (single- or 3-phase) windings on an iron core. The winding receiving energy is called primary; the one delivering energy is called secondary. An inverse change of current accompanies the voltage change.

Defining terms

NEMA and the Institute of Electrical and Electronics Engineers classify transformers as *distribution* and *power* types (instrument transformers will not be considered here). A distribution transformer is that having a rating between 3 and 500 kva inclusive, or any network transformer. A power transformer is any transformer with a rating above 500 kva, except network transformers.

Transformers may be of the *indoor* or *outdoor* type. Because of its construction, an indoor transformer must be protected from the weather, but exposure to the weather will not interfere with an outdoor transformer's operation.

Other transformer classifications include *submersible transformers,* which are submerged in water under predetermined conditions of pressure and time, *subway transformers* installed in underground vaults, and *network transformers* used in vaults to feed variable-capacity systems of interconnected secondaries.

The kva rating of a transformer should satisfy immediate load demand and future growth

Most industrial plant transformers are associated with secondary unit-substations varying from 500 to 5,000 kva, usually of dry-type or gas-filled insulation, ventilated or unventilated and mainly located indoors. Outdoor substations usually have oil-filled transformers.

Practically all industrial transformers are of 3-phase construction. These transformers cost less, have higher efficiency and require less space than single-phase units making up 3-phase banks. They have an excellent service record. The advantage of single-phase units, however, is the ability to operate at reduced 3-phase equivalent capacity by the connection of two units in open-delta in case one unit fails. They also are useful where single-phase voltage is required for single-phase outlets.

Weighing characteristics

When selecting and specifying a transformer for a particular application, the engineer must consider the following characteristics: kva rating, single or 3-phase voltage, frequency, indoor or outdoor service, voltage ratings, voltage-taps, winding connections, type of cooling, basic-impulse-insulation level (BIL), efficiency, grounding system requirements and accessories.

The kva rating of a transformer should satisfy the immediate load demand and possible future load growth. For transformer standard base kva ratings, see Table 1.

The voltage ratio is the ratio of the rms primary terminal voltage to the rms secondary terminal voltage under predetermined load conditions. Voltage ratio and taps are selected to provide correct voltage at terminals, considering variations in supply voltage as well as voltage drop in the transformer and distribution lines.

Taps are usually provided to compensate for variations of several steps of $2\frac{1}{2}$ or 5 percent above and below rated voltage, or to vary the secondary voltage level with load requirement changes (these taps usually provide full-capacity output from the transformer). The adjustable no-load tap is performed manually with the transformer de-energized. When load swings are frequent and voltage levels critical, the automatic tap-changing under load is available.

Connections for the standard two winding power transformers are preferably delta primary and wye secondary. The wye secondary provides a convenient neutral point for system ground or a phase conductor run for phase to neutral.

Section 5.3 will discuss different transformer connections with respective advantages and disadvantages, and where and why to apply each.

The key to a dependable and economic power distribution is the selection of the proper transformer type to suit each application. For certain industrial or climatic environments, unique characteristics of each type make one more suitable than another. These characteristics—and not cost alone—should prevail when selecting the transformer that best suits the desired performance and reliability.

Four basic types to choose from are

TABLE 1   TRANSFORMER STANDARD BASE KVA RATINGS

Single-phase				3-phase			
3	75	1,250	10,000	15	300	3,750	25,000
5	100	1,667	12,500	30	500	5,000	30,000
10	167	2,500	16,667	45	750	7,500	37,500
15	250	3,333	20,000	75	1,000	10,000	50,000
25	333	5,000	25,000	112½	1,500	12,000	60,000
37½	500	6,667	33,333	150	2,000	15,000	75,000
50	833	8,333		225	2,500	20,000	100,000

From IEEE Standard 462-1973.

TABLE 2   TRANSFORMER CAPABILITIES WITH FORCED COOLING

	Self-cooled ratings* (kva)		Percent of self-cooled ratings with auxiliary cooling	
Class	Single-phase	3-phase	First stage	Second stage
OA/FA	501-2,499	501- 2,499	115	—
OA/FA	2,500-9,999	2,500-11,999	125	—
OA/FA	10,000 and above	12,000 and above	133⅓	—
OA/FA/FA	10,000 and above	12,000 and above	133⅓	166⅔
OA/FA/FOA	10,000 and above	12,000 and above	133⅓	166⅔
OA/FOA/FOA	10,000 and above	12,000 and above	133⅓	166⅔
AA/FA†	501 and above	501 and above	133⅓	—

From NEMA TR1-1974.
* *In the case of multiwinding transformers or autotransformers, the ratings given are the equivalent two-winding ratings.*
† *Not applicable to sealed dry-type transformers.*

oil-filled; nonflammable insulating liquid-filled—Askarel and silicon-liquid (silicon-liquid filled is an alternative to Askarel-filled transformers, which are being phased out because of their ecological contamination); open dry-type; and gas-filled. Application criteria for selecting one of these types of transformers are cost, impulse insulation strength, equipment location, maintenance requirements, sound level, future forced-air capability and available space.

Transformer cooling types

NEMA and ANSI classifications and definitions apply to the following types of transformer cooling:

• *Oil-immersed, self-cooled (Class OA)* has core and coils immersed in oil. The cooling is effected by natural air circulation over the cooling surface.

• *Oil-immersed, self-cooled/forced-air-cooled (Class OA/FA)* is similar to Class OA but also has a forced-cooling rating due to forced circulation of air over the same cooling surface.

• *Oil-immersed, self-cooled/forced-air-cooled / forced-air-cooled (Class OA/FA/FA)* is similar to Class OA/FA but has an increased forced-air-cooled rating obtained by the increased forced circulation of air over a portion of the cooling surface.

• *Oil-immersed, forced-oil-cooled with forced-air cooler (Class FOA)* is similar to Class OA but the cooling is by forced circulation of oil through external oil-to-air heat exchanger equipment, utilizing forced circulation of air over its cooling surface.

• *Oil-immersed, forced-oil-cooled with forced-water cooler (Class FOW)* is similar to Class FOA but utilizes forced circulation of water over its cooling surface.

• *Oil-immersed, self-cooled/forced-air-cooled / forced-oil-cooled (Class OA/FA/FOA)* is similar to Class OA/FA, but also has a forced-oil-cooling rating by forced circulation of oil over core and coils, adjacent to the same cooling surface over which air is force-circulated.

• *Oil-immersed, self-cooled/forced-air-forced oil-cooled/forced-air-forced -oil cooled (Class OA/FOA/FOA)* is similar to Class OA/FA/FOA except that its auxiliary cooling controls are set to start some of the oil pumps and fans for the first auxiliary rating and the rest of them for the second auxiliary rating.

• *Oil-immersed, water-cooled (Class OW)* is cooled by natural circulation of oil over the water-cooled surface.

• *Oil-immersed, water-cooled/self-cooled (Class OW/A)* is similar to Class OW but has a self-cooled rating. Cooling is accomplished by natural air circulation over the cooling surface.

Oil-filled transformers have the lowest first cost of any other type of transformers, but their use in confined primarily to outdoor installations. They also can be used indoors but only in approved vaults and under conditions set forth by the NEC. Oil-filled transformers are suited for use in dirty and dusty areas and in adverse weather conditions. They are unsuitable where fire is a hazard and when vaults must be provided; in these cases, economics generally favor a dry-type transformer.

• *Nonflammable insulating liquid-filled transformers, Askarel type,* may be used indoors and outdoors because of their nonflammable insulating liquid. They are best suited for dusty, dirty or corrosive atmospheres, even when fire is a hazard. Having lower sound levels than the dry-type transformers and being lightweight, the nonflammable insulating liquid transformers are suitable for indoor applications. This is especially true for hi-rise buildings, where they permit economical power distribution to various floors by using voltages up to 15 kv and then stepping down to the utilization voltage.

The shortcoming of this type of transformer, as intensive studies have revealed, is that the PCBs (polychlorinated biphenyls) in the nonflammable insulating liquids may escape into the environment during handling or when leaks develop in transformer tanks. PCBs are nonbiodegradable and may cause dangerous ecological contamination that adversely affect plant and animal life. Several government agencies have forbidden their use. Legislation has been passed voiding them entirely. Leading manufacturers have discontinued their fabrication. Silicon-liquid is now the replacement for Askarel. (More about silicon-liquid filled transformers will be discussed in section 5.2).

• *Dry-type self-cooled transformer (Class AA)* is cooled by natural air circulation and is not immersed in oil.

• *Dry-type self-cooled/forced-air-cooled transformers (Class AA/FA)* are not immersed in oil and have self-cooled ratings, with cooling by natural air circulation and forced-air-cooled ratings obtained by forced-air circulation.

• *Dry-type forced-air-cooled transformers (Class AFA)* are not immersed in oil and derive cooling by forced-air circulation.

The provision for increasing the continuous kva rating of liquid-filled and open dry-type transformers rated 500 kva and above, by adding cooling fans and/or pumps, yields a percentage increase of their self-cooled ratings (see Table 2).

Open dry-type transformers are among the lowest first-cost fireproof units available and are extremely reliable when installed in proper locations and atmosphere. Dry-type transformers are lightweight and can be installed overhead on balconies, roof trusses, upper floor buildings or roofs. Fire or toxic fumes are not a hazard with this type of transformer, so fire insurance companies offer lower insurance premiums than for oil-filled transformers. Dry-type transformers do not require any vaults or special venting, so they have a lower installation cost. They require minimal periodic inspection of air circulation or dust accumulation, but they require no oil level checking or oil cleaning, adding and replacing as is the case with oil-filled transformers.

The disadvantage of dry-type trans-

TABLE 3 TRANSFORMER STANDARD BASIC-IMPULSE-INSULATION LEVELS USUALLY ASSOCIATED WITH NOMINAL SYSTEM VOLTAGES

Nominal system line-to-line voltage (volts)	Insulation class (kv)	Basic-impulse-insulation level (kv)			
		Liquid insulated		Dry-type	
		Power	Distribution	Ventilated*	Gas-filled and sealed
120-600	1.2	45	30†	10	30
2,400	2.5	60	45†	20	45
4,160	5.0	75	60†	25	60
4,800	5.0	75	60†	25	60
6,900	8.7	95	75†	35	75
7,200	8.7	95	75†	35	75
12,470	15.0	110	95†	50	95
13,200	15.0	110	95†	50	95
13,800	15.0	110	95†	50	95
14,400	15.0	110	95†	50	95
22,900	25.0	150	150	—	—
23,000	25.0	150	150	—	—
26,400	34.5	200	200	—	—
34,500	34.5	200	200	—	—
43,800	46.0	250	250	—	—
46,000	46.0	250	250	—	—
67,000	69.0	350	350	—	—
69,000	69.0	350	350	—	—
92,000	92.0	450	—	—	—
115,000	115.0	550	—	—	—
		350**	—	—	—
		450**	—	—	—
138,000	138.0	650	—	—	—
		550**	—	—	—
		450**	—	—	—
161,000	161.0	750	—	—	—
		650**	—	—	—
		550**	—	—	—

From IEEE Standard 462-1973 and NEMA 201-1970 and 210-1970.
  * Special ratings for ventilated dry-type transformers, equivalent to the gas-filled type, can be obtained.
  † Ratings are also applicable to primary and secondary unit substation transformers.
  **Optional reduced levels applicable if equivalent reduced rating arresters are properly applied on the system.

formers is that their BIL is about half that of the liquid or gas-filled units, and their cost is 20 to 25 percent higher than the oil-filled transformers. Overall technical and economical considerations dictate their selection.

• *Gas-filled transformers* are indicated where a situation cannot tolerate the presence of a liquid and calls for the higher BIL of a liquid-filled unit.

The gas used in these transformers is fluorocarbon (C_2F_6) which is nonflammable, nonexplosive and nontoxic. This gas is ideally suited for contaminated atmospheres that require fireproof installation. They can be used outdoors as well as indoors, fluorocarbon gas being nonexplosive and nonflammable, and this transformer type requires minimum maintenance.

Cooling fans are not available for gas-filled transformers, since they are designed only for a self-cooling kva rating. Their price is twice as high as that of oil-filled transformers.

More selection criteria

The BIL rating of a transformer winding defines the design and tested capability of its insulation to withstand lightning or surge overvoltages. The BILs are expressed in terms of impulse crest voltages with a nominal 1.2×50 microsecond wave, as described in Paragraph 3.8 of ANSI Standard C57. 12.90-1973.

A winding's line terminal must be assigned a BIL and an insulation class that can be found in ANSI Standard C57. 12.00-1973 (IEEE Standard 462-1973). Transformer BILs usually associated with nominal system voltages are in Table 3.

Impedance of a transformer, based on rated capacity and voltage, is the voltage required to circulate rated current through the primary winding of the transformer when the secondary winding is short-circuited, with the respective winding connected as for rated-voltage operation. Impedance values are usually expressed in percent of the rated voltage of the winding in which the voltage is measured. Tolerances for impedance values can be found in ANSI C57 12.00-1973. Table 4 lists standard impedance values for 3-phase transformers.

Load losses in a transformer are those incident to the carrying of the load. They include I^2R loss in the windings due to load current, stray losses due to stray fluctuations and also any circulating currents in parallel

windings. Impedance and load-loss tolerances are covered by NEMA Standard TR-27-1965.

No-load losses are the losses in a transformer excited at rated voltage and frequency but not supplying load. No-load losses include core, dielectric and copper losses in the winding due to exciting current.

Total losses are the sum of no-load and load losses. The losses by transformer test should not exceed the values shown in Table 13 of ANSI C57 12.00-1973.

Temperature rise is also a factor. The life expectancy of insulating materials used in transformers depends upon the temperatures to which they are

subjected and their duration. The actual temperature is the sum of ambient temperature and temperature rise. The ambient temperature is that of the medium, such as air or liquid, into which the equipment heat is dissipated.

The limits of temperature rise for continuously rated transformers are in Table 5. The temperature of the cooling air (ambient temperature) must not exceed 40 C, and the average temperature of the cooling air for any 24-hr period must not exceed 30 C.

Sound levels shall be below NEMA standards as shown in Table 6 (NEMA TR1-1974). Values are measured in an isolated sound room in accordance

TABLE 4 STANDARD IMPEDANCE VALUES FOR THREE-PHASE TRANSFORMERS

High-voltage rating (volts)	kva rating	Percent impedance voltage
Secondary unit substation transformers*		
2,400-31,800[1]	112.5-225	Not less than 2.0[2]
2,400-13,800	300-500	Not less than 4.5
2,400-13,800	750-2,500	5.75
22,900	All	5.75
34,400	All	6.25

Liquid-immersed transformers, 501—30,000 kva†

	Low voltage, 3,480 v	Low voltage, 2,400 v and above
2,400-22,900	5.75	5.5
26,400 and 34,400	6.25	6.0
43,800	6.75	6.5
67,000		7.0
115,000		7.5
138,000		8.0

Notes: [1]) Ratings separated by hyphens indicate that all intervening standard ratings are included.
[2]) Percent impedance voltages are at self-cooled rating and as measured on rated voltage connection.
* From NEMA 210-1970
† From ANSI C57.12.10-1969.

TABLE 5 LIMITS OF TEMPERATURE RISE

Type of transformer	Winding temp. rise by resistance (degree C)	Hottest-spot winding temp. rise (degree C)
55 C Rise oil-immersed	55	65
65 C Rise oil-immersed	65	80
55 C Rise dry-type	55	65
80 C Rise dry-type	80	110
150 C Rise dry-type	150	180

with audible sound tests defined by the same standard.

Efficiency of a transformer is the ratio of useful power output to total power input.

Transformers may be solidly grounded, resistance-grounded or reactance-grounded. This means that the neutral point of the transformer winding may be grounded solidly, through a resistance (of high or low value) or through a reactance. (Equipment grounding is the grounding of the non-current-carrying parts).

Accessories furnished with transformers include the standard and optional manufacturer's publication.

Dry-type transformers are among the lowest first-cost fireproof units available today

Some optional accessories are winding temperature indicator, sudden pressure relay, alarm contacts for temperature, liquid level, pressure-vacuum gauges and pressure-relief devices. Surge-arresters mounted on the transformer provide surge protection.

The NEC on transformers

The NEC states that transformer and transformer vaults shall be readily accessible to qualified personnel for inspection and maintenance with the exception of dry-type transformers 600 v or less and installations in fire-resistant hollow spaces in buildings (Art. 450-2).

Dry-type transformers installed indoors and rated 112½ kva or less must have a separation of at least 12 in. from combustible material, unless separated by a fire-resistant heat-insulating barrier or unless the transformer is rated 600 v or less and is completely enclosed except for ventilation openings.

Transformers rated higher than 112½ kva must be installed in a fire-resistant transformer room. This does not apply to transformers with Class 80 C rise or higher insulation that are separated from combustible material by a fire-resistant, heat-insulating barrier or at least 6 ft. horizontally and 12 ft. vertically, or that are completely enclosed except for

TABLE 6   AUDIBLE SOUND LEVELS FOR TWO-WINDING SUBSTATION TRANSFORMERS

Self-cooled rating (kva)	Average sound level (decibels)*		
	Liquid type (69 kv and below)	Dry type (15 kv and below) Ventilated	Sealed
151-300	55	58 (67)	57
301-500	56	60 (67)	59
501-700	57 (67)	62 (67)	61
701-1,000	58 (67)	64 (67)	63
1,001-1,500	60 (67)	65 (68)	64
1,501-2,000	61 (67)	66 (69)	65
2,001-3,000	62, 63 (67)	68 (71)	66
3,001-4,000	64 (67)	70 (73)	68
4,001-5,000	65 (67)	71 (74)	69
5,001-6,000	66 (67)	72 (75)	70
6,001-7,500	67 (68)	73 (76)	71
10,000	68 (70)	—	—
12,500	69 (70)	—	—
15,000	70 (71)	—	—
20,000	71 (72)	—	—
25,000	72 (73)	—	—
30,000	73 (74)	—	—
40,000	74 (75)	—	—
50,000	75 (76)	—	—
60,000	76 (77)	—	—
80,000	77 (78)	—	—
100,000	78 (79)	—	—

From NEMA TR 1-1974
Note: The tabulated values represent the average sound level which will not be exceeded on the base transformer and is exclusive of sound emitted by integral load tap-changing mechanisms, disconnecting switches or close-couple switchgear. These values are not necessarily applicable to rectifier transformers or furnace transformers. Refer to NEMA TR 1-1974 for measurements and test conditions. (Noise in dBA at 1 ft from external surface.)
* The values in parentheses represent the sound level with one stage of forced-cooling equipment in operation. (Noise in dBA at 6 ft from external surface.)

ventilation.

Transformers over 35,000 v must be installed in a vault (Art. 450-21). Dry-type transformers installed outdoors must have a weatherproof enclosure (Art. 450-22).

Askarel-insulated transformers installed indoors, if rated over 25 kva, must have a pressure-relief vent. If rated over 35,000 volts, they must be in a vault (Art. 450-23).

Oil-insulated transformers installed indoors must be in a vault, with four exceptions as listed in NEC (Art. 450-24). Combustible material, buildings, fire escapes, door and window openings must be safeguarded from fires originating in indoor oil-insulated transformers. Space separations, fire-resistant barriers, automatic water-spray systems and enclosures containing the oil of a ruptured transformer tank are accepted safeguards. Oil enclosures must consist of fire-resistant dikes, curbed areas or basins, or trenches filled with crushed

stone. Trapped drains are recommended where the quantity of oil involved makes oil removal important (Art. 450-25).

Transformer vaults must be ventilated to the outside air. Vault walls and roofs must be of structural strength for minimum 3-hr fire resistance. Floors must be of concrete at least 4 in. thick. (Art. 450-51-52). The vault doorway must be protected with fire-resistant materials and with locks accessible only to qualified persons (Art. 450-43). Oil drainage must be provided by floors pitched to drains (Art. 450-46). No pipes or duct systems may enter or pass through a transformer vault, and no materials may be stored in the vaults (Art. 450-47).

Based on the described NEMA, ANSI and NEC definitions and requirements, section 5.2 will discuss the pros and cons among dry-type, liquid-filled and gas-filled transformers from a technical and economical point of view.

5.2 Ratings and Characteristics of Dry-Type, Liquid- and Gas-filled Transformers

The first section 5.1, discussed the fundamental definitions and characteristics of different transformer types as reflected in the latest National Electrical Manufacturer's Assn. and American National Standards Institute standards and the National Electrical Code.

This second part deals with specific ratings, characteristics, outlines, weights and prices of dry-type, liquid- and gas-filled transformers. Advantages and disadvantages of each transformer type are discussed from a technical and economic point of view, together with recommendations of when, why and how to use each type. Figures and tables are numbered consecutively.

The four basic types of transformers, as defined by ANSI or NEMA, are oil-filled, nonflammable insulating liquid-filled (Askarel and fluid-silicone), dry-type, and gas-filled. The selection of any one of these transformers depends on first cost, equipment location, maintenance requirements, ambient, hazardous or nonhazardous atmosphere, impulse strength, required maintenance, sound-level requirements, available space and provision for future forced-air-cooled capability.

The Askarel transformers are phased out as a result of a toxic substances bill that became law Oct. 12, 1976. Its insulating liquid, polychlorinated biphenyl material, is nonflammable but also toxic and nonbiodegradable. Should this material get into earth or streams, it can cause environmental problems with the effect of toxicity to fishes, birds, animals and humans.

A newcomer to the family of nonflammable insulated liquid-filled transformers is the silicon-fluid-filled transformer. This was especially developed as an alternative to transformer Askarels and is supposed to answer the need for safe and environmentally acceptable transformer liquid. Silicone liquid is expected to solve the flammability problems of mineral oils and the environmental hazards of Askarels. Users should be cautious of the risk element in placing silicone-filled transformers in hazardous locations until they are fully accepted by NEC and insurance companies. The purchaser has the

Dry-type transformers do not require periodic checking, but oil-filled transformers always do

responsibility to install and operate these transformers safely and to obtain local code approval and insurance coverage for each installation.

Section 450-23 of the 1978 NEC covers transformers to replace Askarel-insulated transformers. The high-fire-point insulated transformer is an alternate to the oil-filled transformer for indoor use, but without a vault. The commercial, institutional and industrial dry-type transformers are covered by NEMA Standard Publication TR27-1974, ANSI C57.12.00-1973 and *Secondary Unit Substation Publication NEMA 210-1970.* During the past 15 years, dry-type transformers have been successfully performing in almost all indoor requirements and many outdoor applications at 15,000 v or less. It has been estimated that approximately 90 percent of indoor transformers are dry-type rather than oil-filled or nonflammable liquid-filled type. Their success is due to the following reasons:

• Dry-type transformers can be installed anywhere in buildings and plants, especially at the indoor load centers, thus eliminating the expensive fireproof vaults NEC requires for oil-filled transformers.

• They do not require maintenance and periodic checking of the oil to make sure it has not lost its insulating qualities by accumulation of water. There are no liquids to handle.

• No gas vents are required, no catch basins are needed, no drains, no gauges and valves require checking and maintenance, no gaskets require replacement or repairs.

• Dry-type are normally nonexplosive, nonflammable and ecologically safe.

• Three-phase dry-type transformers are manufactured in all ratings from 3 to 10,000 kva at primary voltages from 480 v to 34.5 kv, and up to 150-kv BIL levels. Single-phase dry-type transformers are manufactured in ratings to 7,500 kva.

• The low initial cost of dry-type transformers enables engineers to solve difficult installation problems, especially where space is limited. These units can even be recessed into walls.

• They are lightweight and can be installed on balconies, on roof trusses, upper-floor buildings and on roofs.

• They have high operating efficiency, good voltage regulation and quiet operation.

• They have built-in overload capability if specified as Class H insulation 115 C rise.

Transformer insulation types

Insulating materials are classfied as types A, B, F and H. The letters indicate the temperatures to which these insulation classes may be exposed and still have an acceptable life expectancy.

Class A materials consist of cotton, silk, paper and other organic materials that should not be exposed to average conductor temperatures exceeding 95 C, or 55 C rise over 40 C ambient, for normal life expectancy. A maximum gradient of 10 C results in a limiting temperature rise that should not exceed 105 C. This type of insulation is commonly used in oil-filled transformers. In dry types, Class A insulation became outdated years ago.

Class B materials consist of combinations of mica, glass fiber and asbestos, with bonding substances that should not be exposed to average conductor temperatures exceeding 120 C, or 80 C above 40 C ambient. The hot-spot temperature rise should not be more than 30 C above 120 C, thus establishing at 150 C the limiting temperature.

Class F allows a rise of 115 C over 40 C ambient plus another 30 C for the hot-spot temperature, making 185 C the hottest-spot temperature or the total permissable ultimate temperature. This class contains the same materials as Class B: the only difference is the way of bonding and impregnating the materials. Class F is due to fall into disuse in favor of Class H, which is currently used in dry-type transformers.

Class H materials consist of silicon, elastomer, mica, glass fiber or asbestos with appropriate silicone resins. This class of materials allows a rise of 150 C above 40 C ambient to which an additional 30 C hot spot is allowed. The limiting temperature should not exceed 220 C. All dry-type transformers 30-kva and above are manufactured with this kind of insulation. The advantage of Class H insulation lies in size reduction, permitting minimum amounts of conductor and core.

Comparing liquid transformers with dry-type transformers from a temperature-rise point of view, it can be seen that liquid transformers use 120 C insulation systems for either 55 C rise with 112 percent maximum nameplate rating or 65 C rise with 100 percent maximum nameplate rating. On the other hand, dry-type transformers offer a 220 C insulation system and three basic temperature rises, namely: 80 C rise carrying 135 percent maximum nameplate rating at 150 C rise, 115 C rise carrying 115 percent maximum nameplate rating at 150 C rise and 150 C rise carrying 100 percent maximum nameplate rating (see Table 6).

A dry-type transformer specification calling for Class H insulation, 115 C rise is incongruous since the Class H insulation is for 150 C and not 115 C rise (see the insulation designations in Table 7). Such a transformer can be specified, however, and Table 8 explains the advantage of such a transformer. The curve shows that neither the 150 C-rise Class H nor the 115 C-rise Class H operates at rated design potential and both have

additional capacity. At 150 C rise, both transformers operate at rated design potential and thus have the same normal life expectancy.

The Class H, 115 C-rise transformer has a kva capacity larger than its nameplate indicates. Due to this larger size and higher kva continuous rating, it is sold at a price premium. The Class H, 115 C-rise transformer can be considered a "non-standard" transformer that nevertheless has continuous overload kva capability of approximately 15 percent greater than the ratings.

The case for fan cooling

The weakest point of the Class H insulation is its life expectancy at the ultimate temperature of 220 C. Indeed Class H materials must withstand 150 C rise for a minimum of 20,000 hr. At full load and assuming a possible 40 C ambient for 24-hr continuous operation, the 20,000 hr would disappear in

2.3 years. Based on these assumptions, it would be good practice to design for a Class H with 115 C rise only. Because of the short life mentioned, the lower initial cost of 150 C-rise units might not be a good economy. At 115 C rise with a possible 30-yr life expectancy, the dry-type transformer Class H with 115 C rise might be a better buy since for every 10 C decrease in temperature the insulation life expectancy might be doubled. The Class H, 150 C-rise transformer is indicated where lowest initial cost is desired, where the loads are intermittent, or where the transformer will rarely be operated close to the nameplate rating and no load growth is foreseen.

Fans can be added to liquid or dry-type transformers to increase their kva ratings. No additional price is charged for provision for future fan addition.

Liquid-cooled transformers from

TABLE 6   BASIC TEMPERATURE RISES FOR DRY
AND LIQUID TYPES

Insulation class	Liquid 120 C insulation		Dry-type 220 C insulation		
Temp. rise	55° C rise	65 C rise	150 C rise	115° C rise	80 C rise
Max. nameplate rating	112%	100%	100%	115%*	135%*

* When so specified

TABLE 7   INSULATION DESIGNATION BASED ON AMBIENT TEMPERATURE
OF 40 C

Present system	Conductor insulation winding temp. degree C rise			Previous class
	By resistance	Hot spot	Hottest spot	
55° rise	55	10	105	A
80° rise	80	30	150	B
115° rise	115	30	185	F
150° rise	150	30	220	H

TABLE 8   DRY-TYPE TRANSFORMER CHARACTERISTICS

Class H, 115° C		Class H, 150°C
(C) Kva nameplate rating	(D) Continuous overload kva	(B) Kva nameplate rating
30	34.5	30
45	51.8	45
75	86.3	75
112.5	129.4	112.5
150	172.5	150
225	258.8	225
300	345	300
500	575	500

750 through 2,499 kva can obtain a 15 percent increase in kva rating with fan cooling; transformers 2,500 through 11,999 kva can obtain 25 percent increases.

Fans can help dry-type transformers 300 kva and above obtain 33 percent increases in their kva ratings. Fans are controlled by accurate hot-spot relays that can carry heavier overloads, and enable engineers to size transformers more nearly to the actual load and achieve longer transformer life.

Other transformer characteristics

Standards define the transformer's time constant as the number of hours required to raise its hot-spot temperature to 63 percent of its rated hot-spot rise with rated load applied, starting from no load at standard ambient. This is the time it takes for the transformer to reach temperature equilibrium. The higher the time constant, the more short-time (about 30 min) overload can be carried. Table 9 shows that an 80 C dry-type has the same short-time overload characteristic as a liquid-filled, and a 150 C dry-type has a slightly reduced capability.

Standard core and coils of dry-type transformers usually have a lower BIL than liquid-type transformers. However, dry-type transformers with properly applied lightning arresters, or an optional design that increases BIL to match oil-filled types, can be obtained. The BIL for various high-voltage insulation classes for liquid, dry and gas-filled transformers are shown in Table 10.

The comparison in Table 11 for weight and dimensions indicates that dry-type transformers are essentially the same in size and weight as the liquid ones. Dry-type transformers have three advantages over the other types, however: no head room required for untanking, balcony installations over work areas that eliminate floor space requirements, and knockdown cases for rigging into confined locations.

The NEMA standards (Table 12) show sound levels for dry-type transformers as higher than liquid-filled units. The difference ranges from 3 to 6 db for the self-cooled (OA or AA) rating but is essentially the same for the forced cooled (FA) rating.

In general, liquid units have lower no-load losses, whereas dry-type normally have lower load losses. For example, Table 13 compares a 1,000 kva, 15-kv 80 C temperature rise dry-type transformer to a 1,000-kva,

15-kv, 55 C liquid unit. At light loads, liquid units generally cost less to operate, but at heavier loads (75 percent and above) dry-type transformers are more efficient.

A cost comparison must evaluate the total installed cost. The evaluation of installed cost in percent, where 100 percent equals the oil-type first cost, was made for a standard 1,000-kva, 15-kv transformer (Table 14). The oil-type transformer is compared for total installed cost with Askarel,

TABLE 9   TIME CONSTANT OF DRY VS. LIQUID

Type of transformer	Time constant hours
Liquid 55 C or 65 C	1.5
Dry 80 C	1.5
Dry 150 C	1.0

TABLE 10   BASIC IMPULSE LEVELS FOR VARIOUS HIGH-VOLTAGE INSULATION CLASSES

Type of transformer	5 kv	15 kv	25 kv	34.5 kv
Liquid	60	95	150	200
Dry	25	50	125	150
Dry (optional)	60	95	150	150
Gas filled	60	95	125	150

TABLE 11   SIZE AND WEIGHT COMPARISON OF DIFFERENT TRANSFORMERS (EVALUATION BASIS IS A STANDARD 1,000-KVA, 15-KV TRANSFORMER)

Type of transformer	Temp. rise	KV BIL	Ht. in. (approx.)	Floor sq ft area (approx.)	Weight lbs (approx.)
Oil	65° C	95	84	27	6,400
Askarel	65° C	95	86	27	7,200
Dry-type vent	80° C	50	90	33	7,700
		95	90	33	8,600
	150° C	50	90	33	6,800
		95	90	33	7,600
Dry-type	150° C	50	90	33	8,000
		95	90	33	9,000
Gas filled sealed	150° C	95	96	42	10,000
Silicone	65° C	95	86	27	6,500

From Westinghouse Mfg. Corp.

TABLE 12   NEMA SOUND TABLE FOR LIQUID AND DRY-TYPE

Kva	Liquid-type OA	FA	Dry-type AA	FA
300	55	—	58	67
750	58	67	64	67
2,500	62	67	68	71

TABLE 12A   NEMA SOUND TABLE FOR DRY-TYPE 0-300 KVA TRANSFORMERS

KVA 600 v and less*	Sound level in decibels (dB)
0-9	40
10-50	45
51-150	50
151-300	55

*For 5 kv class the average sound level is about 5 dB higher.

TABLE 13   EFFICIENCY TABLE FOR LIQUID AND DRY TYPES

1,000 kva 15 kv transformer	Percent load				
	25	50	75	100	125
Liquid 55° rise	98.75	99.05	99.0	98.7	98.65
Dry 80° C rise	98.30	98.90	99.0	98.8	98.85

TABLE 14 INSTALLED COST IN PERCENT (EVALUATION BASIS, STANDARD 1,000 KVA, 15-KV TRANSFORMER

Type of transformer		BIL	First cost	Installation cost adders: apply when required by insurance or EPA regulations and/or user's standard construction practice			Total installed cost
				Vault & Fire protection	Catch basin	Outside vent	
Oil		95	100%	133%	—	—	100-233%
Askarel		95	135%	—	38%	2%	135-175%
Vent dry-	80°	50	149%	—	—	—	149%
		95	164%				164%
type	150%	50	120%	—	—	—	120%
		95	133%				133%
Dry-type totally enclosed nonventilated		50	160%	—	—	—	160%
		95	175%				175%
Gas-filled sealed dry		95	200%	—	—	—	200%
Silicone		95	143%	—	38%	—	143-181%

From Westinghouse Corp.

TABLE 15 STANDARD ELECTRICAL CHARACTERISTICS STANDARD RATINGS (Kva)

Self-cooled ventilated totally enclosed non-ventilated and gas-filled*	Self-cooled/forced-air cooled ventilated dry type*	High voltage+	High voltage taps at rated kva volts**	Low voltage‡
	3-phase			3-phase
112¹/₂, 150, 225	750/1,000, 1,000/1,333	2,400	2,520, 2,460, 2,340, 2,280	208Y/120-4 wire
300, 500, 750	1,500/2,000, 2,000/2,667	4,160	4,365, 4,260, 4,055, 3,950	or 240 Delta
1,000, 1,500, 2,000	2,500/3,333, 3,000/4,000	4,800	5,040, 4,920, 4,680, 4,560	
2,500, 3,000, 3,750	3,750/5,000, 5,000/6,667	6,900	7,245, 7,075, 6,730, 6,555	480Y/277-4 wire
5,000, 7,500	7,500/10,000			or 480 Delta
10,000	10,000/13,333	7,200	7,560, 7,380, 7,020, 6,840	
		8,320	8,730, 8,520, 8,105, 7,900	2,400△, 2,520△, 4,160△
		12,000	12,600, 12,300, 11,700, 11,400	4,160Y/2,400, 4,360Y, 4,800
		12,470	13,095, 12,780, 12,160, 11,850	
	Single-phase			Single-phase
167, 250	833/1,111, 1,250/1,667	13,200	13,860, 13,530, 12,870, 12,540	120/208Y, 240
333, 500	1,667/2,223	13,800	14,490, 14,145, 13,455, 13,110	277/480Y, 480,
667, 833	2,500/3,333			
1,250, 1,667	5,000/6,667	22,900	24,100, 23,500, 22,300, 21,700	2,400, 2,400/4,160Y, 2,520, 4,160
2,500, 3,333	6,667/8,889	26,400	27,800, 27,100, 25,700, 25,000	2,520/4,360Y, 4,800
5,000, 6,667	7,500/10,000	34,400	36,200, 35,300, 33,500, 32,600	
7,500				

*Totally enclosed non-ventilated not available above 5,000 kva 3-phase or above 3,333 kva 1-phase or with fan cooling. Gas-filled not available below 300 kva or above 5,000 kva 3-phase or below 333 kva or above 3,333 kva 1-phase or with fan cooling.

+On 3-phase units these voltages are delta or wye, not delta/wye.

**Ventilated and totally enclosed nonventilated dry-type transformers are equipped with stub taps and a flexible connector or terminal board for changing taps. Gas filled dry types are equipped with a tap changer with operating mechanism under a sealed cover.

‡Low-voltage taps not available.

From Westinghouse Corp.

dry-type, gas-filled, and silicon transformers.

Applying dry-type transformers

Dry-type transformers have proven their reliability in a wide variety of distribution and power substations, such as hi-rise buildings, utility network systems, steel and aluminum mills, schools, offices, hospitals, textile plants, and nuclear generating stations.

A decade ago the ratio of liquid-filled to dry-type usage was about nine to one. Today, this ratio has become the reciprocal of one to nine. This proves a recognition of dry-type transformer benefits, especially now that the Askarel-filled transformer is phased out.

In addition to the open dry-type, self-cooled, ventilated transformer, a totally enclosed, nonventilated, dry-type transformer can now operate in dirty atmospheres of magnetic dust, abrasive matter or excessive lint, due to its specially designed enclosure that seals out environmental contaminants. No openings permit entry of under able elements to the coil-and-core area.

Such transformers are successfully used in foundries, refineries and textile plants with highly contaminated atmospheres. Totally enclosed non-ventilated transformers are manufactured up to 5,000 kva, 3-phase (AA). Table 15 lists standard ratings available in ventilated, totally-enclosed nonventilated, and single- or 3-phase gas-filled and dry-type transformers.

Future trends are towards smaller sizes and higher operating temperatures due to continuous improvements in high-temperature insulation systems. Improvements in wire insulation, varnishes, flexible sheet insulations, tape and laminates will make possible higher temperature limits that will exceed the current 250 C limit. More and more aluminum replaces copper winding transformer coils because of aluminum's ease of handling and thermal resistance. Continuous advances in resin technology makes possible cast or encapsulated coils for operation above 150 C, thus expanding dry-type transformer manufacturing to a high-voltage field.

Many challenging problems are in store for this field.

In selecting and specifying transformers, the engineer must compare and weigh the advantages and disadvantages of each transformer type. The appropriate choice takes into account all technical and economic requirements related to the specific conditions, such as cost, location, maintenance, environmental factors, available space, fire, explosion or toxic hazards, future load growth, efficiency, sound, BIL and short-circuit strength.

Significant cost savings, longer insulation life, reserve overload capabilities, and ability to operate safely in high ambient areas are important reasons for the engineer to evaluate carefully all operating characteristics before selecting and specifying the proper transformer type.

5.3 Primary and Secondary Winding Connections of Transformers and Their Uses

The previous section 5.2 discussed specific ratings, characteristics, outlines, weights and prices of dry-type, liquid-filled and gas-filled transformers. It covered the advantages and disadvantages of each from a technical and economic point of view.

This third part discusses the various primary and secondary winding connections of transformers, their respective advantages and disadvantages, and where and why to apply each connection type.

A 3-phase transformer can be made up of a bank of three single-phase shell-type or core-type transformers as shown in Figure 1. (More detail on shell and core types is given later, in the discussion of open-Delta connection.) Most larger-industry transformers are of 3-phase construction because these cost less, have higher efficiency and require less space than single-phase units making up 3-phase banks.

The main objective to the 3-phase transformer in one tank is that a breakdown in the winding of one phase puts the whole transformer out of commission. A three-transformer bank that has each transformer in its own tank can operate at reduced 3-phase equivalent capacity by connecting two of the units in open-Δ in case the third one fails.

Various possible connections of 3-phase transformers can be compared from mainly three viewpoints:
- Ratio of kva output to kva bank rating.
- Degree of voltage symmetry, such as third voltage and current harmonics.
- Operating advantages, disadvantages and peculiarities.

The best selection for a given application can be made only when based on these characteristics.

The ratio of kva output to kva bank rating represents the apparatus economy (or utilization factor), which is maximum when this ratio is unity. The majority of 3-phase transformer connections are made up by connecting the phases between lines to form a Δ connection, or by connecting one end of each phase together and other ends to the respective lines to form a Wye connection (see Figure 2).

If three identical single-phase transformers or the three identical phases of a 3-phase transformer are Δ or Y connected the connection is symmetrical and balanced. This means the current and voltages in each of the phases are respectively the same and are identically related to the line currents and voltages.

E and I represent the 3-phase line voltage and current for a Δ-connection. Each phase has a voltage E and a current $\frac{I}{\sqrt{3}}$; for a Y connection the voltage for each phase is $\frac{E}{\sqrt{3}}$ and the current is I. In both cases the rating of each phase is $\frac{E \times I}{\sqrt{3}}$ and the total rating of the 3-phase transformer is

$$3 \times \frac{E \times I}{\sqrt{3}} = E \cdot I \sqrt{3}, \text{ if } \Delta \text{ or Y connected.}$$

As the power associated with an E and I voltage and current is also $E \cdot I \sqrt{3}$ for balanced 3-phase loads, it is evident that the transformer kva is equal to the kva delivered to the circuit (disregarding magnetizing current and regulation drop). The ratio of the kva output to kva bank rating, therefore, is unity.

The fact that in other 3-phase transformer connections this ratio is less than unity explains the preference for Δ or Y over other connections where this ratio is 86.6 percent. This means these connections can only deliver 86.6 percent of their total transformer rating.

The second viewpoint for comparison is the voltage and current symmetry with respect to the lines and neutral. Such symmetry is obtained only in the Δ and Zig-Zag connections. All other connections have varying degrees of asymmetry that may introduce such objectionable operating conditions as current distortion and unbalanced regulation. Indeed the open-Δ and T connections are asymmetrical with respect to lines and thus introduce in the circuit unbalanced regulation and third-harmonic magnetizing currents.

Harmonics are multiples of the fundamental frequency of voltage and current. Harmonic currents cause electromagnetic induction. Power system harmonics can thus cause noise induction in communication circuits that may in turn cause interference on the telephone circuits that parallel utility power lines.

Harmonics in industrial power systems are caused by transformer exciting current with a fairly large third-harmonic component, a smaller fifth and so on. The magnitudes of these harmonics are approximately 40 and 10 percent of the exciting current magnitude with rapid increases as operating density increases. Exciting current is about 5 percent of rated transformer current. This means that the third-harmonic component, for example, is 5 percent times .4, which is 2 percent of the transformer current.

Making connections

In a 3-phase bank of transformers, the triple-frequency harmonic components are all in phase and therefore must have a suitable flow path. Transformer connections to assure this path merit special consideration.

The Y connection introduces third-

Harmonic currents cause electromagnetic induction at harmonic frequencies

FIGURE 1   3-PHASE CORE- AND SHELL-TYPE TRANSFORMERS

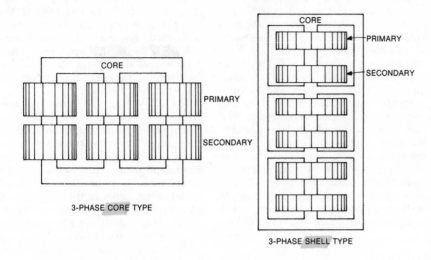

3-PHASE CORE TYPE

3-PHASE SHELL TYPE

FIGURE 2   PRIMARY (OR SECONDARY) DELTA AND
WYE CONNECTIONS OF 3-PHASE TRANSFORMERS

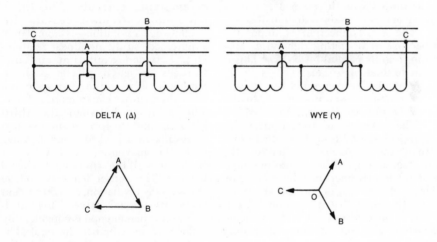

DELTA (Δ)

WYE (Y)

magnetizing currents supplied to such banks are superior to the wave shapes of asymmetrical banks.

If the flux in a transformer magnetic circuit is sinusoidal the exciting current must contain a third-harmonic component. If this component cannot flow because of transformer or system connections, the flux contains a third-harmonic component. This third-harmonic flux introduces a third-harmonic voltage in the transformer winding that may vary between 5 and 50 percent. It is preferable to have at least one Δ-connected winding in a 3-phase transformer bank. The Δ connection furnishes a path for the flow of the third-harmonic current and minimizes the third-harmonic current in the external circuits. Δ-Δ, Δ-Y and Y-Δ connections are equal from a standpoint of symmetry.

When a neutral is used for loading or grounding, the Δ-Δ connection cannot be used. In very high-voltage designs or in very small line current the Y connection lends itself to a less expensive design because the phase voltage is $\frac{E}{\sqrt{3}}$. Conversely, the Δ-connection lends itself to a less expensive design where the current is very large or the voltage small, since the phase current is $\frac{I}{\sqrt{3}}$. These considerations alone may determine the connection to be used.

Where the above considerations do not indicate the connection to be selected, the division of load in the Δ-Δ and Δ-Y or Y-Δ bank might determine the appropriate choice.

When the neutral of the Y winding and that of the load are solidly grounded, no difference exists in the load division characteristics of the Δ-Δ and Δ-Y connections. When one of these two neutrals is isolated, a balanced 3-phase load will be equally divided among the phases in the Δ-Y banks; but in the Δ-Δ bank the division of load is equal only when individual transformers have equal impedances. The Δ-Y connections are insensitive to

harmonic voltage and current asymmetry between lines and neutral that may subject parallel telephone circuits to objectionable interference and may under certain conditions subject the system itself to dangerous overvoltages. This is why the Y-Y connection with isolated neutral is not generally recommended in industrial power systems.

The commonly used Δ-Y or Y-Δ connections remove any tendency to produce triple-frequency voltage since such activity circulates currents in the Δ winding where all triple-frequency

voltages are in phase. The triple-frequency existing current is supplied by the Δ, and no flux distortion is obtained.

The Y-Δ and Δ-Y connections assure complete symmetry for all practical purposes, thanks to the presence of the Δ connection. The Δ winding supplies triple-frequency components of existing current for the bank, keeping it out of the supply lines.

Balanced 3-phase Δ-Δ, Y-Δ and Δ-Y banks do not introduce third harmonics and their multiples into the line. That is why the wave shapes of the off-ratio, whereas in the Δ-Δ connection large currents might circulate in both high- and low-voltage Δ when the transformation ratios in all phases are unequal. Care must be taken when selecting transformers to make up Δ-Δ banks, if full capacity of the banks is to be expected.

On the other hand, this dependence of current division between phases on individual transformers' impedance values provides a flexibility of operation of the Δ-Δ banks not obtainable with the Δ-Y or Y-Δ connection. Δ-Δ banks are operative even when they consist of transformers with different kva ratings, since the phase with the smaller rating has the higher ohmic impedance and thus takes a smaller share of the load. By proper proportioning of impedances, the division of load can be given the same proportion as the ratings. Thus Δ-Δ banks can operate properly even with one phase entirely omitted as in the open-Δ connection. This flexibility allows that a failure in one phase of a Δ-Δ bank should be considered less serious than in a Δ-Y or Y-Δ bank.

Δ-Δ connections in 3-phase banks are flexible because operation can continue after one unit of a 3-phase bank fails, and a single-phase unit can be added to a 3-phase bank to increase output. Although flexibility of a Δ-Δ connection is convenient, it also involves a reduction in output of the transformer bank.

Circulating currents usually are produced in Δ-Δ circuits when an unbalanced voltage exists in the Δ. Unbalanced voltage outside the Δ will not produce circulating currents.

In Δ-Δ transformer banks the division of loads is equal between phases, phase currents are 120 deg apart and equal to .577 times line current, and the apparatus economy of the bank is unity if impedances and kva ratings of all three phases are equal and the 3-phase load is balanced. Any departure from these conditions introduces asymmetry.

It is possible with the open-Δ connection to maintain operation if one phase of a Δ-Δ bank is damaged (see Figure 3). Shell-type transformers can operate in open-Δ when one phase is out. The faulted phase should be disconnected from the rest and short-circuited on itself to prevent fluxes of other phases from inducing voltage in the outaged winding. In the 3-phase core-type transformer it is possible to operate in open-Δ only if the damaged winding is open-circuited and can withstand normal voltage.

The current in the transformer winding of an open-Δ connection is the line-current, and the bank rating is reduced by the ratio of normal transformer current to normal current (57.7 percent of the Δ-Δ rating). The apparatus economy for an open-Δ connection is 57.7/66.6=/86.6 percent. As another example, 100-kva units transforming 3-phase 2,300 v to 3-phase 230-115 v have a bank capacity of $200 \times 86.6 = 173.2$ kva.

In the open-Δ connection the impedance characteristics need not be the same, although it is preferable when it becomes necessary to close the open-Δ bank with a third unit because all three units must have identical impedances. Adding a third 100-kva unit in the above-mentioned example will increase the resultant bank capacity from 173.2 kva to 300 kva.

The Y-Y connection is unpopular because of difficulties arising from its natural instability

The regulation of an open-Δ bank is not as good as a closed-Δ bank, since the drop across the open Δ is greater than across each separate transformer.

The Y-Y connection is unpopular because of operating difficulties arising from its natural instability. This is due to three main causes:
- Magnetizing currents.
- Line-to-neutral unbalanced loads.
- Third-harmonic currents.

The potential of the connection's physical neutral is at some other point than the geometric center of the voltage triangle. The neutral potential of Y-Y transformers may be affected by load characteristics and other circuit conditions so that it becomes hazardous to the transformers and connected systems and may interfere with proper transformer operation. This connection should be used only where there are provisions to prevent or reduce neutral instability.

What makes neutral instability?

Magnetizing current results from differences in the quality or quantity of iron, or differences in joints. These differences may cause appreciable magnetizing current variations in transformers of the same design. The Y-Y connection requires that instantaneous currents in the three branches add to zero. A phase requiring the smaller magnetizing current to produce its normal flux has too much

magnetizing current forced on it by the other phases, so that the voltage across it is more than its share. With the transformer neutrals isolated, this residual unbalanced neutral voltage may be of little importance. If the transformer neutral is ground-connected, however, this asymmetry may shift the neutral appreciably and even reverse the voltage on one phase, thus producing excessive voltages in the other two phases.

The Y-Y connected transformers—with the exception of 3-phase core-type units—cannot supply an appreciable single phase-to-neutral load from line-to-neutral without a shift in the neutral position. This is because the corresponding primary currents of such loads magnetize the primaries of unloaded phases as they flow through. This is true mainly for Y-Y connected single-phase units and shell-type 3-phase units. Conversely, the core-type units, because of interlinking magnetic fluxes in the three legs, may provide tolerable results under single-phase loads from line-to-neutral or unbalanced electrostatic charging currents.

The excitation of Y-connected transformers presents a peculiar case for the third-harmonic and odd-multiples magnetizing currents. The third-harmonic current—necessary for single-wave excitation—is completely suppressed, so the nonlinear relationship between excitation and flux induces in each phase a third-harmonic flux and a corresponding third-harmonic electromotive force. The relation between the third harmonic and the fundamental voltages results in a peaked complex wave with the maximum crest value of induced voltage increased by 50 percent. The consequence is voltage stress on the insulation, also 50 percent above its normal value. This third-harmonic phenomenon is considerably influenced by whether the neutral is connected to ground, and by the amount of connected line capacitance.

The Y-Y connection may be used to interconnect two Δ systems and provide suitable neutrals for grounding them. A Δ-connected tertiary winding is frequently provided to stabilize the neutral. A single-phase short-circuit to ground on the transmission line will cause less voltage drop on the short-circuited phase and consequently less voltage rise in the remaining two phases. Conversely, a 3-phase, three-leg Y-connected transformer without a Δ tertiary winding provides very little stabilization of the neutral. Increasing the neutral stabilization by Δ tertiary winding raises the fault current in the neutral on single-phase short-circuit, and this may improve the system's relay protection efficiency.

The third harmonic component of the exciting current finds a relatively low impedance path in the Δ tertiary of a Y-connected transformer and thus less of the third harmonic exciting current will appear in the transmission lines, reducing interferences with communication circuits. An external load such as a synchronous condenser or static capacitor to improve system operation conditions can be supplied from the Δ tertiary. Failure to provide a path for third-harmonic current in Y-connected, 3-phase, shell-type transformers or banks or single-phase transformers results in excessive third-harmonic voltage from line to neutral. Δ tertiaries are not required in 3-phase core-type Y-connected transformers with very little third-harmonic line-to-neutral voltage. This is because no main return path exists for triple-frequency harmonic fluxes that must return through the tank. The tank acts like a high-reactance Δ winding, reducing the magnitude of the induced triple-frequency voltages.

If the system neutral is grounded, the third harmonic practically disappears because third-harmonic currents for the sine wave excitation are furnished through the connected neutrals. In this case each phase receives independent single-phase excitation. If the primary neutral of a Y-Y transformer bank is isolated and the secondary neutral is grounded, the third-harmonic potentials may be avoided by connecting to the secondary lines a Y-Δ transformer bank or a Zig-Zag transformer whose neutrals are connected to the ground. By these connections the third-harmonic potential becomes negligible because a path exists through the ground for the third-harmonic magnetizing currents that are necessary for sinusoidal excitation of the Y-Y bank. In this case the third-harmonic magnetizing current is a single-phase current flowing in one direction in the lines and returning through the neutral to avoid telephone interferences.

Connecting 3-phase to 3-phase

The most generally used connections are Δ-Δ, Δ-Y, Y-Δ and Y-Y when neutral instability is reduced. These connections are shown in Figure 4. For moderate voltages, the Y-Δ and Δ-Δ connections are used as step-up transformers. The Y-Δ provides a good grounding point in the low-voltage systems, which does not shift with unbalanced loads and is also free from third-harmonic currents and voltages.

The Δ-Δ connection permits operation in open-Δ in case of unit failure. However, these connections are not best for very high-voltage transmission. They may be associated with other connections that may properly ground the high-voltage system. It is preferable to avoid mixing connection systems.

The best connections for high-voltage transmission systems are doubtless the Δ-Y step-up and the Y-Δ step-down. They are most economical and provide a stable neutral with ability to ground the high-voltage system or with a resistance of enough value to damp the system critically and prevent oscillation.

The Y-Y connection may interconnect two Δ systems and provide suitable neutrals for grounding both of them. Sometimes a Y-connected auto transformer may economically be used to interconnect two Y systems with neutral grounds. A Δ-connected tertiary winding can stabilize the neutral and provide a path for the third-harmonic current. A Y-connected transformer with a Δ-connected tertiary, when connected to an ungrounded Δ system or a poorly grounded Y

FIGURE 3   OPEN-DELTA CONNECTION

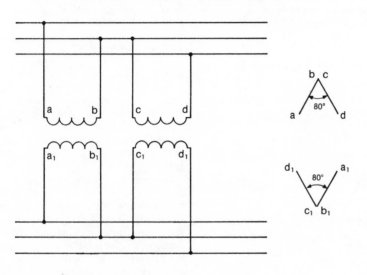

FIGURE 4   MOST-USED TRANSFORMER CONNECTIONS DELTA-DELTA, DELTA-WYE, WYE-DELTA AND WYE-WYE, WITH SPECIAL CONDITIONS

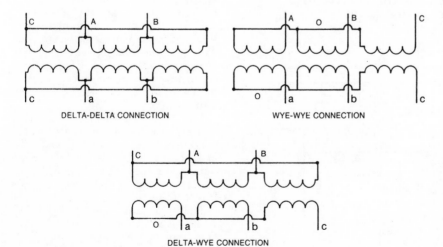

DELTA-DELTA CONNECTION

WYE-WYE CONNECTION

DELTA-WYE CONNECTION

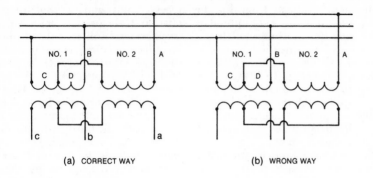

FIGURE 5   T-CONNECTED TRANSFORMERS

(a) CORRECT WAY   (b) WRONG WAY

FIGURE 6   A SCOTT-CONNECTED BANK OF TWO SINGLE-PHASE
TRANSFORMERS, WITH WINDING CURRENTS INDICATED

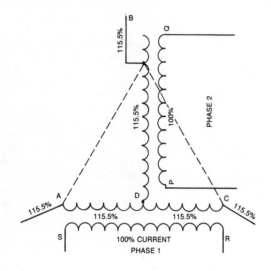

FIGURE 7   CONNECTIONS FOR CHANGING 3-PHASE TO
2-PHASE WITH THREE TRANSFORMERS

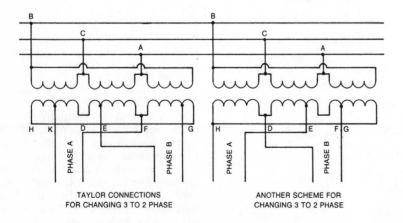

TAYLOR CONNECTIONS
FOR CHANGING 3 TO 2 PHASE

ANOTHER SCHEME FOR
CHANGING 3 TO 2 PHASE

system, increases stability of the system neutral.

The open-Δ or V connection is asymmetrical and is used when one of three single-phase Δ-connected units fails and must be removed. This is an emergency expedient and a temporary solution with the intention of replacing the failing unit after repair. The full-line current in an open-Δ transformer flowing in the windings is out-of-phase with the transformer voltages, and the normal capacity is reduced to 57.7 percent of the 3-phase Δ rating. Because of the absence of the third unit, the third-harmonic current components do not add to zero as they would in a full-Δ connection. With this type of connection the triple-frequency exciting current must be drawn from the system, giving rise to third-harmonic voltages.

Special connections

The T connection uses only two transformers, the "main" transformer connected from line-to-line and the "teaser" connected from midpoint of the first to the third line (see Figure 5). The two transformers should have the same ratio of primary to secondary turns, and tap should be brought out from the central point of one of the transformers. The advantage over the open-Δ connection is that this connection is more nearly symmetrical when the midpoints of primary and secondary windings are available. In the T connection the relative phase sequence of the windings should be the same; otherwise the impedance of the main transformer may be very high and cause imbalance. Figure 5 shows correct and incorrect connections.

The voltage impressed across one transformer is 86.6 percent of that across the other, so that one will have a rating of EI and the other a rating of .866 EI, I being the current in each line and E the voltage between lines. The combined rating will be 1.866, compared with 1.732 EI for three single-phase transformers connected Δ or Y, or 2 EI for two v-connected transformers.

The Scott connection has two single-phase transformers also called main and teaser transformers. The main has a tap in the middle of the winding on the 3-phase side while the teaser has a tap at 86.6 percent of the full winding on the 3-phase side.

The two units usually have full windings and 50 and 86.6 percent taps. One end of the teaser winding is connected to the 50 percent tap of the main winding, while the 86.6 percent

FIGURE 8   3-PHASE TO 6-PHASE TRANSFORMATION, DOUBLE-DELTA

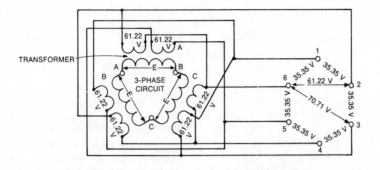

FIGURE 9   3-PHASE TO 6-PHASE, DIAMETRICAL
TRANSFORMATION, DOUBLE WYE

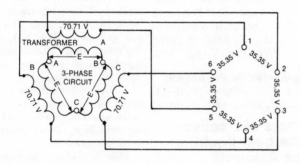

FIGURE 10   ZIG-ZAG CONNECTION

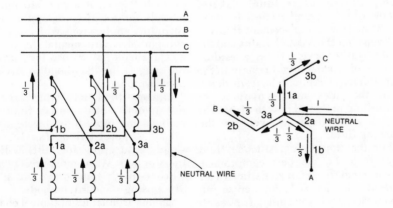

tap of the teaser winding and the two ends of the main winding become the 3-phase terminals (see Figure 6). These connections form a symmetrical 3-phase Δ. The figure shows that the winding on the 3-phase side of a Scott-connected pair of transformers must be designed to carry 15.5 percent more current than the single-phase ratings of the transformers indicate. If no extra copper is provided in the two single-phase transformers for 3-phase currents, the rating of the bank should be reduced to 86.6 percent of the combined single-phase ratings to avoid exceeding rated currents.

In small installations where cost of a spare unit is prohibitive, and to avoid a complete interruption in service when one unit of a bank is outaged, the 3-phase to 2-phase type of connection with three transformers is used (see Figure 8). These connections also are employed when it is intended to change later from 2-phase to 3-phase. The connection in Figure 7 is known as the Taylor connection.

Two Δ-connected banks with the polarity of one bank reversed and connected as shown in Figure 8 provide a double Δ. Two sets connected in Y, with one set's windings connected in reverse of the other's, form the diametrical 3-phase to 6-phase connection (see Figure 9).

The interconnected Y connection shown in Figure 10 is called a Zig-Zag connection. It may be used with a Δ-connected or a Y-connected winding for step-up or step-down operation. The Zig-Zag winding produces the same angular displacement as a Δ winding. The Zig-Zag transformer connection is the most economical method of deriving a 3-phase, four-wire grounded system from an ungrounded Δ system, and is extensively used for establishing a neutral for grounding purposes. The behavior of this connection is similar to a Y-grounded Δ bank, because it reacts similarly to a line-to-ground fault and it does not require triple-frequency exciting current from the lines. Each core has a triple-frequency flux, that produces a triple-frequency voltage in each winding. These voltages are in phase opposition in any two series winding sections connected to provide line-to-neutral fundamental voltage, so they cancel each other.

141

5.4 Silicone Liquid Can Be Used to Replace Askarel. Spec. Guides for Three Dry-Type Transformers

Section 5.3 discussed the various primary and secondary winding connections of transformers, their respective advantages and disadvantages, and where to apply each connection type. The following section discusses alternatives to Askarels and also how to specify different types of dry-type transformers. Tables and figures are numbered chronologically.

Section 5.2 mentioned that polychlorinated biphenyls (PCB's), or Askarels, are being phased out. Because amounts of PCB's have been found in streams, wildlife and humans, and some forms of cancer and birth defects suggest PCB contamination, legislation has curtailed their use in industry. Researchers are very active in finding the best liquid to replace Askarels in power transformers, one having the lowest flammability, heat transfer capacity, electrical strength and compatibility with the environment. (For a chemical substance to be nonflammable, if generally must be highly chlorinated, as are PCB's, but this high degree of chlorination produces a high degree of nonbiodegradability.)

General Electric Co. discontinued the use of PCB's. Westinghouse Electric Corp. also stopped using PCB's as a fire-resistant insulating material in transformers. (The company made no new quotations for units filled with PCB after Dec. 31, 1976.)

The U.S. Environmental Protection Agency has issued regulations covering fines, penalties and controls for spills, discharge and transport of PCB compounds. In cases involving negligence in a spill from a transformer, an individual could be fined $10,000 and/or imprisoned for a year. The regulations define a spill as an amount of one pound or more. In addition, the owner or operator of the facility where the transformer was stored or in operation could be fined as much as $500,000. EPA has proposed a limit of PCB compounds in any process water discharged to navigable waters not to exceed a monthly average

concentration of 1 part/billion PCB compounds.

The handling, use, storage, and disposal of PCB is now regulated by the Toxic Substances Control Act (Public Law 94-469, known as TSCA), which went into effect January 1, 1977. Because of the complexity and sweeping scope of the act, the Environmental Protection Agency, charged with administering the act, was unable to develop and have published the detailed regulations needed to control PCB until February 1978. The PCB regulations are found in the *Federal Register,* February 17, 1978, Part V, pp 7150-7164.

Silicone liquid may be the answer

There are many questions relating to filling existing askarel-filled trans-

Researchers are active finding the best liquid to replace Askarels in power transformers

formers with another fluid. If this is done, each transformer must be analyzed on a unit-by-unit basis to determine its loading and thermal characteristics, its derating if necessary, its gas space, the type of gasketing (where used) and the compatibility of residual Askarel (known by its brand names, Inerteen or Pyranol) with replacement fluids.

Even after the Askarel drains and the unit is flushed several times, a residual amount of Askarel might remain in the transformer. EPA will have to determine the rules and regulations for retrofilling units and how to dispose of the original fluid as well as the flushing fluid.

For the time being, silicone fluid appears to be the best compromise replacement for PCB's. Estimates of current price levels (compared to oil, taken as 100 percent) for each alternative to PCB's are:

Type	Percent
Ventilated dry-type	*120-125*
Askarels(discontinued)	*125*
Silicone liquid	*145-155*
Sealed dry-type	*200*

Underwriters Laboratory evaluated

the silicone liquid for use in transformers and gave it a flammability classification between 4 and 5. Taking the flammability index of water as 0 and that of ether as 100, the flammability indexes are:

Type	Percent
Mineral oil	*20-30*
Silicone fluid	*4.5*
Askarels	*1-2*

After reviewing the available data, some insurance companies have permitted silicone liquids in transformers used by their clients. Because there is no general policy yet, the insurers indicate that evaluations for each application will be made on an individual basis.

Silicone transformer liquids are more environmentally acceptable than Askarels. The product's low toxicity to aquatic, bird, animal and human life is well documented.

Dow-Corning, which manufactures silicone liquids for transformers, has obtained from EPA the following statement:

"EPA is unaware of any instances of adverse health or ecological effects associated with the production, use or disposal of polydimethylsiloxane fluids (silicone fluids) which have been produced in the United States at an estimated level of about 340 million pounds for a variety of applications, including applications which result in substantial environmental discharges, and available laboratory test data do not suggest the likelihood of environmental problems."

Silicone-filled transformers require no special maintenance. Standard maintenance procedures developed for oil or Askarel-filled transformers should also apply for silicone-filled transformers. Also, moisture entering silicone-filled transformers can be dried using standard methods.

Comparison tables of typical characteristics of liquid, ventilated and sealed transformers are shown in Table 16. The dielectric, thermal and physical properties of oil, Askarel and silicone appear in Table 17.

Three important factors make silicone liquids economically and techni-

1,500 kva, 13.8 kv, 480Y/277v

	Liquid		Ventilated		Sealed	
	Oil	Silicone	Air	Air	Freon	Nitrogen
Thermal rating						
Average rise	65°C	65°C	150°C	150°C	150°C	150°C
Hot-spot rise	80°C	80°C	180°C	180°C	180°C	180°C
Dielectric rating						
Impulse	95 Kv	95 Kv	50 Kv	95 Kv	95 Kv	50 Kv
Applied	34 Kv	34 Kv	31 Kv	34 Kv	34 Kv	31 Kv
Induced	27.6 Kv	27.6 Kv	27.6 Kv	27.6 Kv	27.6 Kv	27.6 Kv
Losses						
No load	100%	100%	160%	160%	120%	120%
Total	100%	100%	130%	170%	110%	110%
Sound (dB)	60	60	65	65	64	64
Weight	100%	105%	98%	100%	166%	180%
Dimensions						
Floor space	100%	100%	110%	110%	123%	135%
Height	100%	110%	112%	112%	130%	140%
Application						
Indoors	Yes	Yes	Yes	Yes	Yes	Yes
Outdoors	Yes	Yes	Limited	Limited	Yes	Yes
Resistant to						
Fire	No	Yes‡	Yes	Yes	Yes	Yes
Explosion	No	Yes‡	Yes	Yes	Yes	Yes
Environmental contamination	Yes	Yes	Yes	Yes	Yes	Yes
Maintenance	Medium	Medium	High	High	Low	Low
Cost	100%	140%	125%	138%	200%	235%

* Values stated are approximate average and subject to variation with Kva size, Kv rating, etc.
‡ Subject to interpretation of published data.

Courtesy of I-T-E Transformer Div., Gould Inc.

TABLE 17 TYPICAL LIQUID PROPERTIES

	Oil	Askarel	Silicone
Dielectric			
Dielectric strength kv (ASTM D-877)	30+	30+	30+
Dielectric constant	2.2	4.3	2.7
Power factor (%)	.02	1.2	0.6
Volume resistivity (ASTM D-1169)	1.0	0.5	1,000
(Ohm-cm × 10^{12})			
Thermal			
Flash point °C	160	—	285
Fire point °C	173	—	342
Pour point °C	− 57	− 37	− 55
Relative thermal conductivity 25°C	1.0	1.0	1.3
Specific heat (cal/gm/°C 25°C)	.503	.263	.340
Coefficient of expansion (cc/cc °C)	.00086	.0007	.00104
Physical			
Weight (lb/gal)	7.5	11.5	8
Interfacial tension (dyne/cm)	46	50	31
Viscosity (centistokes)			
25°C	16	15	50
50°C	7	8	30
100°C	2	3	16
150°C	—	2	12
Flammability rating	10-20	2-3	4-5

Courtesy I-T-E Transformer Div., Gould Inc.

cally acceptable for transformer insulation:

- The environmental restrictions and phasing out of transformer Askarels.
- Today's shortage of acceptable hydrocarbon-based oils.
- The narrowing cost differential between Askarels and silicone liquids.

A word of caution: Until silicone-filled transformers are fully accepted by the National Electrical Code, and full approval is forthcoming from insurance companies, engineers should recognize that there may be an element of risk in placing silicone-filled transformers in hazardous locations. It is the sole responsibility of the purchaser to install and operate the transformer safely and to obtain local code approval as well as insurance coverage for each installation.

Specifying dry-type transformers

The pros and cons of dry-type transformers against liquid-filled ones were discussed in section 5.2. Since dry-type transformers are air insulated, there are no liquids to handle, no gas vents required, no catch basins needed, no drains, no gauges or valves to maintain, no gaskets to repair or replace, and no expensive reconditioning of coolants. In addition, dry-type are non-explosive, nonflammable and ecologically safe.

Dry-types can be built to meet the needs of practically any transformer application for the utility, manufacturing or construction industries. They have proved their reliability in a wide variety of distribution and power substations, such as pulp and paper mills, aluminum mills, nuclear generating stations, textile plants, hi-rise buildings and offshore drilling rigs.

The open dry-type transformer is one of the lower-first-cost, fireproof units available. The 300-1,000 kva-5kv open dry-type transformer is also the lightest transformer available, which makes it well suited for applications where floor loading is critical and space at a premium. The addition of fan cooling increases kva rating $33^{1/3}$ percent without any increase in the transformer's dimensions. Dry-type transformers are manufactured in sizes up to 750 kva in single-phase and 10,000 kva in 3-phase units.

The limitation of the open dry-type unit is its lower BIL rating, but this can be overcome by surge protective equipment (lightning arresters) or by special high-voltage BIL manufacturing. Dry types are suitable for indoor installation in reasonably clean and dry locations, require 'lower installa-

tion and maintenance cost and, because they are nonflammable, are subject to lower insurance rates.

Here is a specification guide for different types of dry-type transformers.

A. Part of specification common to all types of dry-type transformers
1.0 Scope
This specification with the associated sketches and requisition covers the design testing and furnishing of dry-type transformers complete with all equipment and devices as specified hereinafter.

2.0 Codes and standards
All materials and equipment shall be in accordance with the latest editions of the following codes and standards:

a. Institute of Electrical Engineers

For the time being, silicone fluid appears the best compromise replacement for PCB's

---

(IEEE)

b. American National Standards Institute (ANSI)

c. National Electrical Manufacturers Assn. (NEMA)

d. Occupational Safety and Health Act (OSHA)

e. National Electrical Code (NEC)

f. State and local codes

g. Underwriters Laboratory (UL)

h. Environmental Protection Agency (EPA)

3.0 General
3.1 Unless shown otherwise on sketches, transformer shall be of the two-winding design with delta-connected primary and wye-connected secondary.

3.2 Transformer neutral shall be brought out to a bushing at the throat connection of the low-voltage side.

3.3 All electrical characteristics, such as voltage, frequency, ratio of transformation, cooling data and accessories, shall be as shown in sketches and requisition.

3.4 Bushing location shall be as shown in sketches. Primary and secondary bushing compartments (throat connection if required) shall be furnished to make possible the connection of primary disconnect switch and/or secondary switchgear or bus to form an integral unit.

3.5 If part of a unit substation, the transformer shall be arranged to permit

mounting in either left-hand or right-hand arrangement.

4.0 Construction
4.1 Transformer shall have provisions to facilitate moving and maintenance as follows:

a. Structural steel base with jack-step skids to allow movement in either direction.

b. Pulling eyes.

c. Lifting lugs for transformer lifting.

d. Possibility to expose core and coils in field for repair purposes.

e. Handhole in cover of minimum 18-in. dia for access to interior of tank.

4.2 High-voltage terminal compartment

a. High-voltage section shall consist of a terminal compartment with the transformer case for (cable) or (bus) entrance.

b. Terminal connectors shall be located so as to allow sufficient space for stress cones.

c. Sufficient barriers shall be provided between H.V. terminal compartments and the transformer to prevent the temperature surrounding the cable from exceeding NEMA standards.

4.3 High-voltage lead facilities

Provision shall be made for connecting the transformer case directly to a high-voltage switch housing or other H.V. switchgear and also the H.V. leads to this equipment.

4.4 Low-voltage lead facilities

Provision shall be made for connecting transformer to a low-voltage switchgear housing and leads as shown in sketches.

5.0 Controls
5.1 All controls and wiring, including alarms, shall be brought out to terminal blocks in a control enclosure easily accessible.

5.2 Tagging of wiring and terminal strips shall be provided for testing and circuit identification.

5.3 Plates requiring field drilling shall be removable.

5.4 All wiring shall be THHN-THWN not smaller than No. 14 AWG and shall be run in galvanized steel conduit outside the control panel.

6.0 Inspection and testing
6.1 The transformer shall be completely assembled, wired and tested by manufacturer at his factory.

6.2 Factory tests shall be in accordance with latest ANSI and NEMA TR-27 standards as follows:

a. Resistance measurements of all windings.

b. Ratio test at rated voltage and all tap connections.

c. Polarity and phase-relation tests at rated voltage connection.

d. No load loss at rated voltage.

e. Excitation loss and current.

f. Impedance and load loss at 25, 50, 75 and 100% rated current on rated voltage connections.

g. Temperature tests. For transformers with auxiliary cooling equipment providing more than one rating, temperature tests shall be provided at each rating.

h. Applied potential tests.

i. Induced potential tests.

j. Impulse tests on all terminals.

7.0 Manufacturer's drawings

7.1 Outline dimensional drawings and weights shall be furnished showing overall dimensions, base details, location and arrangement of H.V. and L.V. bushings or leads, control cabinets, etc.

7.2 Manufacturer's drawings and operating and maintenance instruction manuals shall be in accordance with terms and conditions for purchase-forming part of these specifications.

7.3 Wiring diagrams shall be furnished showing all controls and alarms.

8.0 Identifications

8.1 Identification shall consist of marking on a nameplate the purchase order number, specification number and item or tag number.

8.2 Manufacturer's model and serial numbers shall be included where applicable.

9.0 Warranty and performance guarantees

9.1 Manufacturer shall guarantee that equipment will meet performance requirements as stated in this specification.

9.2 The cost of energy losses during the life of the equipment will be considered by evaluating bids by the purchaser.

(A sketch forming part of the specification should show outlines of transformer, location of high- and low-voltage bushings and terminal compartments, sizes and top or bottom entry of high- and low-voltage busduct or cable and conduit, or close-throat connection with eventual switchgear.

B. Specification addition for ventilated dry-type transformer

The indoor (outdoor), standard or (tamper-resistant) transformer shall be rated as follows:

____kva, ____phase, ____Hertz, ventilated dry type, ____°C rise, 220°C insulation system (complete with fans for increased rating to ____kva).

HV: ____volts, 3-wire, with plus two 2¹/₂%, and minus two 2¹/₂% de-energized full-capacity taps, delta-connected, ____BIL.

LV: ____volts, 4-wire, (z-wire) wye (delta)-connected, ____BIL.

High-voltage taps

Tap leads shall be terminated at the coils and equipped with provisions for changing taps.

Insulation

The transformer shall be of non-explosive, fire-resistant, air-insulated, dry-type construction, cooled by the natural circulation of air through the windings. Solid insulation in the transformer will consist of inorganic materials, such as porcelain or glass roving, in combination with a sufficient quantity of high-temperature binder to impart the necessary mechanical strength to the insulation structure.

Case

For ease in fitting through limited openings, the knockdown case shall be

---

Standard maintenance developed for Askarels should also apply for silicone transformers

---

of 13-gage sheet-steel construction and equipped with removable panels with ornamental ventilating grills for access to the core and coils on the front and rear. A bolted cover section shall be supplied for access to the core and coil lifting loops for lifting the complete assembly.

Paint finish

The case shall be phosphatized. The color shall be light gray ANSI No. 61 (indoor) or dark gray ANSI No. 24 (outdoor).

Lightning arresters

Three low-ratio lightning arresters shall be mounted in the transformer case and connected to the high-voltage leads, for use on a ____-kv grounded (ungrounded) system.

Impedance

The impedance of the transformer at normal rating and frequency will be manufacturer's standard ± 7¹/₂% tolerance.

Sound level

The transformer shall be designed to meet the standard NEMA sound levels.

Accessories shall include the following:

Diagram instruction plate.

Provision for lighting and jacking.

Removable case panel for access to high-voltage taps.

Drip-proof cover.

Ground pad.

All manufacturer's standard accessories.

Standard tests

As listed in common specification for all dry-type transformers.

C. Specification addition for totally enclosed nonventilated dry-type transformer.

All instructions are the same as those for ventilated dry-type transformers, except for the following:

Case

For ease in fitting through limited openings, the knockdown case shall be of 13-gage sheet steel construction and equipped with removable panels on the front and rear for access to the core and coils. The case shall totally enclose the core and coils and be semi-dust-tight. A bolted cover section shall be supplied for access to the core and coil lifting loops for lifting the complete assembly.

D. Specification addition for gas-filled, sealed, dry-type transformer

The rating, sound-level and impedance instructions are the same as those for ventilated dry-type transformers.

Sealed tank

The transformer shall be of sealed-tank construction to prevent breathing. Tank shall be hermetically sealed with metallic seals throughout and tested at 15-psi pressure. It shall be provided with welded-on ¹/₄-in. thick Yukon coolers.

Shot blast

The case and coolers shall be cleaned by shot blast and phosphatized before the paint is applied.

Finish

Paint finish shall be manufacturer's standard, applied over a properly prepared surface. The color shall be light gray ANSI No. 61 (indoor) or dark gray ANSI No. 24 (outdoor).

Insulation

The transformer shall be of non-explosive, fire-resistant, flourocarbon-insulated, dry-type construction, cooled by the natural circulation of fluorocarbon through the windings. Solid insulation in the transformer shall consist of inorganic materials, such as porcelain or glass roving, in combination with a sufficient quantity of high-temperature binder to impart the necessary mechanical strength to the insulation structure. The transformer shall be insulated and cooled with C_2F_6 fluorocarbon gas. It shall be shipped filled with this C_2F_6 gas to a gauge pressure of approximately 1¹/₂ psi at 25°C ambient.

Bushings

The transformer shall be equipped

with rolled-flange, inert, arc-welded bushings for the H.V. and L.V. connections to ensure that the tank is hermetically sealed.

Accessories shall include the following:

I-beam base for rolling in any direction.

Cover shall be welded to the tank flange.

Yukon cooler 1/4-in. thick.

Lifting hooks—4 total.

Jack pads—4 total.

Vacuum pressure guage.

Dial-type gas thermometer with alarm contact.

3/4-inch filling plug—2 total.

Diagram nameplate.

Welded handhole cover for access to H.V. and L.V. bushings.

De-energized tap changer, externally operated.

Ground pad.

Welded-on main tank cover.

All manufacturer's standard accessories.

Tests

The following tests shall be performed in accordance with NEMA TR-27:

Resistance measurements of all windings.

Ratio test at rated voltage and all tap connections.

Polarity and phase-relation tests at rated connection.

Excitation loss.

Excitation current.

Impedance and load loss at 25, 50, 75 and 100% of rated current on rated voltage connections.

Temperature test shall be made on one unit only of an order covering one or more units of a given rating if essentially duplicate data is not available.

Applied potential tests.

Induced potential tests.

Summary

A wide selection of transformers certainly exist: liquid filled with oil or silicone fluid, dry-type ventilated, totally enclosed, nonventilated, gas filled with fluorocarbon or nitrogen, etc. Based on the advantages and disadvantages of each type, as discussed in sections 5.1-5.4, the engineer can select the proper unit for any of the varied applications encountered in the industrial and commercial areas by applying sound engineering judgement. The tables shown in these sections comparing the various characteristics of different types of transformers will help in selecting the proper type of transformer for each particular application.

Section 5.4 discussed the use of silicone liquid to replace Askarel, other alternatives, and how to specify different dry-type transformers. The following, section 5.5, discusses transformer paralleling and its relation to polarity, phase rotation, angular displacement and voltage diagrams. Tables and figures are numbered chronologically.

Transformer paralleling in industrial plants is often required because of increases in power demand beyond the capacity of an existing transformer. Conversely, when power demand is temporarily reduced, it is sometimes more economical to operate one smaller transformer close to its full kva capacity rather than one large transformer at reduced capacity. In such cases of fluctuating demand, two or more transformers in parallel may be better than one large transformer. The system is more flexible because it has the ability to shed or add part of the paralleled transformers as needed.

Transformers are sometimes paralleled when reliability and continuity considerations are more important than economical ones, as shown in Figure 11. Here two transformers are continuously paralleled, if one transformer fails, the other one continues to supply load without any interruption. Each transformer's kva rating has to satisfy all the load demand, and when both transformers are operating, each operates at almost half load.

Two single-phase transformers operate in parallel if they are connected with the same polarity. Two 3-phase transformers operate in parallel if they have the same winding arrangement (i.e., wye-delta), are connected with the same polarity, have the same phase rotation and their angular displacement is the same.

Voltage diagrams of the two transformers to be paralleled must coincide. Of course, the two transformers must be of similar impedance, voltage rating and frequency. The load current division in proportion to the kva ratings of paralleled transformers is conditioned by their having the same voltage rating, turn ratios, percentage impedances and reactance to resistance ratios.

If these conditions are not met, the load currents may not divide in proportion to the kva ratings of the two paralleled transformers and a phase difference may occur between currents.

Transformers sometimes parallel when reliability considerations are great

rents. To make the application of paralleling transformers intelligible, an understanding of polarity, phase rotation, angular displacement and voltage diagram is necessary.

Polarity

Transformer windings are marked to show polarity and also to designate high and low voltage. For the purpose of terminal marking, "primary" and "secondary" are meaningless because these terms depend on the input and output connections. Usually high-voltage leads are marked with H1, H2 and H3; low-voltage windings are marked with X1, X2 and X3 in a 3-winding transformer.

In addition, terminals are numbered to indicate direction of induced voltage. If a high-voltage winding is marked H1-H2 and the secondary winding is marked X1-X2, the voltage in each winding is induced in such a manner as if the voltage at H1 is positive with respect to H2, and the voltage induced at X1 is positive with respect to X2.

National Electrical Manufacturers Assn. Standard 9-17-1941 defines lead polarity as a designation of the relative instantaneous directions of the currents in the transformer leads. Primary and secondary leads have the same polarity when, at a given instant, the current enters the primary lead and leaves the secondary lead in the same direction as though the two leads formed a continuous circuit.

The terms additive and subtractive polarity pertain when viewing the transformer terminals from only one side of the transformer tank. The direction of induced voltage is assumed in all cases to be from the lower-numbered terminal to the higher. In Figure 12a, H1 and X1 are both on the left when viewing the terminals from one side of the transformer.

In Figure 12b, H1 and X2 are both on the left. If a lead would be connected from H1 to the adjacent low-voltage lead X1 in the former example, the voltage across the remaining leads X2 to H2 would be the difference of two voltages and thus subtractive. In the same manner, the polarity is additive in the latter instance where the voltage from H2 to X1 is the sum of the voltages when H1 is connected to X2.

NEMA Standard 9-17-1941 defines the lead polarity of single-phase transformers as follows: if one pair of adjacent leads from the two windings in question is connected together and voltage is applied to one winding, then the lead polarity is additive if the voltage across the other two leads of the winding is greater than that of the higher-voltage winding alone. The lead polarity is subtractive if the voltage across the other two leads of the winding in question is less than that of the higher-voltage winding alone (see Figures 12c and 12d).

The polarity of a 3-phase transformer is defined by NEMA by the internal connections between phases as well as by the relative location of leads. It is usually designated by means of a voltage vector diagram showing the angular displacements of windings and a sketch showing the lead markings. The vectors represent the induced voltages, and its recognized

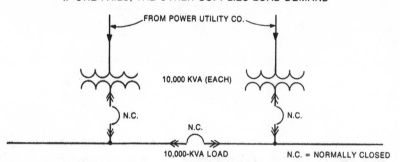

FIGURE 11   TWO TRANSFORMERS PARALLELED—
IF ONE FAILS, THE OTHER SUPPLIES LOAD DEMAND

← FROM POWER UTILITY CO. →

10,000 KVA (EACH)

N.C.   N.C.

N.C.

10,000-KVA LOAD   N.C. = NORMALLY CLOSED

FIGURE 12a   SUBTRACTIVE POLARITY WINDING
ARRANGEMENT OF SINGLE-PHASE TRANSFORMER

FIGURE 12b   ADDITIVE POLARITY WINDING
ARRANGEMENT OF SINGLE-PHASE TRANSFORMER

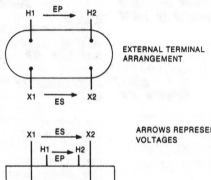

H1   EP   H2

EXTERNAL TERMINAL
ARRANGEMENT

X1   ES   X2

ARROWS REPRESENT
VOLTAGES

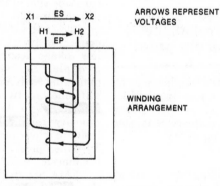

X1   ES   X2

H1   EP   H2

WINDING
ARRANGEMENT

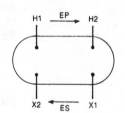

H1   EP   H2

X2   ES   X1

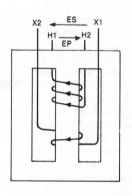

X2   ES   X1

H1   EP   H2

FIGURE 12c   SUBTRACTIVE POLARITY TEST
$E = E1 - E2$ VOLTS

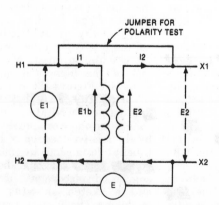

JUMPER FOR
POLARITY TEST

H1   I1   I2   X1

E1   E1b   E2   E2

H2   X2

E

FIGURE 12d   ADDITIVE POLARITY TEST
$E = E1 + E2$ VOLTS

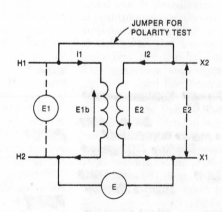

JUMPER FOR
POLARITY TEST

H1   I1   I2   X2

E1   E1b   E2   E2

H2   X1

E

counter-clockwise direction of rotation is used. The vector that represents any phase voltage of a given winding is drawn parallel to the corresponding phase voltage of any other winding under consideration.

In single-phase transformers the primary and secondary voltages are either in phase or in opposition, defined by the polarity or the marking of the leads. In 3-phase transformers or banks of three single-phase transformers, the vector relationships are more complicated and are represented by voltage diagrams. The mere lettering of the leads does not indicate the polarity. In polyphase connections, polarity alone is inadequate to represent true vector relationships. Only by voltage diagrams can vector relationships be adequately understood.

Construction of voltage diagrams

Voltage diagrams for 3-phase transformers are best explained by an example:

The main 3-phase connections commonly used are wye-delta, delta-wye, delta-delta and wye-wye.

Figure 13 shows a wye-delta-connected 3-phase transformer. Figure 13b represents the induced voltages of the wye-connected winding. The voltage diagram of the delta-connected winding is drawn as follows:

Coils X1-X2 and H-N (see Figure 13a) are wound in the same direction, as their induced voltages. Draw X1-X2 (see Figure 13b) parallel to and in the same direction as H1-N. On the middle leg (Figure 13a), coil X2-X3 is wound in the same direction as H2-N; therefore, their respective voltages are drawn parallel and in the same direction as shown in Figure 13b. Use a similar procedure for the third phase and the diagram is completed.

If the delta were improperly connected in Figure 13a, the delta in Figure 13b would not close, showing an unbalanced voltage short-circuited through the delta. Inspecting Figures 13a and 13b shows that the connection has subtractive polarity, 30 deg angular displacement and standard phase rotation. The angular displacement is defined by NEMA 11-12-1953 as the time angle between lines drawn from neutral to H1 and X1. Angular displacement is also called phase relation.

"Phase rotation" refers to a perfectly definite order in which the leads are to be considered. In Figure 13b, phase rotation is clockwise in the order H1-H2-H3, but counterclockwise in

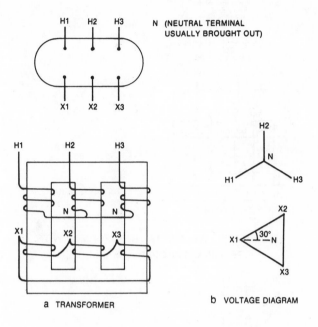

a TRANSFORMER

b VOLTAGE DIAGRAM

FIGURE 14   WYE-DELTA 3-PHASE TRANSFORMER WITH ADDITIVE POLARITY, 30 DEGREES ANGULAR DISPLACEMENT

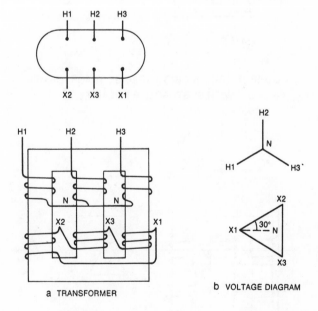

a TRANSFORMER

b VOLTAGE DIAGRAM

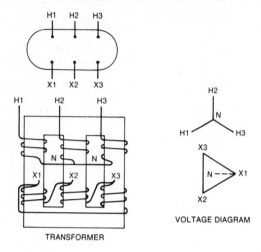

FIGURE 15a WYE-DELTA 3-PHASE TRANSFORMER WITH
TERMINALS IMPROPERLY MARKED

VOLTAGE DIAGRAM

TRANSFORMER

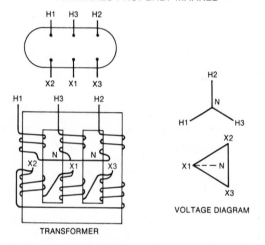

FIGURE 15b WYE-DELTA TRANSFORMER WITH
TERMINALS PROPERLY MARKED

VOLTAGE DIAGRAM

TRANSFORMER

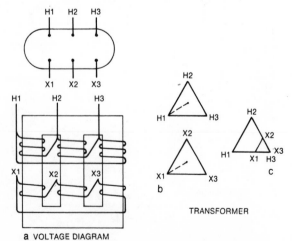

FIGURE 16 DELTA-DELTA 3-PHASE TRANSFORMER
WITH SUBTRACTIVE POLARITY

a VOLTAGE DIAGRAM

TRANSFORMER

the order H2-H1-H3. The phase rotations of H1-H2-H3 and X1-X2-X3 are the same, but those of H1-H2-H3 and X3-X2-X1 are opposed. Remembering the necessity of specifying the order of leads, the standardization rules specify that leads shall be marked so that the phase rotation of high- and low-voltages in the lead order H1-H2-H3 and X1-X2-X3 shall be the same.

If a 3-phase motor is transferred from the high- to low-voltage circuit by transferring its terminals from H1 to X1, H2 to X2 and H3 to X3, its rotating direction is the same.

Figures 14a and 14b have additive polarity, 30 deg angular displacement and standard-phase rotation. The voltage diagrams of Figures 13a, 13b, 14a, 14b, 14c and 14d are identical, but the lettering of the leads is different because of different internal arrangements. Different lead lettering is equivalent to interchanging the leads, because similarly-lettered leads are connected for multiple operation.

By interchanging leads, identical voltage diagrams are obtained on wye-delta transformers with different internal arrangements. All wye-delta or delta-wye connections can be reduced to the same diagram by properly selecting the order of the leads. This is not possible with delta-delta or wye-wye connections.

To prove the point, construct the voltage diagram for the connections shown in Figure 15a, which will be similar to Figure 15b. Interchange two leads on the high side, H3 with H2, and two on the low side, X1 with X2 (see Figure 15c). The voltage diagram in Figure 15d shows that it is identical in form and lettering to Figures 13b, 14b and 14d and proves that all wye-delta or delta-wye connections can be reduced to the same diagram by properly selecting the lead sequence.

Delta-delta connection diagrams are shown in Figures 16a, b, c and 17a, b, c. Trying all possible delta combinations in the high- and low-voltage coils shows that only two diagrams can be operative (see Figures 16a, b and c and Figures 17a, b and c).

The polarity of Figure 16 is subtractive and that of Figure 17 is additive. Phase rotation of high- and low-voltages of these connections must be referred to a perfectly definite order in which the leads must be considered. In Figure 16b the phase rotation is clockwise in the order H1-H2-H3, but counterclockwise in the order H2-H1-H3. The phase rotations of H1-H2-H3 and X1-X2-X3 are the same but those of H1-H2-H3 and X3-X2-X1 are opposed. The necessity of specifying the order of leads is standardized and provides that the leads shall be marked so the phase rotation of high- and low-voltage in the lead order H1-H2-H3 and X1-X2-X3 shall be the same.

In Figure 16b, H1-H2-H3 and X1-X2-X3 have the same rotation and therefore the correct phase rotation. In Figure 17b the phase rotations H1-H2-H3 and X1-X2-X3 are the same and are also correct. While Figure 16b and 17b have opposite polarities and different angular displacements, they have the same phase rotation.

Voltage diagrams indicate only the relative phase rotation of primary and secondary windings and do not offer any information regarding the actual phase rotation on either side, this being determined by the supply circuit. Changing the lettering or interchanging the leads (leaving coil connections unchanged) cannot alter the voltage diagrams of Figures 16 and 17. The transformer in Figure 16a cannot give the diagram of Figure 17b by manipulating its external leads. Only by changing the internal connections of the coils can this be done. With delta-delta-connected transformers the lead lettering is the same

regardless of the angular displacement (see Figures 16a and 17a).

Wye-wye connecting diagrams are shown in Figures 18a, b and 19a, b. Constructing voltage diagrams for wye-wye connected transformers is the same as that described for the wye-delta transformer. Figures 18b and 19b show that only two connections are possible. The first has subtractive polarity, zero-phase displacement and standard-phase rotation. The second has additive polarity, 180 deg angular displacement and standard-phase rotation. No manipulation of external leads can change the diagrams, though it may change the order of lettering for the voltage diagrams.

Figures 18a and 19a show that with wye-wye-connected transformers, the lettering of the leads is the same regardless of the angular displacement.

Obtaining diagrams by test

All the voltage diagrams described were based on a given design. If the design is unknown, the coils and connections inaccessible, and no vector diagrams are furnished, voltage diagrams can be obtained by test.

Voltage diagrams can be determined by the following method, neglecting the polarity and phase-rotation tests:

connect a high- and low-voltage lead and excite the transformer with a voltage that is safe for the low-voltage circuit. Measure the voltage between all other high- and low-voltage leads and plot them to scale.

If the same test is applied to wye-wye connected transformer of the same polarity (Figures 18a and 19a), diagrams similar to Figures 16c and 17c would be obtained. Using such tests it would be impossible to determine whether the internal connection of the transformer is delta-delta or wye-wye, but this distinction is unnecessary so far as parallel operation is concerned.

The test indicates the angular displacement between high- and low-voltage circuits but does not distinguish between connections that belong to the same group—i.e., connections that will successfully parallel transformers with each other. With very small low voltages, obtaining voltage diagrams by such measurements becomes difficult.

FIGURE 17   DELTA-DELTA 3-PHASE
TRANSFORMER WITH
ADDITIVE POLARITY

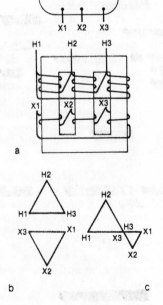

FIGURE 18   WYE-WYE 3-PHASE
TRANSFORMER WITH
SUBTRACTIVE POLARITY,
ZERO PHASE DISPLACEMENT

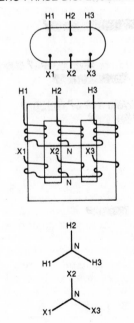

FIGURE 19   WYE-WYE 3-PHASE
TRANSFORMER WITH
ADDITIVE POLARITY, 180 DEGREE
ANGULAR DISPLACEMENT

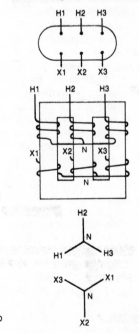

5.6 Transformers Operating in Parallel Must Have the Same Vector Relationship, Equal Turn Ratios, and Similar Impedance

Section 5.5 discussed polarity, phase rotation, angular displacement and voltage vector diagrams of transformers. This sixth and last section 5.6 discusses conditions for proper parallel operation of transformers based on polarity, phase rotation, angular displacement, voltage diagrams and NEMA as well as ANSI Standards.

Single-phase transformers connected in parallel have a common voltage impressed on the primary winding and a resultant common voltage on the secondary winding. The internal impedance drop is given by the phasor difference between the impressed high voltage divided by the turns ratio and the terminal low voltage. It follows logically that the impedance drop of two transformers connected in parallel must be identical.

As shown in Figure 20, E_1 is the phasor representing the terminal high voltage, E_2 (reduced to equivalent high voltage by multiplying by turns ratio) is the phasor representing the terminal low voltage, and (vectorially) $E_1 - E_2 = IZ$ is the impedance drop that is common to both. Consequently, under any load condition, the current will be divided such that the product of current and the impedance in one of the transformers equals the product of current and impedance in the other. It is evident, that if the transformers are not equal in all respects, from the fact that the terminal high and low voltages are identical, a constant circulating current must flow between the transformers, even at no load conditions.

For a suitable parallel operation and a load division in proportion to transformer capacities, the ratio of turns and the voltage ratings of both transformers must be identical, their per-unit impedance equal and the ratio of reactance to resistance the same. Any departure from these conditions will bring about an uneconomical division of current or a circulating current that lowers the efficiency and decreases the maximum safe load the bank can carry.

Paralleling consideration

The following conditions are considered impractical for operating transformers in parallel:

• When the division of load is such that, with a total load equal to the combined kva rating, the load current

When voltage diagrams coincide, polarities and phase rotations must agree

flowing in any one of the two transformers is greater than 1.1 times its normal full-load value.*

• When the no-load circulating current in any transformer, exceeds one-tenth of the full-load rated value.

• When the mathematical sum of the circulating and load currents is greater than 1.1 times the normal full-load current.

"Circulating current" is the current flowing at no-load in the high- and low-voltage windings of paralleled transformers, exclusive of exciting current. "Load current" is the current flowing in the transformers underload, exclusive of exciting and circulating currents.

If the ratios are not the same, they may be equalized by using an autotransformer or by removing taps on the windings. Differences in the impedances may be corrected by adding external impedance to one transformer.

The polarity of single-phase transformers is an indication of direction of current flow from a terminal at any one instant, and is quite similar to the polarity marking on a battery.

Facing the high-voltage side of the transformer, the terminal on the right is always marked H_1 and the other

*As stated in ANSI "Guide for Loading Oil-Immersed Distribution and Power Transformers" appendix C57.92 (1962 Ed.) to C57.17 standards.

high-voltage terminal is marked H_2. This is standard procedure. For additive polarity, the low-voltage terminal on the right, facing the low-voltage side, should be marked X_1 and the left one marked X_2. For subtractive polarity, the low-voltage terminal on the left, facing the low-voltage side, should be marked X_1.

When making transformer connections, the polarity of individual transformers must be checked. Thus, if two transformers are to be connected in parallel, the two H_1 terminals should be connected together, then the two H_2 terminals, the two X_1 terminals, and the two X_2 terminals. By observing these connections, single-phase transformers can satisfactorily operate in parallel regardless of whether they are of the same polarity or one is additive and the other subtractive.

Polarity and other criteria

American National Standards Institute Standard 12.00-1973 states that polarity of single-phase transformers 200 kva and below having high-voltage ratings of 8,660 v and below (winding voltage) shall be additive. All other single-phase transformers shall have subtractive polarity.

It also states that the angular displacement between high- and low-voltage phase voltages of delta-delta, wye-wye, delta-zig-zag and zig-zag-delta connections shall be zero degrees. The angular displacement between high- and low-voltage phase voltages of 3-phase transformers with wye-delta and delta-wye connections shall be 30 deg with the low voltage lagging the high voltage as shown in Figure 21.

The same ANSI standard defines the angular displacement of a polyphase transformer as being the time angle expressed in degrees between the line-to-neutral voltage of the reference identified high-voltage terminal (H_1) and the line-to-neutral voltage of the corresponding identified low-voltage terminal (X_1).

The vector diagrams of any 3-phase

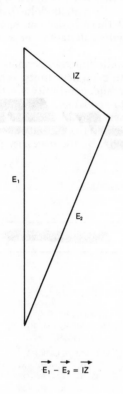

$$\vec{E_1} - \vec{E_2} = \vec{IZ}$$

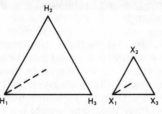

DELTA-DELTA CONNECTION

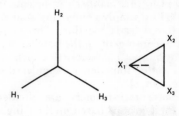

WYE-DELTA CONNECTION

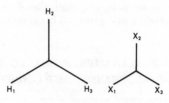

WYE-WYE CONNECTION

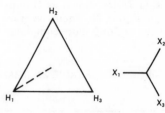

DELTA-WYE CONNECTION

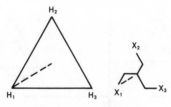

DELTA-ZIG-ZAG CONNECTION

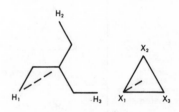

ZIG-ZAG-DELTA CONNECTION

(ANSI C57.12.00-1973)

transformers defining both the angular displacement and phase sequence can be verified by connecting the H_1 and X_1 leads together and exciting the unit with a suitable low 3-phase voltage and then taking voltage measurements between various pairs of leads. By plotting these values and comparing them for their relative order of magnitude using the corresponding diagram in Figures 22 (3-phase transformer) and 23 (3-phase transformer) as shown in NEMA Standard TR27-1974 Part 5, the typical check measurements for voltage, angular displacement and phase sequence can be verified. As in the corresponding single-phase test, the reading may not show sufficient decisive percentage differences if the ratios between the primary and secondary windings of the transformers are greater than 30 to 1.

Terminal markings of transformers must be in accordance with the 'American National Standard Terminal Markings and Connections for Distribution and Power Transformers' C 57. 12.70-1964 (Revised on 1971).

Parallel operation of 3-phase transformers is satisfactory if their polarity,

phase rotation, angular displacement and voltage rating are the same. Delta-delta and wye-wye transformers have correct angular displacement when their polarity and phase rotation are correct. This is not necessarily true for delta-wye or wye-delta transformers. However, these can be adjusted by the proper selection of the leads sequence.

If the voltage diagrams of the transformers that are to operate in parallel are available, it is then only necessary that these diagrams coincide and corresponding terminals be connected together. It is unnecessary then to raise questions of polarity and phase rotation because when the voltage diagrams coincide, leads that are to be connected together will have the same potential, this being the basic requirement for paralleling; whereas polarity, phase rotation, etc, are merely means to arrive at this condition. When voltage diagrams coincide, polarities and phase rotations must necessarily agree, although the converse of this statement is not necessarily true.

As an example, an industrial plant purchased a wye-delta transformer to operate in parallel with an existing

wye-delta transformer. In spite of the fact that the added transformer was connected in the field with its terminals H_1, H_2, H_3 and X_1, X_2, X_3, respectively, to bus phases 1, 2, 3, the transformers did not operate properly in parallel. Motors on the low-voltage sides were rotating in opposite directions. Drawing the voltage vector diagrams shown in Figure 24, it was apparent that the way the added transformer was connected (B), the vector diagram on the delta side was not the same as that of the existing transformer. By interchanging the terminal markings H_1 and H_3 on the delta side of the added transformer (C), the same voltage diagram is achieved for both transformers and connecting as such, brings them to operate satisfactorily in parallel, with all motors on the low-voltage sides rotating in the same direction.

Standardized connections

To simplify the connections of transformers in parallel and to avoid the necessity of testing polarity, phase rotation, etc., ANSI C 57.12.70-1964 (R-1971) has standardized the marking and connections for distribution and power transformers. Transformers marked in this manner can operate in parallel by simply connecting similarly lettered leads together. This is, of course, contingent on the transformers having proper characteristics such as turns ratio, impedance, angular displacement, etc.

3-phase transformers are divided into three groups based on their angular displacement, as shown in Figure 25. Four of the usual 3-phase to 6-phase diagrams are shown as Groups IV and V, in Figure 26. Their construction involves nothing more complicated than the method indicated for 3-phase to 3-phase connections.

To operate in parallel, the transformers must belong to the same group. No interchange of external leads can change one group into another one. Thus, two delta-delta transformers, one belonging to Group I and the other to Group II cannot operate in parallel. If the high-voltage diagrams of these transformers were superimposed, the low-voltage diagrams would not coincide. All wye-delta or delta-wye transformers, however, can be reduced to the same diagram, and therefore are classed in one group. This is achieved by having the secondary voltages reversed, if the turns ratios are such as to make the voltages equal as seen in Figure 24. A wye-wye bank can operate in parallel with a similar wye-wye bank or with a delta-delta bank but neither of these banks can operate in parallel with a delta-wye or wye-delta bank.

For paralleling transformers in either existing or new units, economy, reliability and continuity are the key factors to consider. Paralleling of transformers may be required by load growth beyond the capacity of existing transformers, by the necessity of hav-

FIGURE 22   TRANSFORMER LEAD MARKINGS AND VOLTAGE VECTOR-DIAGRAMS
FOR 3-PHASE TRANSFORMER CONNECTIONS

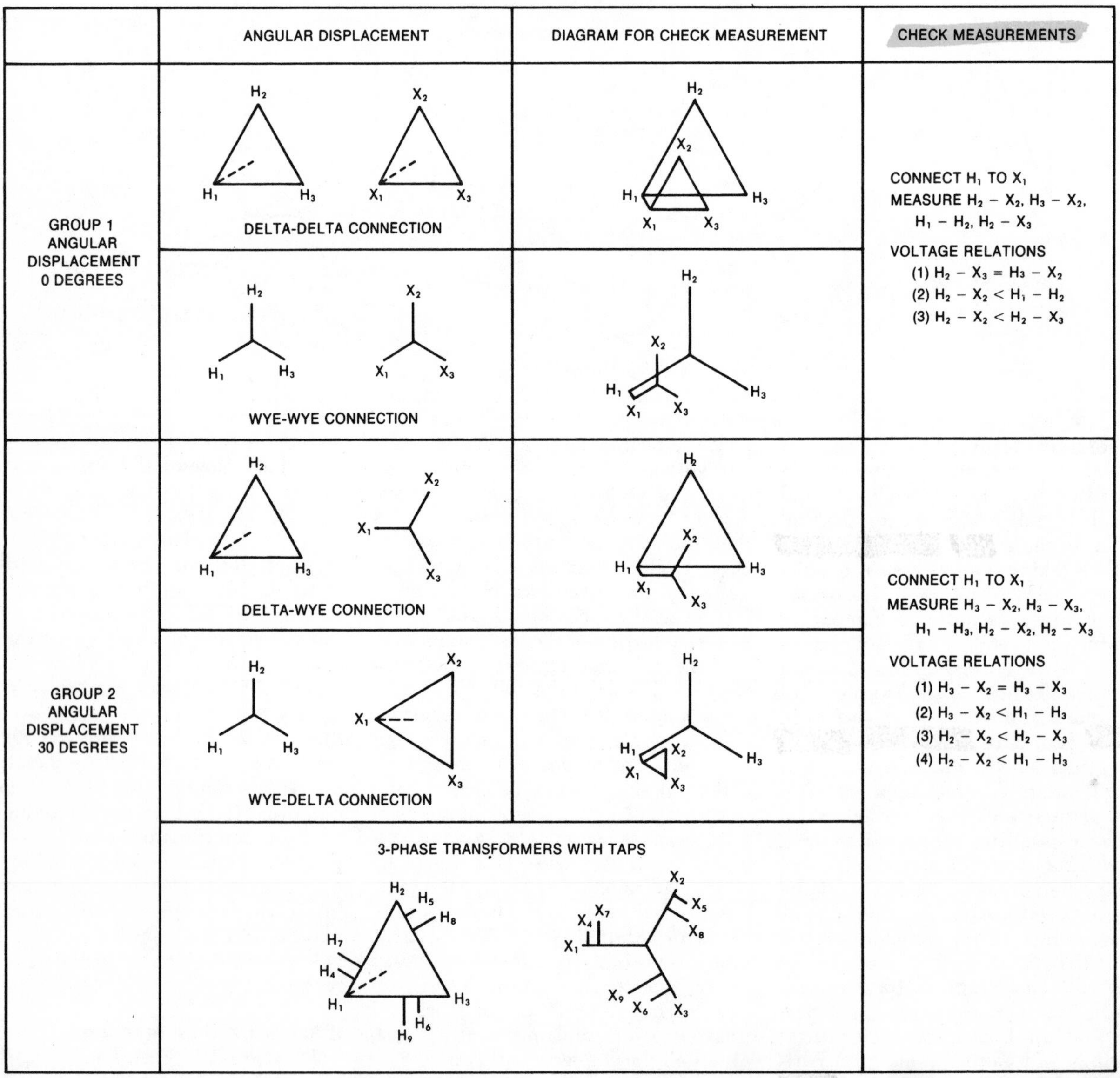

	ANGULAR DISPLACEMENT	DIAGRAM FOR CHECK MEASUREMENT	CHECK MEASUREMENTS
GROUP 1 ANGULAR DISPLACEMENT 0 DEGREES	DELTA-DELTA CONNECTION / WYE-WYE CONNECTION		CONNECT H_1 TO X_1 MEASURE $H_2 - X_2$, $H_3 - X_2$, $H_1 - H_2$, $H_2 - X_3$ VOLTAGE RELATIONS (1) $H_2 - X_3 = H_3 - X_2$ (2) $H_2 - X_2 < H_1 - H_2$ (3) $H_2 - X_2 < H_2 - X_3$
GROUP 2 ANGULAR DISPLACEMENT 30 DEGREES	DELTA-WYE CONNECTION / WYE-DELTA CONNECTION / 3-PHASE TRANSFORMERS WITH TAPS		CONNECT H_1 TO X_1 MEASURE $H_3 - X_2$, $H_3 - X_3$, $H_1 - H_3$, $H_2 - X_2$, $H_2 - X_3$ VOLTAGE RELATIONS (1) $H_3 - X_2 = H_3 - X_3$ (2) $H_3 - X_2 < H_1 - H_3$ (3) $H_2 - X_2 < H_2 - X_3$ (4) $H_2 - X_2 < H_1 - H_3$

(ANSI TR 27-5.04)

154

FIGURE 23 TRANSFORMER LEAD MARKINGS AND VOLTAGE-VECTOR DIAGRAMS
FOR 6-PHASE TRANSFORMER CORRECTIONS

	ANGULAR DISPLACEMENT	DIAGRAM FOR CHECK MEASUREMENT	CHECK MEASUREMENTS
GROUP 1 ANGULAR DISPLACEMENT 0 DEGREES	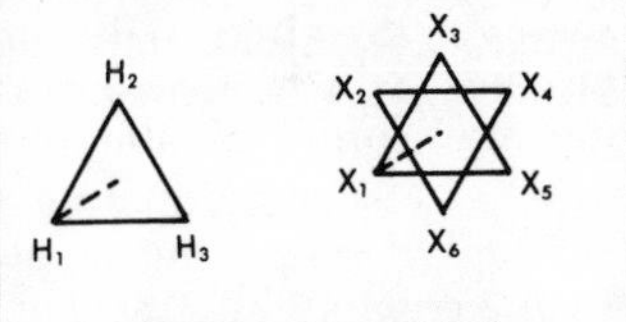 DELTA-DOUBLE DELTA	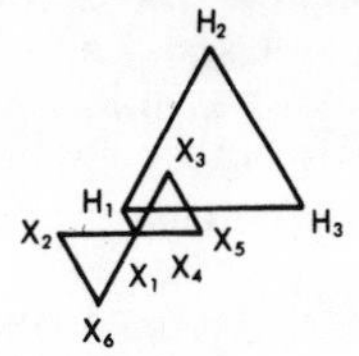	CONNECT H_1 TO X_1 TO X_4 MEASURE $H_2 - X_3$, $H_1 - H_2$, $H_2 - X_5$, $H_2 - X_6$, $H_3 - X_2$, $H_2 - X_2$, $H_3 - X_3$ VOLTAGE RELATIONS (1) $H_2 - X_5 = H_3 - X_3$ (4) $H_2 - X_6 = H_3 - X_2$ (2) $H_2 - X_3 < H_1 - H_2$ (5) $H_2 - X_6 > H_1 - H_2$ (3) $H_2 - X_3 < H_2 - X_5$ (6) $H_2 - X_2 < H_1 - X_6$
GROUP 2 ANGULAR DISPLACEMENT 30 DEGREES	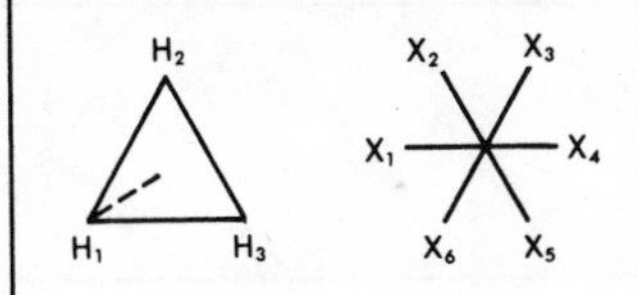 DELTA DIAM	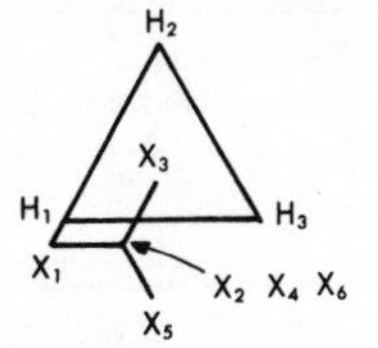	CONNECT X_2 TO X_4 TO X_6 H_1 TO X_1 MEASURE $H_3 - X_3$, $H_3 - X_5$, $H_1 - H_3$, $H_2 - X_3$, $H_2 - X_5$ VOLTAGE RELATIONS (1) $H_3 - X_3 = H_3 - X_5$ (2) $H_3 - X_3 < H_1 - H_3$ (3) $H_2 - X_3 < H_2 - X_5$
	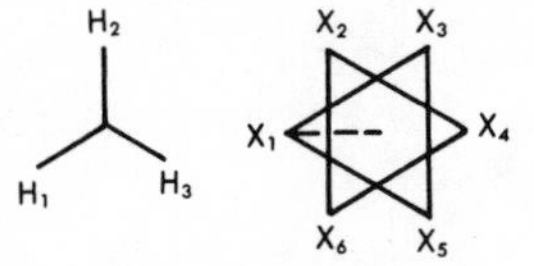 WYE-DOUBLE DELTA	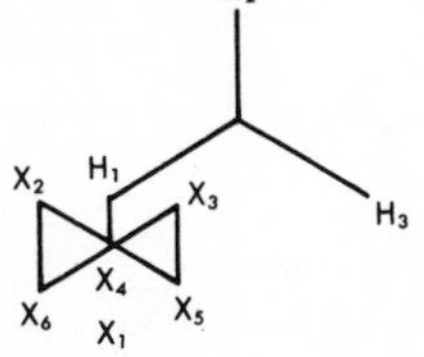	CONNECT H_1 TO X_1 TO X_4 MEASURE $H_3 - X_3$, $H_3 - X_5$, $H_1 - H_3$, $H_2 - X_3$, $H_2 - X_5$, $H_3 - X_2$, $H_3 - X_6$, $H_2 - X_2$, $H_2 - X_6$ VOLTAGE RELATIONS (1) $H_3 - X_3 = H_3 - X_5$ (2) $H_3 - X_3 < H_1 - H_3$ (3) $H_2 - X_3 < H_2 - X_5$ (4) $H_3 - X_2 = H_3 - X_6$ (5) $H_3 - X_2 > H_1 - H_3$ (6) $H_2 - X_2 < H_2 - X_6$

6-PHASE TRANSFORMER WITH TAPS

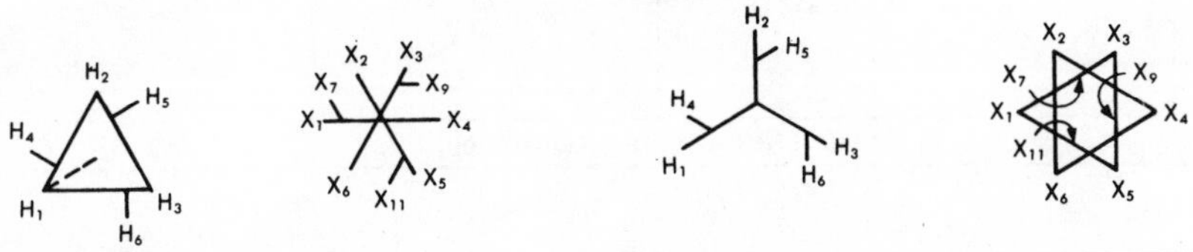

(ANSI TR 27-5.04)

FIGURE 24 INCORRECT AND CORRECT CONNECTIONS FOR PARALLEL OPERATION OF TRANSFORMERS

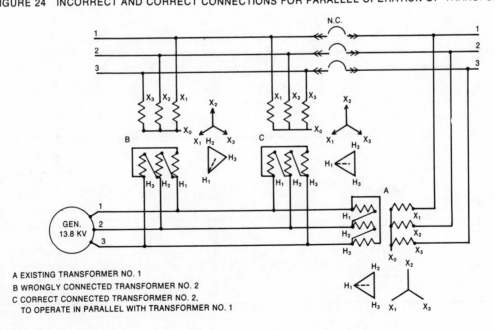

A EXISTING TRANSFORMER NO. 1
B WRONGLY CONNECTED TRANSFORMER NO. 2
C CORRECT CONNECTED TRANSFORMER NO. 2,
   TO OPERATE IN PARALLEL WITH TRANSFORMER NO. 1

ing half the total transformer capacity available in case of one unit's failure or by requirements to continue supplying should one transformer fail.

Transformers operating in parallel must have the same vector relationship, approximately equal turn ratios and the same or similar impedance. In the case of new units to be operated in parallel, a statement to this effect must be included in the specifications. When a new transformer is to operate in parallel with an existing unit, the impedance and the kva rating of the existing unit must be shown in the specifications. It is advisable that the manufacturer have the nameplate drawing and serial number of the existing unit if possible. It should also be indicated whether cooling equipment for future provision has been added to the existing transformer.

It is advisable to request nameplate drawings for approval, with the design impedance indicated. The actual tested impedance must be stamped on the metal nameplate. Reviewing these drawings will assure a final check, which is important for proper transformer parallel operation.

FIGURE 25   TRANSFORMER GROUPINGS 1, 2 or 3

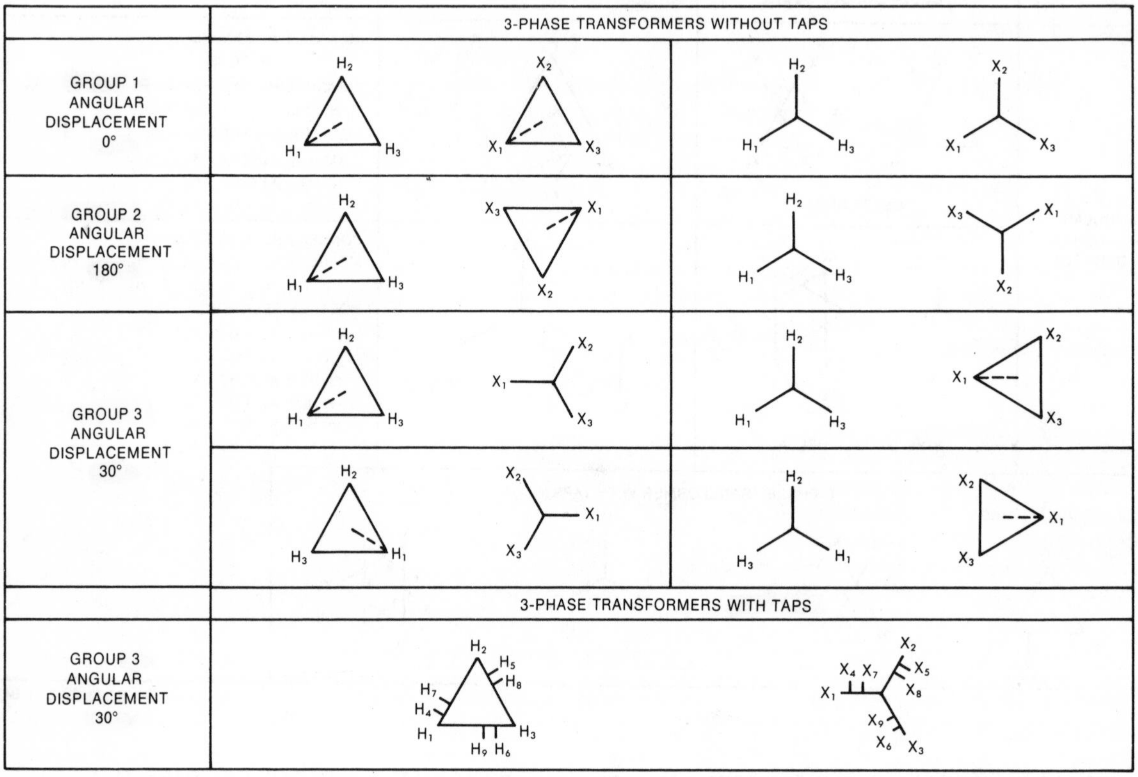

FIGURE 26 TRANSFORMER GROUPINGS 4 or 5

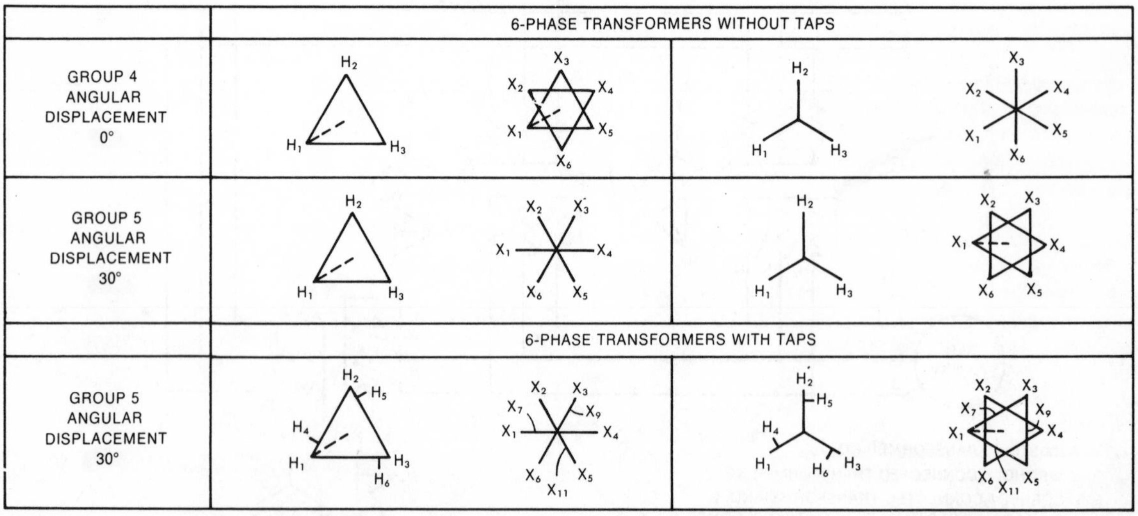

156

6

System Grounding in Industrial Power Systems

6.1 Factors Influencing the Engineer's Choice of Grounding Methods for Industrial Power System Design

One of the most important and controversial problems in industrial power system design is the selection of system grounding for each particular case. The term "grounding" in electric power systems is used to indicate both system and equipment grounding, which are different in their objectives.

This chapter will concentrate on system grounding of three-phase power system neutrals that comprise one or several system grounds, such as neutral points of transformers or generator windings established either solidly or by several means of current-limiting devices.

In this first section, criteria, definitions and basic factors influencing the selection of grounded or ungrounded systems are discussed, including respective advantages and disadvantages of each system.

System grounding insures longer insulation life for motors, transformers, and other components by suppressing transient and sustained overvoltages associated with certain fault conditions. System grounding improves protective relaying by providing fast, selective isolation of ground faults. Further more, system grounding is required by the National Electrical Code and for personnel safety.

System neutral resistance grounding provides extra protection to rotating machinery when ground faults occur by preventing the burning of the iron in whose slots the conductors are embedded.

To obtain maximum benefits from system grounding, each type must be considered in relation to the voltage of the particular industrial power system, and the specific requirements of the manufacturing or process operation. System grounding is a highly controversial subject. Design engineers planning electrical distribution must first decide whether to ground an electrical system, and then must choose the proper method of power system grounding.

Some engineers argue that power systems should be ungrounded, so that a single accidental ground will not shut down any part of the system. Today's consensus, however, is that some form of system grounding should be used to minimize transient overvoltages. An ungrounded system is in reality grounded through the capacitance-to-ground of the system conductors, and therefore, can be considered as a capacitively-grounded system.(see Figure 1).

If the engineer decides in favor of a grounded system he must then select

FIGURE 1   VOLTAGE-TO-GROUND DIAGRAMS UNDER STEADY-STATE CONDITIONS

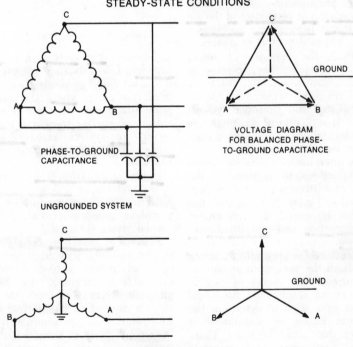

PHASE-TO-GROUND CAPACITANCE

UNGROUNDED SYSTEM

VOLTAGE DIAGRAM FOR BALANCED PHASE-TO-GROUND CAPACITANCE

GROUNDED WYE SYSTEM

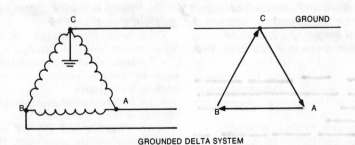

GROUNDED DELTA SYSTEM

157

the best method of grounding. The large number of factors that must be considered cannot always be analyzed in terms of dollars and cents, and thus weighed against each other. The best method of power-system grounding is, therefore, more difficult to select than any other feature of its design.

American practice has shifted from ungrounded, to resistance grounded, to solid- or effective-grounded methods. In the past, most systems were operated with their neutrals free, unconnected to ground. In this way an insulator failure on a phase could be tolerated for a short time until the fault was located and repaired. Relaying had not come into general use, so prolonged outages were avoided by ungrounded operation.

With the rapid growth of electrical systems—both in mileage and voltage—limitation of ungrounded operation became necessary. The increase of ground-fault currents prompted an increase of transient grounds, which were no longer self-clearing. Furthermore, the "arcing grounds" phenomena—whereby alternate clearing and restriking of the arc bring about high-surge voltages—became a problem for engineers.

By 1920, the majority of power systems became either solidly- or resistance-grounded. Recent transient-overvoltage comparisons between isolated and grounded systems showed that isolated systems are subject to higher overvoltages during faults, or switching operations.

While ungrounded operation is still more hazardous to equipment, the degree of difference between ungrounded and grounded operation has somewhat improved through proper surge protection and coordination in insulation.

The tendency in grounding practice was to limit the maximum amount of fault currents by means of neutral resistances or reactances. Empirical formulas were used to determine the maximum value of resistance or reactance that could be used. These formulas were expressed in terms of cable length, charging current to ground and connected generating kva of the system. Recent studies confirm that the maximum permissible neutral grounding resistance or reactance should be inversely proportional to the total line-to-ground charging kva. Other practical considerations, such as relaying, might dictate a lower maximum limit to grounding resistance than the arcing phenomena would require.

For system neutral grounding for industrial plants, the trend is toward solid grounding for systems rated 600

and below. For systems rated 2.4 to 13.8 kv, low-resistance grounding is prevalent. Solid grounding is also used in a few cases where the available ground-fault current is not objectionable, or where line-to-neutral loads are served. For systems rated 22 kv and higher, solid grounding is usually adopted.

In the transmission field, particularly on systems of 115 kv and above, solid or effective grounding—now the prevalent grounding method in the United States—is used.

Systems approaching 69 kv normal system voltages, with high concentrations of power subjected to high ground-fault currents, use neutral-grounding reactors of moderate ohmic size for grounding transformer banks. Europeans have predominantly used "Peterson" coils as ground-fault neutralizers. There are some similar installations in the U.S., and in many instances, these have reduced outages caused by ground faults.

The basic reasons for system neutral grounding are threefold:

• To limit overvoltages connected with various fault conditions.

• To limit electric potential differences between uninsulated conducting parts in a local area.

• To isolate faulty equipment and circuits at fault occurrences.

• An ungrounded system might offer better service continuity than a grounded system, since a line-to-

ground fault would not generate a fast tripping of the faulted circuit. Despite this fact, a second ground fault on another phase of another circuit would cause a phase-to-phase fault, consequently tripping both faulted circuits (see Figure 2).

The service continuity in a well-maintained ungrounded system, in which a first ground fault was promptly located and removed might be better than in a solidly-grounded system. Yet grounded industrial systems that obviate the various dangers and disadvantages of an ungrounded operation are becoming the norm.

The basic methods of system neutral grounding are: Solid grounding; high or low resistance grounding; high or low reactance grounding; and ground fault neutralizer grounding. The above designations refer to the nature and extent of the circuit from the system neutral point to ground, rather than to the degree of grounding.

The following factors influence the design engineer in his choice of a grounded or ungrounded system:

Service continuity—Phase-to-phase ground faults generally result in the immediate isolation of the faulted circuit. For many years industrial plant distribution systems have been operated ungrounded in order to gain an additional degree of service continuity. The choice of an ungrounded system may rest on the advantage that any contact between

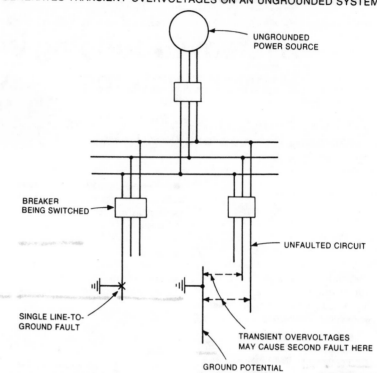

FIGURE 2   SWITCHING OF CIRCUIT HAVING A GROUND FAULT, GENERATES TRANSIENT OVERVOLTAGES ON AN UNGROUNDED SYSTEM

UNGROUNDED POWER SOURCE

BREAKER BEING SWITCHED

UNFAULTED CIRCUIT

SINGLE LINE-TO-GROUND FAULT

TRANSIENT OVERVOLTAGES MAY CAUSE SECOND FAULT HERE

GROUND POTENTIAL

System grounding

one phase and ground will not cause an immediate outage. Where continuity is the most important factor, an ungrounded system might be the answer. Experience has proven, however, that many systems can obtain good service continuity with a grounded neutral system.

Multiple faults to ground—If the neutral of a system is not grounded, destructive transient overvoltages may appear from line-to-ground during normal switching of a circuit subjected to a line-to-ground fault.

Repeated restriking of the arc during interruption of a line-to-ground fault may generate dangerous overvoltages. These in turn may cause insulation failures at other system locations besides the point of fault. A line-to-ground fault on one circuit usually results in damage to equipment and service interruption in other circuits (see Figure 3).

In an ungrounded neutral system, a second ground fault may occur on another phase before the first fault is removed. The resulting line-to-line fault may actuate relays or circuit breakers, and trip one or both circuits. A single minimal line-to-ground fault may result in considerably high line-to-line faults with the interruption of both circuits.

A ground fault on a line of an ungrounded system causes full line-to-line voltage to appear throughout the system. This voltage is 73 percent higher than normal (see Figure 4). The insulation between line and ground can withstand full line-to-line voltage; but prolonged exposure may result in a failure or degradation of the insulation. The only advantage of the ungrounded system is that the circuit is not instantly tripped at the occurrence of the first ground fault. Provided the fault remains as a single line-to-ground fault, and no other fault occurs, the circuit may continue operating until the fault is removed. Ground detectors in ungrounded systems indicate that a ground fault has occurred, but do not give the fault location. There are some fault-location detectors, but time is still required to locate and remove the fault, and repair the fault feeder. Production losses can occur while a fault location is found in an ungrounded neutral system. Double ground faults are frequent in un-grounded systems, because the first ground is usually left on line with the hope that the operator will find it before the second ground fault occurs.

With ungrounded systems, audible or visible ground detectors should be installed, and an organized maintenance program should locate and remove grounds immediately after their detection. Locating faults in ungrounded systems should be performed with the system energized and without interrupting the service on any circuit. Multiple ground faults are seldom encountered in grounded neutral systems.

Arcing fault burndowns—Arcing faults, especially in low-voltage power systems, can produce severe burndowns, damages, and even complete destruction of electrical equipment. An arcing fault may occur between two or more phase conductors in un-grounded systems, or between phase conductors and ground in solidly-grounded neutral systems. The arc releases large amounts of energy at the fault point, accompanied with violent hot gas generation and arc plasma. The heat produced may vaporize the copper or aluminum conductors and even the surrounding steel enclosures. Often the equipment involved in arcing faults must be replaced.

Arcing faults are not sensed by the normal phase-overcurrent protective devices, because arcing fault current levels are so low, these devices are not actuated. By the time the devices are actuated, it is usually too late to prevent the burndown.

The prevention of arcing-fault burndowns relies on sensitive and fast detection, with interruption of such faults in a maximum of 10-20 cycles. This is possible in solidly-grounded neutral systems because an arcing fault produces a current in the ground path—either the fault starts as a line-to-ground fault, or instantly involves ground, even though initiated as a line-to-line arcing fault.

Under normal conditions there is no appreciable current flowing in the ground-return path. Monitoring the solidly-grounded neutral system for currents flowing in the ground circuit provides a means for detecting and removing destructive arcing faults to ground. The sensitivity and speed of

Power system definitions

American National Standard Institute's Standard C114.1-1973, a basic source of technical guidance for industrial and commercial power system grounding, provides the following definitions:

System ground—a system of conductors in which at least one conductor or point (usually the middle wire of the neutral point of transformer or generator windings) is intentionally grounded, either solidly or through a current-limiting device. Grounded systems may be subject to various steady-state and transient overvoltages, all depending on the ratios X_o/X, and R_o/X, as viewed from the fault location. R_o, X_o and X are respectively the zero-sequence resistance, the zero-sequence reactance and the positive-sequence subtransient reactance. (For the meaning of these values, see "Coordinating Protection for Electrical Systems in Plants" *Specifying Engineer,* May, 1976.

Ungrounded—without an intentional connection to ground, except through potential indicating or measuring devices.

Solidly grounded—grounded through an adequate ground connection in which no impedance has been intentionally inserted.

Resistance grounded—ground through an impedance, the principal element being a resistance.

Reactance grounded—grounded through an impedance, the principal element being a reactance.

Ground-fault neutralizer—A grounding device providing an inductive component of current in a ground fault that is substantially equal to, and therefore neutralizes the rated frequency component of the ground fault current and renders the system resonant grounded.

Grounding transformer—a transformer intended to provide a neutral point for grounding purposes.

Equipment-grounding—an intentional solid connection to ground from one or more of the noncurrent-carrying metal parts of the wiring system or apparatus, such as: metal conduits, metal raceways, metal amor of cables, outlet boxes, cabinets, switch boxes, motor frames and metal enclosures of motor controllers. The main purpose of equipment grounding is personnel safety.

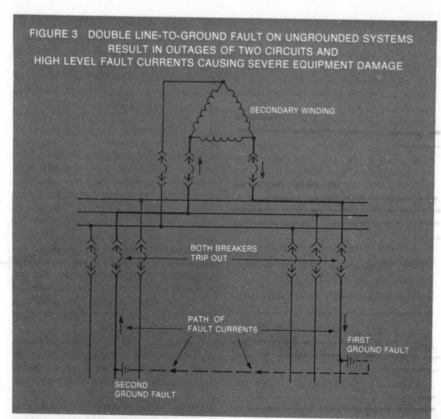

FIGURE 3   DOUBLE LINE-TO-GROUND FAULT ON UNGROUNDED SYSTEMS
RESULT IN OUTAGES OF TWO CIRCUITS AND
HIGH LEVEL FAULT CURRENTS CAUSING SEVERE EQUIPMENT DAMAGE

such relaying is independent of the normal load currents and phase-overcurrent protective devices' settings. Phase-overcurrent relays usually have tap settings from 4 to 16 amp, whereas ground relays have tap settings from .5 to 2 or 1.6 to 6 amp. The solidly- as well as low-resistance-grounded neutral systems provide the best protection against destructive phase-to-ground arcing fault burndowns. The ungrounded, or high-impedance grounded systems, while less subject to arcing faults, provide less protection against arc blast and flash hazard due to arcing faults. No system, however, is completely protected against low-level, line-to-line arcing fault burndowns.

Ease of fault locations—Ground faults on ungrounded systems do not open the circuit—audible or visual detectors must be installed. Detectors indicate the presence of a ground fault and the phase involved, but do not show on which feeder the fault has occurred. Each feeder in turn must be removed from service until the detector signals that the faulty feeder has been disconnected from the

[handwritten margin note: Because current in neut. is high enough]

[handwritten margin note: current in neutral ground is too low]

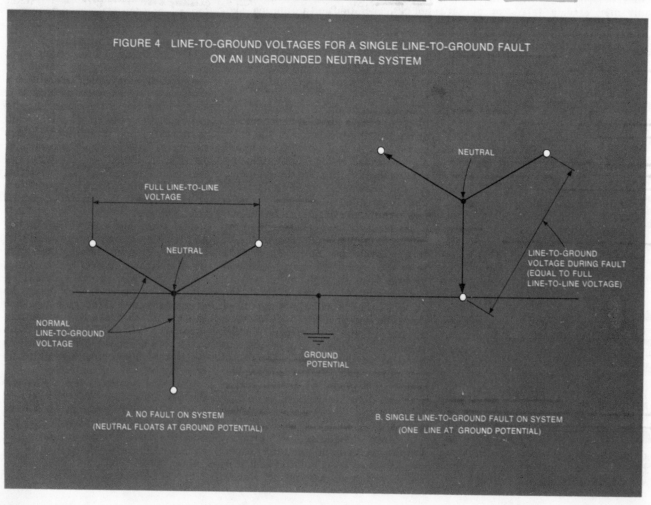

FIGURE 4   LINE-TO-GROUND VOLTAGES FOR A SINGLE LINE-TO-GROUND FAULT
ON AN UNGROUNDED NEUTRAL SYSTEM

A. NO FAULT ON SYSTEM
(NEUTRAL FLOATS AT GROUND POTENTIAL)

B. SINGLE LINE-TO-GROUND FAULT ON SYSTEM
(ONE LINE AT GROUND POTENTIAL)

system. In a multi-fault situation, it may be necessary to disconnect all feeders and restore them individually after the detector has shown that the faults have been removed. There are various types of ground-locating equipment. Some operate without deenergizing the system feeders, but all require some time to find the fault location.

Conversely, an accidental ground on a grounded system is indicated and located by an automatic interruption of the grounded circuit or equipment.

Safety of personnel and equipment—Poor or nonexisting grounding is a source of hazards to personnel and equipment. While equipment grounding is not included in this series of articles, it is worth mentioning that regardless of whether a system is grounded, safety of personnel and equipment requires thorough grounding of equipment, metallic structures, and all noncurrent-carrying metal parts.

In ungrounded systems, contact with an energized phase conductor presents serious lethal shock hazards. During the period a ground fault remains on one phase, personnel accidentally contacting one of the other phases and ground are subject to 1.73 times the normal system voltage. This is not the case with a solidly-grounded neutral system. Inadequate grounding of equipment in either grounded or ungrounded neutral systems results in fire and shock hazards.

Abnormal voltage hazards—Overvoltages on ungrounded systems cause more equipment failures than on grounded systems—and can cause multiple equipment failures. These multiple failures may involve several different feeders, because in a ungrounded system, a fault in one phase imposes an overvoltage on the normally-rated insulation. This imposition, together with other sustained or transient overvoltages, may cause failure or shortening of the insulation's life expectancy.

On grounded systems, overvoltages are less likely to damage equipment and insulation.

Power system overvoltages— Lightning overvoltages are usually suppressed by surge arresters installed at the incoming service. Surge arresters may be required on the low side of transformers to protect equipment from surges that are passed through the transformer by the high-side arresters. Through normal switching operations, switching surges

can cause short-duration overvoltages three times the normal voltage. These overvoltages result from transient oscillations in the circuit inductance and capacitance and from stored energy in the circuit capacitance at the moment of interruption.

Neutral grounding will not totally reduce the magnitude of overvoltages produced by lightning or switching surges, but it can distribute the voltage between phases and reduce excessive voltage stress on the phase-to-ground insulation of a particular phase.

Overhead open-wire lines may be subject to static overvoltages resulting

System grounding should be used to minimize transient overvoltages

from special atmospheric conditions. These static buildups can be effectively prevented by a system ground connection.

A broken high-voltage conductor falling on a low-voltage conductor, or breakdown between high- and low-voltage windings, can produce a breakdown of insulation if the low-voltage system is ungrounded. An effectively grounded low-voltage system will hold the system neutral close to ground potential, and thus reduce the overvoltages-to-ground on the low-voltage system.

In an ungrounded system, if one phase of a three-phase system becomes grounded, the insulation of the other phases is taxed with 73 percent above-normal voltage, thus reducing the insulation's life. Solidly-grounded neutral systems cannot be subjected to these overvoltages.

Ungrounded systems can be subjected to resonant overvoltages. With the high phase-to-ground capacitance of larger systems, there may be a resonance condition during a line-to-ground fault through an inductance such as a faulty coil in a motor starter. In this case, the voltage-to-ground of the unfaulted phases can be in excess of the line-to-line voltage. Similar resonant conditions can be encountered in smaller systems where tuned inductive capacity circuits are used for welders. A grounded neutral system prevents these overvoltages by holding the phases to their approximate normal voltage-to-ground.

Arcing, restriking, or vibrating ground faults on ungrounded systems may produce surge voltages as high as six times the normal voltage. Neutral

grounding is effective in reducing transient-voltage buildup from intermittent ground faults by reducing neutral displacement from ground potential, and destructive effects of high-frequency voltage oscillations following arc initiations or restrike.

Cost—The cost of grounded-neutral systems varies. Cost depends on system voltage and whether the system to be grounded is an existing or a new system. 208/120-v, Wye-connected systems provide system neutrals grounding for themselves, and therefore, no extra cost is involved. Wye-connected unit substations for grounded 480-v systems may cost up to 6 percent more than Delta-connected substations. For 2.4-kv systems, Wye-connected transformers may be obtained at a slight cost premium over 2.4 kv Delta transformers. In addition, there is the cost of a resistor or other grounding impedance.

For 4.16 and 13.8 kv systems, Wye-connected transformers are standard, with no transformer price increase for grounding these systems involved. However, the grounding resistor is an extra cost. Changing existing systems to grounded systems can be expensive, especially where grounding transformers with protective equipment are necessary.

In a grounded-neutral system three overcurrent elements are required in the protective devices. Generally it is unnecessary to carry the neutral wire along with the three-phase circuits, unless they supply single-phase loads connected from line-to-neutral (For example, 208/120-v Wye-connected circuits or 480/277-v, four-wire systems supplying 120 or 277-v lighting loads). Therefore, there is no additional circuit cost for grounded-neutral arrangements.

The additional costs of grounded-neutral transformers and controls with three overcurrent elements are small when compared to total system cost.

With grounded-neutral systems, savings can be realized since cables for grounded-neutral service are less expensive than those for ungrounded systems. This applies to 13.8 kv systems and above, as well as for systems where automatic ground-fault relaying is used.

6.2 Ungrounded, Solidly Grounded, and High-Resistance-Grounded Systems Are All Suitable for Low-Voltage Applications

Section 6.1 discussed the importance and definitions of system grounding, as well as the basic factors influencing the engineer's selection of the properly grounded or ungrounded neutral systems. This second part summarizes grounded system advantages in 480-v, 2.4 to 15-kv systems; explains how to obtain the system neutral of transformers and generators; discusses Wye-Delta and Zig-Zag grounding transformers and describes frequently-employed system neutral grounding methods for low-voltage industrial power systems. Figures and tables are numbered consecutively.

In selecting the appropriate type of system grounding, the engineer's objective is to gain the best compromise between the conflicting advantages and disadvantages of grounded versus ungrounded neutral systems.

Table I presents a summary of the advantages of grounded systems as compared with ungrounded systems for 480-v, 2.4- to 15-kv systems. Generally preferred for low-voltage power systems (600 v and less) is the solidly grounded (sometimes the high resistance grounding) method. For medium-voltage power systems (2.4-15 kv), the low-resistance grounding method is preferred.

To obtain the system neutral point, select the source transformers or generators with Wye-connected windings. Their neutral is thus readily available for the selected method of system grounding.

System grounding is most advanta-geous for 120/208-v, Wye or 277/480-v Wye systems. For 4.16-, or even 2.4-kv systems, Wye-connected source transformers provide the system ground point. On existing Delta-connected systems, grounding Wye-Delta or Zig-Zag transformers can be connected to establish the system neutral. This procedure particularly applies to older existing systems of 600-v or less, and equally to many existing 2,400-, 4,800- and 6,900-v systems.

In these systems the neutral is provided by installing grounding transformers whose neutral is then connected solidly or through a resistance or reactance to ground. The same principle applies to many 2.4- to 15-kv systems having only Delta-connected equipment. Grounding transformers are of two types: Wye-Delta and Zig-Zag connected. These transformers provide a low impedance path for the flow of zero-sequence currents associated with ground-fault conditions. Consequently, the zero-sequence currents can flow at the point of fault and back through the neutral of the grounding transformer. Figures 5a and 5b show the connections and ground-fault current flowing in a Wye-Delta and a Zig-Zag grounding transformer connected to an un-grounded 3-phase system.

The impedance of both types of grounding transformers to a normal 3-phase current is high, so that when no fault exists on the system only a small magnetizing current flows in the transformer windings.

The total ground-fault current at the fault point, as well as at the grounding transformer, is divided into three equal parts—i_1, i_2, i_3—which are all single-phase currents. Each current represents one-third of the total ground-fault current. They are all equal and in time phase with each other and are thus called zero-sequence components of currents.

There are two types of grounding transformers: Wye-Delta and Zig-Zag

After entering the main system, the ground-fault current divides, with one part flowing to the load and the other part flowing to the source. During normal system conditions, the operating characteristics of the Wye-Delta grounding transformers are the same as those of a Wye-Delta power transformer operating unloaded.

A Zig-Zag grounding transformer operates in the same way as a Wye-Delta grounding transformer. Zig-Zag grounding transformers provide a stable neutral point which makes them suited for grounding an isolated neutral system.

The type of grounding transformer more commonly used is a 3-phase Zig-Zag transformer without a secondary winding. The short-time kva rating of such a transformer is equal to the rated line-to-neutral voltage multipled by the rated neutral current. Grounding transformers are designed to carry their rated current for a limited time only—about 10 seconds. Consequently, a grounding transformer may be one-tenth as large physically as an ordinary 3-phase transformer for the same rated kva.

The continuous rating of a Zig-Zag grounding transformer is necessary for establishing the rating and setting of the transformer protective device. In general, a continuous current capability of at least 10 percent of the 10-second rating allows for reasonable

TABLE 1—ADVANTAGES SUMMARY OF SOLIDLY-GROUNDED 480-V SYSTEMS AND LOW-RESISTANCE GROUNDED 2.4-15 KV SYSTEMS

	480v		2.4 to 15 kv	
	Grounded neutral systems *Safest*	*Ungrounded systems* *Less safe*	*Grounded neutral system* *Safest*	*Ungrounded systems* *Unsafe*
Safety	277 v to ground at any time	480 v to ground on two conductors, when one phase is grounded	Single line-to-ground fault immediately tripped	Subject to severe overvoltages
	System voltage limited to 277 v at failure of primary to secondary in transformer supplying system	On secondary, system voltage may be as high as primary voltage on failure of primary to secondary in transformer supplying system		
	Ground faults in control wiring puts only 58 percent of line voltage, on line-to-line connected contactor closing coils	Ground faults in control wires may be full voltage on contactor-closing coils		
	Highest	*Less satisfactory*	*Highest*	*Less satisfactory*
Service reliability	Ground faults are readily located without interruption of system	Must take part or all of system out of service to find ground faults	Ground faults readily located and removed	Must take part or all of system out of service to locate and remove faults
	Ground faults are localized and immediately removed	If ground faults are not rapidly removed, a second ground fault trips two circuits at once, thus loosing twice as much production equipment	Limited fault current causes minimum damage to equipment	If ground fault is not removed immediately, a second ground fault trips two circuits at once, loosing twice as much production equipment
	Minimizes transient overvoltages	Overvoltages likely	Minimizes transient overvoltages on the system	High fault currents associated with line-to-line faults, result in more equipment damage
	Floating ground unlikely	Floating or arcing faults likely		
	Lowest	*May be costly*	*Lowest*	*May be costly*
Maintenance cost	Ground faults are easily located and removed	Time is spent hunting ground-fault location	Ground faults are easily located and removed	Time is spent hunting ground-fault location
High-voltage fluorescent	Provides 277 v for fluorescent lighting, resulting in cost savings and elimination of lighting transformers and also copper reduction	Must use step down transformers from 480 to 277 v		
First costs	About same as Delta-connected substation with ground detector	Requires ground detector and fault locator equipment to be comparable	About same—adds cost of resistor and neutral relaying	Requires ground detector and fault locator equipment to be comparable

163

FIGURE 5a—WYE-DELTA GROUNDING TRANSFORMER CONNECTION AND CURRENT DISTRIBUTION, WHEN LINE TO GROUND FAULT OCCURS IN A 3-PHASE UNGROUNDED SYSTEM

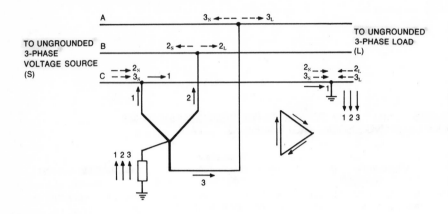

FIGURE 5b—ZIG-ZAG TRANSFORMER CONNECTION AND CURRENT FLOW, WHEN FAULT OCCURS IN A 3-PHASE UNGROUNDED SYSTEM

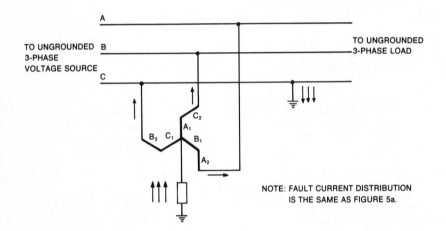

NOTE: FAULT CURRENT DISTRIBUTION IS THE SAME AS FIGURE 5a.

protective relay setting.

Common methods for connecting Zig-Zag grounding transformers on 2.4 kv and above, and 600 v and below, ungrounded systems are shown in Figures 6a, 6b and 6c. Grounding transformers are mainly connected to existing systems, since on new systems the neutral can be obtained without the expense of a grounding transformer.

The transformer's physical location depends on the arrangement of the existing equipment. The grounding transformer may be located at the system bus or at the main transformer secondary terminals. The connection method depends on the transformer's location, degree of protection desired, protective device selectivity, and the nature of the load.

In general, when the transformer is connected to a system bus, protective devices must be included, especially when the bus is enclosed in a metal-clad switchgear.

The grounding transformer should be protected against faults in the transformer, and back-up protection must be provided for ground faults in the system that are not cleared by other protective devices.

For system voltages of 2,400 v and above, the protective devices are actuated by current transformers and relays. At 600 v and below, series trip devices are commonly used. Currently, systems of 2,400 v and above are grounded through a resistor, whereas at 600 and below, system neutrals are solidly grounded.

For systems 600 v and less, the solid

neutral grounding of 208/120 v, Wye is universally adopted. Modern standard load center unit substations are available with a Wye-connected secondary winding rated 480/277 v, Wye or 208/120 v, Wye, which allows system neutral grounding. Usually, these load center substations are available with Delta primary windings at all commonly used high voltages.

The low-voltage neutral is generally brought out through a bushing connected to a low-voltage ground bus. The low-voltage neutral connection point is left off when grounding is not desired. In general, substations rated 240 v are Delta-connected. To obtain the neutral operation the engineer can use either 208/120-v or 240-v Delta substations with grounding transformers.

Low-voltage systems are solidly grounded since relatively high ground-fault currents are required to operate protective devices in 600 v and less circuits.

In low-voltage systems three levels of ground-fault currents are possible: ground-fault currents greater, equal or less than 3-phase fault. In systems supplied by transformers only, it is desirable to aim for ground-fault current values equal to 3-phase faults. This condition can be achieved by a solidly-grounded system. If generator neutrals are solidly grounded, the ground-fault currents would be greater than the 3-phase fault currents. In these cases, it is necessary to use a low value of neutral reactor to bring the ground-fault current down to the 3-phase fault current valve.

When grounding transformers are used (in ungrounded systems), the ground-fault current must be limited to a value less than the 3-phase fault current to keep grounding transformer sizes within practical limits. This is usually accomplished by inserting a low value resistance in the transformer neutral. Special ground relays are not commonly used in low-voltage circuits whose neutral is grounded. For single line-to-ground faults, all 3 poles of the circuit breakers are opened simultaneously. This is not the case with fused switches, where the faulted phase opens first and the remaining fuses may or may not open depending on the magnitude of the overload imposed by the remaining single-phased circuits.

It is advisable to limit available ground-fault currents to the minimum consistent with the limitation of transient overvoltages to acceptable levels (approximately 250 percent). Ground-fault currents should also stay

FIGURE 6a—COMMON METHOD OF GROUNDING TRANSFORMER CONNECTION ON 2.4 KV AND ABOVE SYSTEMS

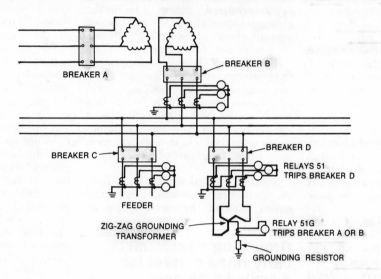

FIGURE 6b—ALTERNATE METHOD OF GROUNDING TRANSFORMER CONNECTION ON 2.4 KV AND ABOVE SYSTEMS

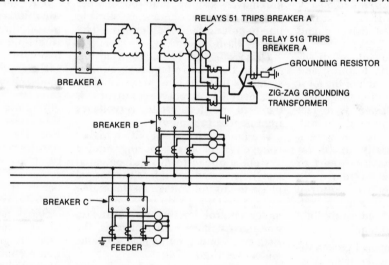

FIGURE 6c—GROUNDING TRANSFORMER CONNECTED TO BUS, WITH CIRCUIT BREAKER ON A 480-V DELTA SYSTEM

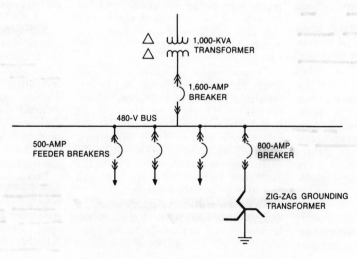

within the requirements of the protective relaying system. The energy released at the fault location is approximately proportional to the square of the fault current. The National Electrical Code states which classes of low-voltage systems must be solidly grounded. The most important methods used in low-voltage power system grounding are the:

- Ungrounded system
- Solid neutral grounding
- High resistance grounding There are some other system grounding methods—low reactance grounding, mid-phase grounding, corner of Delta grounding, etc.—but these are used infrequently.

Low resistance grounding is not used on low-voltage systems because the limited available ground-fault current is insufficient to operate the series trip units of breakers and fuses used for phase-to-phase and phase-to-ground fault protection. Although this system limits fault currents to 50-150 amp, that current is sufficient to cause serious damage if not detected and quickly cleared.

Following are the advantages, disadvantages, characteristic features, and area of application of each of the most commonly used grounding methods.

The ungrounded system is in fact capacity-coupled to ground through the phase conductors of the system. This method is especially suitable for two-wire, single-phase systems or three-wire, 3-phase systems. No grounding equipment is required except potential transformers, a voltage relay or a ground-indicating light for ground-fault detection.

Except for the additional ground detection expense, cost is the same as for the solidly-grounded neutral system with phase relaying only. The system-charging current $\frac{3 \times E_{l\text{-}n}}{X_{co}}$ is less than one percent and usually less than 1 amp, where $E_{l\text{-}n}$ is the line-to-neutral voltage and X_{co} is the system line-to-ground capacitive reactance including surge capacitors, if present.

In 208-v systems sustained arcing for line-to-line faults is a small probability, but it may occur. In 480- to 600-v systems, a high probability of sustained arcing fault exists. At no ground fault, shock hazard exists from phase-to-neutral voltage of each phase to ground.

At ground fault on a phase conductor, line-to-line voltage appears on two phases. With repetitive restrikes to ground or a series resonant L-C circuit, voltages to ground are in excess of line-to-line voltage, and can cause trapped charges to build voltages from 500 to 600 percent of normal—thereby placing high stresses on equipment, conductor insulation.

Advantages: There is no tripping of overcurrent devices at the first line-to-ground fault, provided a second line-to-ground fault on another phase occurs before the first one is removed. The faulty circuit continues in operation, which, in certain process industries, is regarded as a great advantage.

No flash hazard to personnel from an accidental line-to-ground fault exists, unless the system has an

Grounding transformers carry rated current for a limited time only

unremoved ground fault on another phase. If this occurs, a double line-to-ground fault is accompanied by serious flash hazards.

Disadvantages: The main disadvantage of the low-voltage ungrounded system is that this kind of system does not provide effective control for transient and steady-state overvoltages from neutral to ground.

If a fault-path contact with a higher voltage system occurs, the ungrounded system's phase-to-ground potential may be elevated as high as the normal phase-to-ground voltage on the higher voltage system. In directly-connected motor control circuits using line-to-line rated voltage contactor coils, the first or second ground may start the motor (see Figure 7a).

An unremoved ground fault puts greater than normal voltage on the system insulation, which may result in severe overvoltage conditions, with the consequence of increased shock hazard, multiple insulation failures and eventual equipment and circuit outages.

Ground faults in ungrounded systems are very difficult to locate, requiring time and shutdowns. Maintenance costs are relatively high because of reduced insulation life and labor involved in fault locations. Ground faults in motors cannot be easily detected and removed until the fault has burned into another coil, resulting in greater damage.

The typical area of application for ungrounded systems is in the process industries and in manufacturing operations where immediate shutdown at the first ground fault is undesired. Preventing an immediate shutdown avoids severe financial production losses, damage to equipment and danger to equipment and personnel.

The advantage of the ungrounded system is the sustaining of service continuity when a single ground fault occurs. However, the disadvantages of the ungrounded power distribution system—such as insulation failures and increased shock hazard from transient and steady-state overvoltage conditions—has brought about the gradual diminishment of its use in favor of the solidly-grounded and high resistance-grounded systems. The ungrounded systems, still used in specific plants and industries, require excellent maintenance and rigorous ground-fault detection and removal practices to provide the service reliability and continuity equivalent found in solidly- and high resistance-grounded neutral systems.

The solidly-grounded system is suitable for serving: four-wire, 3-phase; three-wire, 3-phase; two-wire, single-phase, 1 side grounded; and two-wire, single-phase systems. Typical ground-fault currents are several thousand amp and may exceed the calculated 3-phase fault current. No grounding equipment is required for Wye systems with neutral available. For Delta systems, a grounding transformer is required. The probability of sustained arcing for line-to-line faults at 208 v is small but it may occur. In 480- to 600-v systems the probability is high.

Shock hazard for no ground fault is phase-to-neutral voltage from each phase to ground; at ground fault on a phase conductor, the shock hazard is phase-to-neutral voltage on two phases. Solid grounding meets the requirements of the National Electrical Code which does not prohibit the use of low resistance or ungrounded systems.

Advantages: The solidly-grounded neutral system controls to safe levels the transient and steady-state overvoltages from neutral to ground due to insulation breakdowns, resonant inductive capacitive circuits, restriking ground faults, etc. The solidly-grounded system uses low-cost phase protective devices to provide selective isolation and automatic tripping for the first ground fault.

Phase overcurrent devices will operate for solid ground faults or high-level arcing faults to ground. For low-level arcing faults to ground, the application of sensitive ground-fault relays is necessary to disconnect faulty circuits before burndowns occur.

Sensitive zero-sequence ground-fault relays are now installed in many industries where protection of equipment and personnel is very important. These types of relays discriminate between low-level ground faults and normal load currents. These ground relays minimize the possibility of arcing-fault burndown.

Phase-to-ground shock resulting from a fault-path contact with a high voltage system is limited approximately to the line-to-neutral voltage of the low-voltage system. Shock hazard from neutral to ground during a line-to-ground fault is almost zero voltage for low impedance main-

Generally, transformers connected to a system bus require protective devices

grounding conductors.

For ground faults in directly-connected motor control circuits using line-to-line rated voltage coils, only 58 percent of the line-to-line voltage will appear on the contactor coil, and motor start is unlikely (see Figure 7b).

Locating the first line-to-ground fault is not difficult since the fault is usually self-isolating via the phase overcurrent protective device operation. However, ground-fault relaying is indicated to isolate low-level faults on high-current circuits. Noise, smoke and flash help in locating faults.

System maintenance cost is minimal since the insulation's life expectancy is not shortened and ground faults are rapidly located.

Faults to ground in motor windings can be quickly detected and removed before serious damage occurs by means of phase overcurrent devices or ground sensor zero-sequence relays.

Disadvantages: There is a high probability of sustained arcing line-to-ground faults at 480- to 600-v systems. There is also a high probability of escalating single phase line-to-ground arcing faults into line-to-line or 3-phase arcing faults, particularly for 480- to 600-v systems.

There is a safety hazard for faults in directly-connected motor control circuits using line-to-line rated voltage contactor coils, especially where the motor is already running. It may not cease operation when the "stop" button is pressed. Pushing the "start" button with a ground fault in the control circuit may allow line-to-ground fault current to flow through

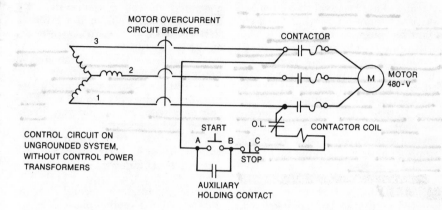

FIGURE 7a   IF A FIRST GROUND FAULT OCCURS AT LINE 3, A SECOND FAULT AT "B" OR "C" IMPRESSES LINE-TO-LINE VOLTAGE AT THE CONTACTOR COIL AND STARTS THE MOTOR

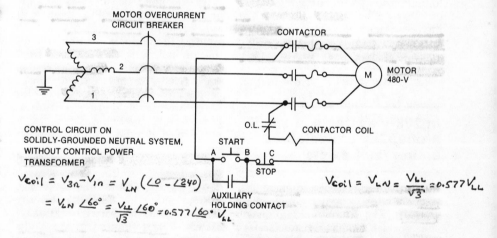

FIGURE 7b   ACCIDENTAL STARTING OF MOTOR IS IMPROBABLE SINCE ONLY 58 PERCENT OF LINE TO LINE VOLTAGE CAN BE IMPRESSED AT CONTACTOR COIL IF A GROUND FAULT OCCURS AT "B" OR "C"

$$V_{coil} = V_{3n} - V_{1n} = V_{LN}(\angle 0 - \angle 240)$$
$$= V_{LN}\angle 60° = \frac{V_{LL}}{\sqrt{3}}\angle 60° = 0.577\angle 60° V_{LL}$$

$$V_{coil} = V_{LN} = \frac{V_{LL}}{\sqrt{3}} = 0.577 V_{LL}$$

the push button causing a momentary personnel hazard until a protective device operates.

Persisting low-level arcing faults may result in equipment burndowns. Sensitive zero-sequence ground-fault relays should be installed to eliminate this problem. There may be severe flash hazards to personnel for ground faults on any phase of a high-capacity system.

The typical area of application for the solidly-grounded neutral system is in industrial and commercial service for loads affecting public welfare and safety, involving lighting, elevators, fire pumps, ventilation, etc. The solidly-grounded system is especially effective in 3-phase, four-wire, low-

voltage power distribution circuits as well as in critical process loads.

The main characteristics of the solidly-grounded neutral system are the effective control of all overvoltage conditions and the rapid isolation of the faulted circuit by economic overcurrent trips at the occurence of ground faults. Furthermore, due to the possible addition of zero-sequence grounding relays, the solidly-grounded neutral system provides effective protection against destructive low-level arcing faults. These advantages explain the extensive use of the solidly-grounded neutral system in industrial and commercial service.

The shortcoming of this grounding system is the severe flash hazard at the occurence of an arcing fault involving ground. This hazard can be obviated by working on the equipment and circuits only when the system is deenergized.

In the solidly-grounded neutral system prompt removal of a circuit in which a ground fault has occurred might be considered undesirable. The requirement to avoid an abrupt shutdown at the first ground fault and the continued supply of power to a critical process or service might take precedence over all other considerations. In these cases, high resistance in the neutral connection to ground to limit fault current and to avoid tripping on the first ground fault is the method indicated.

The high resistance-grounded neutral system has a high value resistor inserted in the neutral connection to ground, limiting the ground-fault current to a value equal to, or somewhat greater than the capacitive-charging current of the system. Typical ground-fault currents are to 10 amp on the primary system. Ohmic rating of the resistor is usually selected to limit ground-fault current to 10 amp or less. The main purpose of high-resistance grounding is to avoid automatic tripping of the faulted circuit at the first ground fault occurance.

This method of grounding is

In 208-v systems, a small probability of sustained arcing fault exists

suitable for three-wire, 3-phase systems and for two-wire, single-phase systems. The grounding equipment consists of a neutral resistor for Wye systems and a neutral resistor and grounding transformer for a Delta system. The installation of a ground-fault indicating device which requires relay and indicating lights or alarm is recommended.

The cost is higher than for the solidly-grounded system with phase relaying, because of the addition of a resistor and ground-fault indicating equipment.

The probability of sustained arcing faults for line-to-line faults is small in 208-v systems, but it may occur. With 480- to 600-v systems, sustained arcing faults are a high probability. Shock hazards from phase-to-ground at no ground faults is limited to phase-to-neutral voltage from each phase to ground. For ground faults on phase

conductors, the shock hazard is approximately line-to-line voltage on two phases.

Advantages: A high resistance-grounded neutral system controls to safe limits the transient overvoltages generated in the power system by resonant capacitive-inductive circuits, static charges and repetitive restrikes of ground faults. The transient overvoltages are limited to about 250 percent of normal voltage. The probability of sustained arcing for line-to-ground faults would be difficult to initiate, and would very likely be self extinguishing.

Single-phase line ground faults would be self extinguishing. No immediate shutdown of the faulty circuit for the first ground fault will happen provided a second line-to-ground fault on another phase does not occur before the first one is removed. The faulty circuit will continue to operate, which is desirable in certain process industries.

The safety hazard for ground faults in directly-connected motor control circuits using line-to-line contactor coils is avoided, because less than the normal line-to-neutral voltage will appear on the contactor coils, and the motor will not start. During line-to-line ground fault, shock hazard from neutral to ground is essentially zero, since neutral is not run with phase conductors. No flash hazards exist for personnel from accidenal line-to-ground fault, unless the system has an unremoved ground fault on another phase.

Disadvantages: Phase-to-ground shock hazard resulting from a fault-path contact with a higher voltage system may be as high as the line-to-neutral voltage of the primary system. Line-to-ground arcing faults cannot be distinguished from load currents, but are very likely self extinguishing. Arcing line-to-line faults will trip the phase overcurrent devices, but if their current level is low they may go undetected, causing equipment burndown.

Unremoved ground faults, subject to greater than normal voltage may affect the system's insulation resulting in possible service damage for motors and equipment. Locating the first fault to ground is as difficult as for the ungrounded system, and it may require many hours and repeated shutdown of the faulty circuit equipment.

System maintenance cost is somewhat higher than for the solidly-grounded system because of above-

normal voltage affecting insulation life during ground faults and increased costs with the time spent in locating ground faults.

The typical area of application for the high-resistance-grounded neutral system is in the process industries, where control of transient overvoltages is desired, but an immediate shutdown on the first ground fault is not wanted. The main objective is the prevention of immediate service interruption con-

Ground faults in ungrounded systems are very difficult to locate

nected with financial losses, as well as the elimination of personnel flash hazard due to ground faults.

The main reasons for using a high resistance grounding are the same as for an ungrounded system, except that transient overvoltage control is also a prime objective. Compared with solidly-grounded systems during ground faults, the high resistance-grounding system offers zero flash hazard and voltage dip, provided simultaneous ground faults on different phases do not occur. It is imperative to monitor and remove ground faults rapidly, otherwise they may cause further insulation breakdown.

Because the neutral point is elevated to almost normal line-to-neutral voltage above earth during a ground fault, this method is not suitable for 4-wire, 3-phase systems with line-to-neutral connected loads.

Obviously no single method of system grounding satisfys all possible situations. The application engineer must solve the problem on the basis of individual requirements. In general, the solidly-grounded neutral system has proven satisfactory for low-voltage power systems. In some instances, the high resistance-grounded neutral system may be preferred. Each system grounding method has technical advantages and disadvantages.

The next Section (6-3) will discuss the recommended system neutral grounding methods for medium-voltage systems of 2.4 to 15 kv and high-voltage systems above 15 kv; it will present industrial versus utility practices; and will outline the selection of the system grounding point and neutral circuit arrangement.

6.3 Medium-Voltage Systems Should Not Be Operated Ungrounded

Section 6.2 discussed the basic factors influencing the engineer's selection of properly grounded or ungrounded neutral systems. The second part, section 6.2, presented the advantages and disadvantages of frequently employed methods of system neutral grounding for low-voltage systems. This section discusses recommended neutral grounding methods for medium-voltage 2.4- to 15-kv systems, and for systems above 15 kv. Figures and tables are numbered consecutively in the series.

The main neutral grounding methods used in medium-voltage power systems are: ungrounded, solid grounding, low- or high-resistance grounding, reactance grounding and ground-fault neutralizers.

The main characteristics and recommended applications for each of these methods follow:

Ungrounded systems are not recommended for medium-voltage installations because there is a high probability of failures due to transient overvoltages caused by restriking ground faults. Transient fault currents can be relatively high frequencies, ranging from one to eight kHz with associated current magnitudes ranging from less than 100 to perhaps 1,000 amp.

These disturbances are usually caused by arcing faults in the system—such as conductors nearly touching a grounded enclosure or repetitive restriking of the arc during line-to-ground fault interruptions.

With an arcing ground fault, successive arc restrikes and series resonance can cause trapped charges to build up voltages ranging from 500 to 600 percent of normal, subjecting the equipment and conductor insulation to considerable dangerous stresses. Furthermore, maintenance costs may be high because ground faults are difficult to ˙locate in ungrounded systems.

Service reliability is poor, since part or all of the system has to be taken out of service to find the fault location. If a ground fault is not rapidly detected and removed, a second ground fault may cause two circuits to fail at the same time. High fault currents associated with two line-to-ground faults usually result in more equipment damage. In addition, ungrounded systems in medium-voltage distri-

Solid grounding has the lowest initial cost of all grounding methods

butions require ground detector fault locator equipment and well-trained personnel.

In summary, medium-voltage systems should not be operated ungrounded because of the high failure probabilities resulting from transient overvoltages caused by restriking ground faults, and because of unsatisfactory service reliability and maintenance. Ground detectors and fault locators may be costly.

Solid grounding, which has the lowest initial cost of all grounding methods, is recommended for overhead distribution systems supplied by transformers protected by primary fuses. The solid grounding provides enough fault current to melt the primary fuses at the occurrence of a secondary ground-fault current.

However, this method is not preferred for industrial and commercial power system grounding because of the severe damage it can produce to the rotating machinery windings. Rotating machinery directly connected at medium voltages is very common. Low-resistance grounding is preferred because it reduces the fault current and consequential damages that may result from a ground fault in the machine windings.

Small systems supplied with transformers and without appreciable rotating machinery connected at medium-voltage, may use the solid grounding system in the interest of economy and because ground-fault currents are not too large.

Solid grounding combats most of the difficulties associated with ungrounded systems, since it eliminates the resonance-based overvoltage possibilities by avoiding line-to-ground capacitance.

On the other hand, ground-fault currents in solidly-grounded systems may become very high in many cases, causing flash hazards and excessive damage at fault points.

Another disadvantage of the solidly-grounded system is that a phase-to-ground fault must be immediately interrupted, de-energizing the affected circuit. In some process industries this forced outage is undesirable, especially where continuity of operation is very important. The alternative is a high-resistance grounding system.

In summary, solid grounding is mainly used in low-voltage and

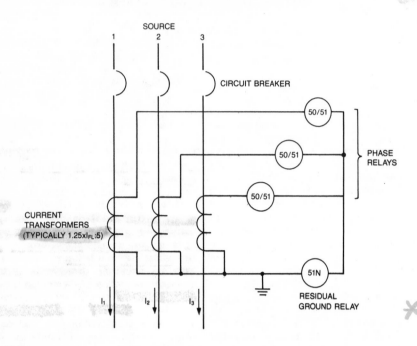

FIGURE 8   RESIDUAL RELAYING SCHEME—GROUND RELAY IN
CURRENT TRANSFORMER NEUTRAL CONNECTION CARRIES CURRENT ONLY
AT THE OCCURENCE OF A GROUND FAULT

applied to low-voltage systems. However, low-voltage circuit breakers are now available with three built-in current transformers, residually connected, with solid-state trip devices providing ground-fault protection. The basic residual scheme is shown in Figure 8. Each phase relay is connected in the output circuit of the respective current transformers and the ground relay is connected in the residual circuit measuring the

Ground sensor relays use a window- or donut-type current transformer

ground-fault current. Under normal conditions, no current flows in the residual leg, since the net result of the three current transformers fluxes is zero. When a ground fault occurs, the net flux is not zero and current flows in the residual leg operating the ground-fault relay. With a residual relaying scheme, the minimum pick-up relay is limited to the current transformer ratio.

Ground sensor scheme—This scheme uses a window-type current transformer, (also known as a donut-type current transformer). The three phases pass through the same opening in the current transformer, so all phases are surrounded by the magnetic core of the window-type current transformer (see Figure 9). For loads connected line-to-neutral, the window or donut-type current transformer also encloses the neutral conductor.

Under normal conditions, short circuits not involving ground and passing through the current transformer result in a zero net flux. Consequently, no current flows in the ground relay. If a ground fault occurs, the current transformer detects the unbalance in the magnetic fluxes surrounding the 3-phase conductors. The resulting flux, which is proportional to the ground-fault current, generates a current that flows in the relay circuit operating the ground-fault relay.

Neutral ground scheme—This scheme senses ground-fault current as transformed by a window-type current transformer connected in the resistance-grounded system neutral grounding conductor (see Figure 10). This scheme uses a time-delay overcurrent relay connected in the secondary of a current transformer whose primary is in the neutral of a wye-connected transformer, generator

high-voltage transmission systems over 15 kv. Solid grounding is seldom used in medium-voltage systems because of extremely high ground-fault currents with the possibility of heavy damage to rotating machinery operated at these voltages.

Low-resistance grounding is preferred for systems between 1,000 and 15,000 v, especially where there is directly connected rotating machinery.

Neutral resistance grounding in medium-voltage systems provides the following benefits:

• It provides longer insulation life expectancy for motors, transformers and other components by reducing the magnitude and duration of overvoltages.

• It provides improved protective relaying, since ground faults can be rapidly and selectively detected by sensitive relays. Tripping of standard overcurrent relays is accomplished with low values of fault-current magnitude.

• It provides extra protection for rotating machinery in which conductors lie close to machine iron slots. The resistance grounding system limits the ground-fault current in the machine windings, preventing the burning of the iron.

• It provides reduced electric-shock hazard to personnel.

The neutral resistor "ohm" value is selected to produce a ground-fault current that will accommodate the prevailing system's ground-fault philosophy.

Low-resistance grounding uses a resistor producing a bolted ground-fault current of such a magnitude to insure proper operation of ground relays. Most low-resistance grounded systems have ground-fault current levels of 50 to 1,200 amp. The circuit becomes resistive and the ground-fault current has negligible switching currents and overvoltages. Consequently, overvoltages and transient currents connected with ground-faults are minimal and well controlled.

In medium-voltage systems, ground-fault protection is commonly provided by three relaying schemes:

Residual relaying scheme—This scheme detects ground-fault current by sensing the current remaining in the secondary of the three phases of the circuit as transformed by the current transformers. The current transformers are connected so the ground relay responds to a current proportional to the ground-fault current. This scheme is not usually

170

or a derived neutral developed by a zig-zag connected transformer. Positive tripping is accomplished with low magnitudes of current. This is why low-resistance grounding is commonly used in medium-voltage systems.

With adequate ground relaying, 50 to 150 amp of ground-fault current is enough to obtain 10 percent relay sensitivity. For example, when combining a 50/5 zero sequence current transformer with a .25-.5 amp instantaneous ground-current relay having a pick-up of 5 amp, a maximum ground fault of 50 amp is enough for 10 percent sensitivity.

Conventional residual relaying would require hundreds and perhaps thousands of amp of ground-fault current to obtain the same 10 percent sensitivity. This is due to the high ratios of current-transformers associated with residual relaying schemes.

With a grounding resistor limiting the maximum ground-fault current to not greater than 100 amp, the neutral ground (zero-sequence) scheme will protect approximately 95 percent of the motor winding. To obtain 95 percent motor winding protection with the residual scheme, a grounding resistor of 2,000 amp would be required. This is another advantage of zero-sequence relaying, which allows the use of smaller grounding resistors while providing adequate relaying.

With the residual scheme, the larger the motor, the smaller the fraction of winding that will be protected for a given grounding resistor size. The zero-sequence scheme is independent of the motor size.

In low-resistance grounding, the phase-to-ground fault-current is usually kept at 20 percent of 3-phase fault current, and downward to 400 amp, which is frequently adopted for power systems using ground sensor (zero-sequence relaying).

A system properly grounded by resistance is not subject to transient overvoltages, unless the resistance is so high as to limit the ground-fault current to less than the system charging current.

Where lightning arresters are required, an ungrounded neutral type may be selected.

High-resistance grounding limits ground-fault current to a very low value, usually under .1 percent of the 3-phase fault-current.

Typically, the current is limited from 1 amp to a maximum of 10 amps by selecting the high-resistance neutral grounding to satisfy the value $R_n \geqq \dfrac{E_{l-n}}{I_c}$. E_{l-n} is the

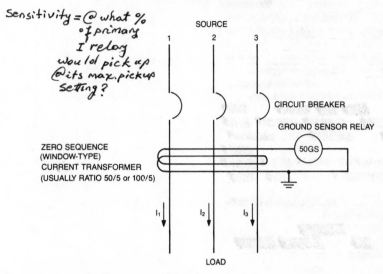

FIGURE 9   GROUND SENSOR SCHEME—ZERO-SEQUENCE CURRENT TRANSFORMER ENCIRCLES ALL PHASE CONDUCTORS. GROUND SENSOR RELAY DETECTS UNBALANCE IN THE MAGNETIC FLUXES SURROUNDING THE 3-PHASE CONDUCTORS THAT OCCURS ONLY ON GROUND FAULTS

FIGURE 10   NEUTRAL GROUND SCHEME—NEUTRAL GROUND RELAY SENSES GROUND-FAULT CURRENT ONLY, AS TRANSFORMED BY ZERO-SEQUENCE CURRENT TRANSFORMER CONNECTED IN RESISTANCE-GROUNDED SYSTEM NEUTRAL GROUNDING CONDUCTOR

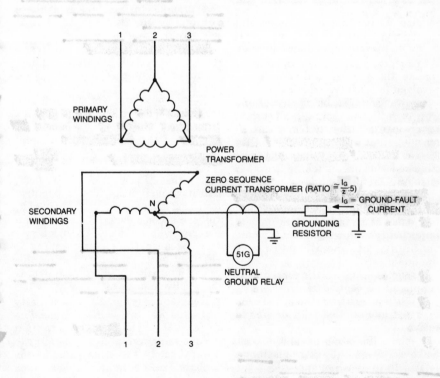

171

system line-to-neutral voltage; I_c is the total capacitance charging current of all three phases.

This high value resistance will dampen the resonant circuit to a point where no substantial overvoltages can be developed. Due to the presence of a high neutral resistor, the resistive current adds 90 deg to the capacitance current, producing a total current that is approximately one half or more greater than the ungrounded system fault current. Such a magnitude of ground-fault current may be tolerated for some time before removal becomes necessary. With this system, the first ground-fault is allowed to persist until the fault is detected and removed. High-resistance grounding is often used in essential services where power supply continuity is of great importance.

Ground-fault escalation tendency limits high-resistance grounding to approximately 8 amp ground-fault current for 2.4- and 4.16-kv systems.

Fault-current magnitude is predictable for all fault locations, since the resistance value inserted in the neutral is large compared to the remainder of ground-fault path impedance. This provides for a ground-fault current

High-resistance grounding limits ground-fault current to a low value

satisfactory for relaying purposes and overvoltage control, and yet sufficiently low to prevent immediate tripping.

Load processes are not interrupted due to the low ground-fault values involved in sensitive relaying.

Allowance must be made for the flow of sufficient ground-fault current to compensate the system's capacitance-to-ground charging current. Otherwise, transient overvoltages could be triggered during switching or other changing circuit conditions.

High-resistance grounding should be applied in the following situations:

• When it is important to prevent immediate shutdowns in plants where continuity of operations is very important.

• When a single rotating machine is supplied by a captive transformer.

• When an existing system has been operated ungrounded without ground relays.

• Where limitation of fault damage and overvoltage is desired, and ground relay selectivity is not applied.

The protective scheme associated

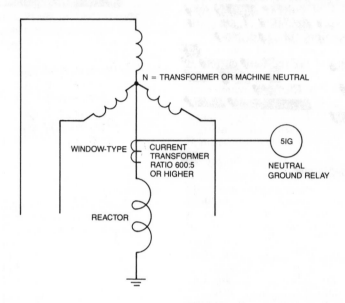

FIGURE 11 REACTANCE GROUNDING—REACTOR CONNECTED BETWEEN TRANSFORMER OR MACHINE NEUTRAL AND GROUND

N = TRANSFORMER OR MACHINE NEUTRAL

WINDOW-TYPE

CURRENT TRANSFORMER RATIO 600:5 OR HIGHER

REACTOR

5IG

NEUTRAL GROUND RELAY

with high-resistance grounding is detection and alarm rather than immediate trip-out. Lightning arresters, if used, may be rated for ungrounded neutral. Alert and well-trained personnel are essential in plants with high-resistance grounding.

High-resistance grounding has been used more frequently on low-voltage systems, because there are no inexpensive ground-sensing devices at these voltage levels that would permit selective relaying at low cost.

Reactance grounding implies a reactor connected between a transformer or machine neutral and ground (see Figure 11).

To minimize transient overvoltages, the reactor must be selected to limit the ground-fault current to a minimum 25 percent of the 3-phase fault current which corresponds to a ratio of $\frac{X_o}{X_1} = 10$.

At less than 25 percent of 3-phase fault, transitory overvoltages due to repetitive restriking in an arc of a ground-fault circuit can become dangerous. This is not the case with resistance-grounded systems because the electric energy is absorbed by the resistor. The resistor cannot return the energy to the system as the reactive equipment can.

Reactance grounding is usually restricted to low-voltage generators under 600 v. The purpose is to limit ground-fault current in any winding to approximately the same value as the 3-phase fault current. Without some impedance to ground, the current from

an AC generator would exceed the 3-phase fault current for which the generators are usually rated.

Medium-voltage generators are generally resistance grounded because this restricts ground-fault current to low values—often less than 5 percent of 3-phase fault current. Therefore, reactor grounding is usually not considered as an alternative to resistance grounding in medium-voltage systems.

In summary, for small systems supplied by generators, reactor grounding producing not less than 25 percent of 3-phase fault may be used in the interest of economy and because ground-fault currents are not too large. If the system is small and supplied by transformers, solid grounding may be used for the same reasons.

The use of grounded neutral lightning arresters connected to overhead lines is the main reason for selecting reactance or solid grounding for industrial power systems of 2.4 to 15 kv.

At medium-voltage levels, reactance grounding is used only if the following conditions are present:

• Overhead circuits are directly connected to rotating equipment and subject to lightning exposure.

• Reactance grounding does not result in excessive ground fault. In this case, the neutral reactor of the generator must be selected so that $\frac{X_o}{X_1} \geq 1$ and the $\frac{X_o}{X_1}$ ratio of the system must be equal to or less than 3 to permit the use of grounded neutral lightning arresters.

Ground-fault neutralizers have a reactor that has specially selected relatively high value of reactance connected between the neutral of the system and ground.

A line-to-ground fault impresses a line-to-neutral voltage across the neutralizer characterized by an inductive current (see Figure 12). This inductive current is 180 deg out of phase and is approximately equal to the resultant of the system-charging currents Ib and Ic of the two unfaulted phases. Inductive and capacitive components of currents neutralize each other and the remaining current in the fault is due only to resistance, corona and insulator leakage. This current is generally of low magnitude and as it is in phase with the line-to-neutral voltage, the current and voltage pass through zero at the same moment. The arc is extinguished without flashovers or restriking and without removing the faulted section from service.

Using ground-fault neutralizers improves service continuity especially in systems in which faults in air are relatively frequent. The number of circuit breaker operations necessary to remove faults is reduced, and service continuity improved. This system is primarily used on 15 kv and more overhead transmission lines.

In general, ground-fault neutralizers are used in systems with the following characteristics:

• Large existing systems, with maximum two current transformers per circuit.

• Systems with heavy charging current subject to lightning exposure in which damage to rotating machinery may result from a ground fault if the system is left ungrounded.

• Systems susceptible to arcing grounds, especially overhead lines.

Care should be taken to keep the ground-fault neutralizer tuned to the system capacitance to minimize the generation of transient overvoltages.

High-voltage systems above 15 kv should be solidly grounded to permit the use of equipment with insulation to ground, rated for less than full line-to-line voltage. Neutral grounding at these high voltages is very expensive. At 15 kv and above, there are usually transmission circuits with open lines in which grounded-neutral type lightning arresters are used for a better overvoltage protection at lower cost. Rotating equipment is seldom connected directly at these high voltages, and limiting ground-fault current to prevent burning of iron laminations is not the important factor, as in medium-voltage systems. Voltages above 15 kv are not carried inside buildings, therefore, shock hazard due to high-fault currents is not a factor.

Industrial versus utility

Grounding practices differ between industrial and utility systems, but the basic principles of neutral grounding apply in both systems. In general, utility practices favor solid grounding because this permits the use of neutral-type lightning arresters which reduce investment and improve protection levels.

Solid grounding results in savings in the transformer-graded insulation at 115 kv and above. Most of the ground faults on utility systems occur from insulator flashovers. High ground-

FIGURE 12   GROUND-FAULT CURRENT IN SYSTEMS GROUNDED BY GROUND-FAULT NEUTRALIZERS—INDUCTIVE I_n CURRENTS AND CAPACITIVE COMPONENTS OF CURRENTS I_c, I_b, NEUTRALIZE EACH OTHER. THE REMAINING CURRENT IN THE FAULT IS DUE TO RESISTANCE, CORONA AND INSULATOR LEAKAGE

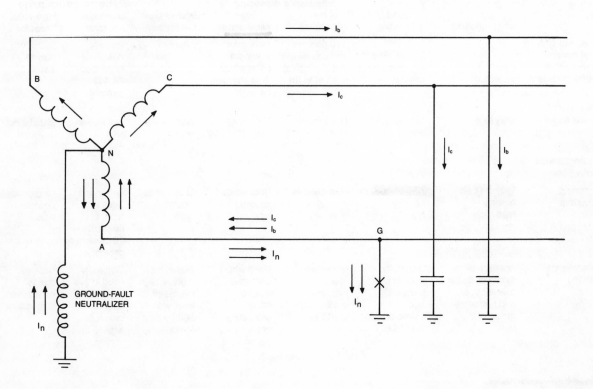

fault currents, due to solid grounding, do not cause expensive damages at the fault points.

This is not the case with industrial power systems with usual voltage levels of 2.4 to 13.8 kv. Here, the main objective is to insure reduced magnitudes of ground-fault current and provide better protection for motor and generator windings and iron laminations. Table 2 summarizes industrial versus utility grounding practice requirements.

Based on current practices, the most desirable methods for system neutral grounding in industrial plants are:

• For systems 600 v and below solid grounding is usually adopted.

• For 2.4- to 15-kv rated systems, low-resistance grounding is used in most cases. Solid grounding in cases where available ground fault is not objectionable, and especially where a majority of line-to-neutral loads are served.

• For systems rated 22 kv and higher solid grounding is usually adopted.

High resistance grounding is usually considered when the industrial system user does not want to adopt the neutral grounding methods.

Table 3 summarizes the characteristics of the various grounding methods and suggests application guides and limits based on the magnitude of transient overvoltages; damage at the fault point in relationship with the magnitude of fault current; proper application of standard relaying for a selective ground-fault tripping; and lightning protection.

Each method of system ground has advantages and disadvantages, and no single method can be declared best for all cases. The choice of grounding methods is dictated by such factors as: voltage level, transient overvoltage possibilities, type of system equipment, desired continuity of service, caliber and training of maintenance personnel, availability of a convenient grounding point, cost of protective and maintenance devices, and personal safety. Selection must be based on the particular and specific requirements of the plant considered.

The next section (6.4) will discuss neutral circuit arrangement, selection of system grounding point, protection of grounding equipment and calculation procedure for ground-fault current magnitude in industrial power systems.

TABLE 2—SUMMARY OF INDUSTRIAL VERSUS UTILITY GROUNDING PRACTICES

	Industrial	Utility
High continuity of power requirements	Yes	Yes
Prevalent method of conducting power	Cables	Overhead lines
Percent of system subject to lightning hazard	Small	Large
Lightning arresters investment	Small	Large
Voltage levels above 15 kv	Few systems	Many systems
Rotating machinery at distribution or transmission voltage level	Mostly yes	Not ususally

TABLE 3—SUMMARY OF VARIOUS GROUNDING SYSTEM CHARACTERISTICS

	Ungrounded	Solid grounding	Resistance grounding Low resistance	Resistance grounding High resistance	Ground-fault neutralizer	Reactance grounding Low-value reactor	Reactance grounding High-value reactor
Phase-to-ground fault current in percent of 3-phase current	Less than 1 percent	Varies, may be 100 percent greater	Δ20 percent and downward to 400 amp (a) to 25 amp (b)	Less than 1 percent but not less than charging current	Nearly zero fault-current	Usually designed to produce 26-100 percent	5 to 10 percent
Transient overvoltages	Very high	Not excessive	Not excessive	Not excessive	Not excessive	Not excessive	Very high
Automatic segregation of faulty-zone	no	yes	yes	no	no	yes	yes
Lightning arresters	Ungrounded neutral-type	*Grounded neutral-type	Ungrounded neutral-type	Ungrounded neutral-type	Ungrounded neutral-type	Grounded neutral-type, if current is 60 percent or greater	Ungrounded neutral-type
Recommendations	Not recommended, due to overvoltages and nonsegregation of fault	Generally used in systems 600v and below, or over 15 kv	Generally used on industrial systems of 2.5-15 kv	Used when characteristics of other grounding systems are not desired	Suited for high-voltage overhead-lines with self-healing faults	Generally used in systems 600v and below, or over 15 kv	Not used due to excessive overvoltage

$$X_o/X_1 \leqq 3.0 \text{ and } R_o/X_1 \leqq 1.0$$

*Provided at the arrester location
Δ (a) Lower limit for power systems using ground sensor relaying
Δ (b) Lower limit for portable excavating machine power supply systems

6.4   Proper Neutral Circuit Arrangement

Section 6.1 discussed the basic factors influencing the engineer's selection of properly grounded or ungrounded neutral systems.

Section 6.2 presented the advantages and disadvantages of frequently employed methods of system neutral grounding for low-voltage systems.

Section 6.3 dealt with recommended neutral grounding methods for medium-voltage 2.4- to 15-kv systems.

This section discusses neutral circuit arrangement, selection of system grounding points, and symmetrical component calculation procedure for determining ground-fault current magnitudes in industrial power systems. Figures and tables are numbered consecutively.

The question often arises as to how many generator or transformer neutrals should be used for grounding, and whether each neutral should be connected independently to ground, or if a neutral bus with a single ground connection should be used. The answer depends on whether a single power source or multiple power sources are involved.

When the power system has only a single power source generator or transformer, grounding is accomplished as shown in Figure 13. It is not necessary to provide a switch or circuit breaker in the neutral circuit, because the potential to ground is practically zero, except during fault time. Besides, it is not advisable to operate the system ungrounded while the generator or transformer are operating. If a disconnecting means is required, a metal clad circuit breaker is preferred to an open disconnect switch. An open disconnect switch may constitute a hazard to

FIGURE 13   GROUNDING OF A SINGLE POWER SOURCE

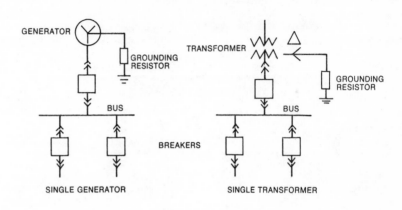

FIGURE 14   GROUNDING OF MULTIPLE SOURCE SYSTEM

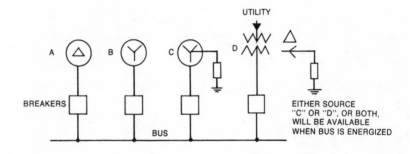

TABLE 15   GROUNDING BY MEANS OF COMMON NEUTRAL BUS: ONE GROUNDING RESISTOR AND SWITCHGEAR

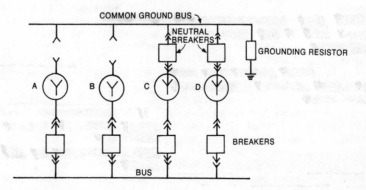

FIGURE 16   EACH VOLTAGE LEVEL MUST BE INDEPENDENTLY GROUNDED

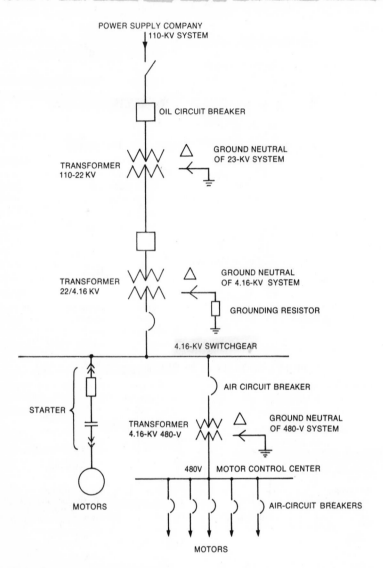

they must be of the metal-enclosed type and interlocked with the supplying transformer or generator main disconnect breaker, to prevent disconnect switch operation when the main breaker is in a closed position.

System grounding point

To achieve the proper protection and advantages of neutral grounding, each voltage level must be grounded independently (see Figure 16.)

For example, if the 4.16-kv system in the one-line diagram were not grounded, it would have the characteristics of an ungrounded system, whereas the 23-kv and the 480-v levels would have the characteristics of grounded systems. Therefore, it is mandatory to ground the neutral lead of the generators, power transformers, or grounding transformers at each voltage level.

A sufficient number of generators or transformers must be grounded to assure that at least one ground on the system is connected at all times. Power sources are fewer in number than loads, and are less likely to be disconnected. Ground-fault current may be excessively high when all load ground points are in service. Consequently, the grounding should be made at the power source and not at the load, as shown in Figure 17.

When there are several major source bus sections, each one should have at least one grounded neutral point since the bus tie circuit may be opened (see Figure 18).

Generally 3-phase ungrounded faults impose the most severe duty on

personnel if a ground fault occurs at the time the switch is being opened or closed.

When there are multiple power sources with a few generators or transformers in a station, individual neutral impedances are used (see Figure 14). When there are more than two or three generators or transformers at one station, it is preferable to use a single resistor with each power source connected to the resistor through a neutral bus and neutral switching equipment as shown in Figure 15.

This system keeps the ground-fault current to a minimum, because the ground-fault current cannot be greater than can be supplied through a single resistor.

The same value of ground current will be assured regardless of the number of generators or transformers in use, thus simplifying the ground relaying. The neutral circuit breakers isolate the generator or transformer neutrals from the neutral bus when they are taken out of service.

If the total ground-fault current with several individual resistors exceeds 4,000 amps, it is advisable to use a neutral switchgear bus and a single resistor.

If disconnect switches are used instead of the preferred circuit breakers,

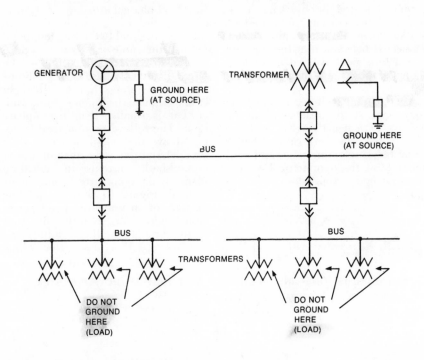

FIGURE 17 GROUND AT THE SOURCE AND NOT AT THE LOAD

NOTE: WHEN POWER SOURCES ARE DELTA CONNECTED, USE
GROUNDING TRANSFORMER RATHER THAN GROUNDING AT LOAD.

FIGURE 18   GROUNDING A SYSTEM WITH TWO OR MORE SECTIONS
WHICH MAY OPERATE INDEPENDENTLY

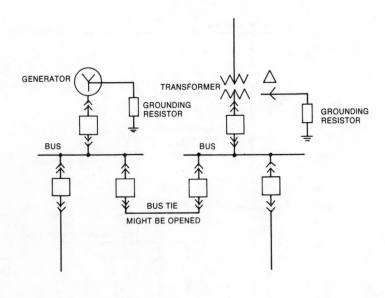

protective devices. Short-circuits on a balanced 3-phase system produce balanced 3-phase faults; whereas line-to-ground faults, as well as line-to-line faults, produce unbalanced 3-phase faults. If unusual reactance values exist, a phase-to-ground fault may sometimes provide a larger short-circuit current than a 3-phase fault. Therefore, 3-phase faults, as well as line-to-ground faults, must be calculated. Since the line-to-ground fault is unbalanced, symmetrical component analysis is used for an accurate determination of such faults.

The theory of symmetrical components consists of reducing an unbalanced 3-phase system of vectors into three balanced systems known as the positive, negative and zero phase sequence components.

The reactances of the sequence components are designated as $X_1 =$ positive-sequence reactance; $X_2 =$ negative-sequence reactance; and $X_0 =$ zero-sequence reactance. These values represent the reactances of the system to the flow of positive, negative and zero-sequence currents. For a more detailed discussion of symmetrical components, see the "Coordination Protection for Electrical Systems in Plants" (section 4.7).

The following formula (developed by Fortescue) is based on symmetrical components theory and expresses the value of single line-to-ground fault I_{fL-G} in amperes:

$$I_{fL-G} = \frac{3 \times E_{l-n}}{X_1 + X_2 + X_0}$$

Where E_{l-n} is the voltage of the system line-to-neutral in volts; X_1, X_2 and X_0 are positive, negative and zero reactances expressed in ohms per phase on the voltage base (if the networks are set up on ohms on a voltage base).

Reactances of transformers and rotating machinery are usually expressed in percent or per unit values on their own kva rating. Since different units may be involved it is necessary to reduce all of them to a chosen base. Formulas for such conversions were shown in chapter 4, section 4.5.

Synchronous machinery has typical reactance values such as synchronous (X_d), transient (X'_d) and subtransient (X''_d) while are positive-sequence reactances (X_1). Usually the negative-sequence reactance (X_2) is equal to the subtransient, except for water-wheel generators without damper windings. The zero-sequence reactance of rotating machinery (X_0) is less than any of the others.

Transformers have identical positive- and negative-sequence reactances. The zero-sequence reactance also has the same value as the positive and negative ones, except for 3-phase core transformers with connections blocking the zero-sequence current.

Zero-sequence currents will not flow if the transformer neutral is ungrounded; X_0 is considered infinite when zero-sequence current cannot flow.

When zero-sequence currents can flow, X_0 is equal to the positive-sequence reactance. In a Wye-Delta connected transformer, the zero-sequence current flows through the neutral connection of the Wye if the neutral is grounded, but no zero-sequence currents can flow in the Delta-side connection. In a Wye-Wye connected transformer, zero-sequence currents can flow in both primary and secondary if enough connections from neutral-to-ground provide current path.

Resistance of the transformer winding is usually neglected in fault-current calculations. For transmission lines and cables, the positive and negative reactances are considered equal; the zero-sequence is different, because the zero-sequence current returns via the earth or overhead ground wire. Usually, the zero-sequence reactance in transmission lines is larger than the positive and negative sequences. An exact value of zero-sequence reactance for cables and transmission lines involves complex calculations. For fair estimates, a ratio of X_0 provides practical values. For example, a 3-conductor cable with non-metallic sheath or conduit and earth return will have a X_0 ratio of 3 to 5.

The following three network diagrams are necessary (phase-to-neutral of power system):

• The positive-sequence network showing generator voltages, reactances of generators, transformers and lines.

• The negative-sequence network is usually a duplication of the positive-sequence network except no generator voltages are shown since no generator operates with reverse phase order. Negative-sequence reactances of synchronous machinery may occasionally differ from positive-sequence reactances.

• The zero-sequence network is usually similar to the negative-sequence network except special attention should be given to transformer connections. Wye-Wye grounded transformers allow zero-sequence current to flow from one side of the bank to the other. Wye-Delta connected banks allow current to flow in the grounded neutral, but block passage of zero-sequence current from one bank to the other. Resistors and reactors connected between transformers and/or machine neutrals and ground are shown at three times their normal value.

After reducing all reactances to an equivalent single reactance for the positive (X_1), negative (X_2), and zero (X_0) sequence network values, the formula for single line-to-ground fault derived by the symmetrical components method is applied:

$$I_{fL\text{-}G} \quad \frac{3 \times E_{l\text{-}n}}{X_1 + X_2 + X_0}$$

Usually X_2 is equal with X_1. If X_0 is equal with X_1, then the formula is reduced to $\dfrac{E_{l\text{-}n}}{X}$ which is the expression for the 3-phase fault current. Consequently, the 3-phase fault current in this case is equal to the line-to-ground fault. If the value of X_0 is less than X_1, the line-to-ground fault current will be larger than the 3-phase fault. In industrial power systems, X_0 is usually higher than X_1, and the line-to-ground fault current is smaller than the 3-phase fault. The following numerical example shows the calculation procedure for determining the magnitude of ground-fault currents in industrial plants by the symmetrical components method. Figure 19 shows a one-line diagram of an industrial plant power system with a 132-kv utility line supplying through an oil circuit breaker a 10,000-kva, 4.16-kv transformer which

FIGURE 19   ONE-LINE DIAGRAM OF AN INDUSTRIAL POWER SYSTEM

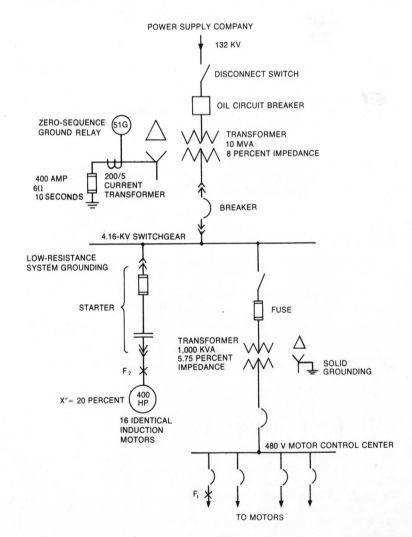

FIGURE 20 3-PHASE FAULT CALCULATION AT FAULT POINT F₁

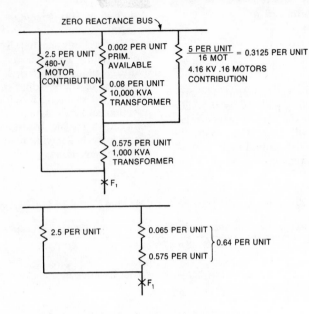

ZERO REACTANCE BUS

2.5 PER UNIT 480-V MOTOR CONTRIBUTION

0.002 PER UNIT PRIM. AVAILABLE

0.08 PER UNIT 10,000 KVA TRANSFORMER

$\dfrac{5 \text{ PER UNIT}}{16 \text{ MOT}}$ = 0.3125 PER UNIT

4.16 KV .16 MOTORS CONTRIBUTION

0.575 PER UNIT 1,000 KVA TRANSFORMER

✗F₁

2.5 PER UNIT

0.065 PER UNIT
0.575 PER UNIT
} 0.64 PER UNIT

✗F₁

$$\frac{1}{0.082} + \frac{1}{0.3125} = \frac{1}{X}$$

$$\frac{0.082 \times 0.3125}{0.082 + 0.3125} = 0.065 \text{ PER UNIT}$$

$$\frac{1}{2.5} + \frac{1}{0.64} = \frac{1}{X}$$

$$X = \frac{2.5 \times 0.64}{2.5 + 0.64} = 0.51 \text{ PER UNIT}$$

$$\text{3-PHASE FAULT} = \frac{10,000 \text{ KVA}}{0.48 \text{ KV} \times 1.73 \times 0.51} = \frac{23,612 \text{ AMP}}{\text{SYMMETRICAL}}$$

POSITIVE-SEQUENCE REACTANCE = X = 0.51 PER UNIT

NEGATIVE-SEQUENCE REACTANCE = X_2=XI= -.51 PER UNIT

ZERO-SEQUENCE REACTANCE = X_0 = 0.575 PER UNIT
(REACTANCE OF 1,000 KVA TRANSFORMER)

FIGURE 21   LINE-TO-GROUND FAULT CALCULATION AT FAULT POINT F₁

THE REACTANCE DIAGRAM OF THE POSITIVE, NEGATIVE AND ZERO SEQUENCE REACTANCES PER PHASE AT FAULT LOCATION F₁ IS:

X_1 = 0.51 PER UNIT POSITIVE-SEQUENCE REACTANCE

X_2 = 0.51 PER UNIT NEGATIVE-SEQUENCE REACTANCE

X_0 = 0.575 PER UNIT ZERO-SEQUENCE REACTANCE

THE GROUND FAULT PHASE TO NEUTRAL I_{L-G} AT F₁ IS GIVEN BY THE SYMMETRICAL COMPONENTS FORMULA:

(1) $I_{L-G} = \dfrac{3 \times E_{L-G}}{X_1 + X_2 + X_0}$

WHERE E_{L-G} IS IN VOLTS AND X_1, X_2, X_0 IN OHMS/PHASE

THE VALUES CALCULATED FOR X_1, X_2 and X_0 WERE EXPRESSED IN PER-UNIT (p.u.) ON THE SELECTED BASE

TO CONVERT THEM IN OHMS, USE FORMULA:

$$X \text{ ohm} = \frac{X \text{ p.u.} \times KV^2 \times 1,000}{KVA \text{ BASE}}$$

$$X_1 = X_2 = \frac{0.51 \times 0.48^2 \times 1,000}{10,000 \text{ KVA}} = 0.0118 \text{ OHMS}$$

$$X_0 = \frac{0.575 \times 0.48^2 \times 1,000}{10,000 \text{ KVA}} = 0.0132 \text{ OHMS}$$

SUBSTITUTING IN FORMULA (1)

$$I_{L-G} = \frac{3 \times \dfrac{480V}{1.73}}{0.0118 + 0.0118 + 0.0132} = 22,618 \text{ AMP SYMMETRICAL}$$

THE LINE-TO-GROUND FAULT I_{L-G} AT POINT F IS LOWER IN VALUE THAN THE 3-PHASE FAULT AT THE SAME LOCATION (SEE FIGURE 20)

FIGURE 22   3-PHASE FAULT CALCULATION AT FAULT POINT F₂

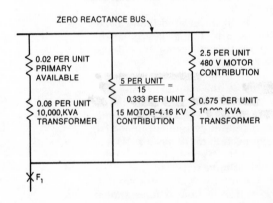

ZERO REACTANCE BUS

0.02 PER UNIT PRIMARY AVAILABLE

0.08 PER UNIT 10,000,KVA TRANSFORMER

$\dfrac{5 \text{ PER UNIT}}{15}$ = 0.333 PER UNIT

15 MOTOR-4.16 KV CONTRIBUTION

2.5 PER UNIT 480 V MOTOR CONTRIBUTION

0.575 PER UNIT 10,000 KVA TRANSFORMER

✗F₁

$$\frac{1}{0.082} + \frac{1}{0.333} + \frac{1}{3.075} = \frac{1}{X}$$

$12.195 + 3 + 0.325 = \dfrac{1}{X}$ X = 0.0644 PER UNIT

$$\text{3-PHASE FAULT} = \frac{10,000 \text{ KVA}}{4.16 \text{KV} \times 1.73 \times 0.0644} = 21,576 \text{ AMP SYMMETRICAL}$$

POSITIVE-SEQUENCE REACTANCE, X_1 = 0.0644 PER UNIT

NEGATIVE-SEQUENCE REACTANCE, X_2 = X_1 = 0.0644 PER UNIT

ZERO-SEQUENCE REACTANCE X_0 = 0.08 PER UNIT
(REACTANCE OF 10MVA TRANSFORMER)

---

in turn supplies power to a 4.16-kv switchgear. This switchgear supplies a 1,000-kva transformer stepping down the voltage to 480 v and terminating in a 480-v switchgear. The 4.16-kv switchgear supplies 16 400-hp induction motors.

Based on the previous sections and on the plant conditions, a solid-grounded neutral system is recommended for the 480-v transformer

TABLE 4   REACTANCE CONVERSION CALCULATION
Selected base = 10 mva
Primary available - 5,000 mva

Circuit element	Reactance on own rating base	Per unit reactance on chosen kva base
Primary available	50,000 mva	$\dfrac{10,000 \text{ kva}}{5,000,000 \text{ kva}}$ = 0.002 per unit
10,000 kva transformer	8 percent	0.08 per unit
1,000 kva transformer	5.75 percent	$0.0515 = \dfrac{10,000 \text{ kva}}{1,000}$ = 0.575 per unit
4.16 kv—400 hp induction motor	20 percent = "d	$0.2 \times \dfrac{10,000 \text{ kva}}{400}$ = 5 per unit

179

and a low-resistance grounded neutral system for the 4.16-kv transformer. The calculation for the 3-phase and ground-fault currents at 480 v and 4.16 kv is shown in Table 4, and Figures 19 through 23.

Neutral grounding resistor

Grounding resistors are normally rated to carry the current for a limited time only. With relays arranged to protect the grounding equipment, the standard time interval for industrial systems is 10 seconds.

The voltage rating of the grounding resistor is ~~in~~ the line-to-neutral voltage rating of the electrical system. The current rating corresponds to the current that will flow through the resistor with the rated resistor voltage applied. The ground protective relay will automatically interrupt the ground-fault current before the thermal limits of the resistor are exceeded. The rating of the resistor for low-resistance grounded neutral systems is based on the following:

- To provide sufficient current for proper functioning of the relaying scheme.
- To limit the ground-fault current to a value minimizing damage at the fault point without generation of system overvoltages.

In general, the ground-fault current is limited by the neutral resistor to a value considerably less than the 3-phase fault value. This value depends on the nature of equipment protected, their connection to the system (Wye or Delta) and the type of protective relay (residual, ground sensor etc.).

Table 5 provides values for grounding resistor selection. Values shown are minimum recommended ground-fault current in percent of rated current of current transformers, or in amperes for ground sensor protection.

For ground sensor protection, a zero-sequence current transformer is usually selected for half the ground-fault current; for a ground-fault current of 400 amp, a zero-sequence current transformer of 200/5 amp would be selected.

For the 10,000-kva transformer in the numerical example, an outdoor neutral grounding resistor made of corrosion-resistant steel is selected, rated for 4,160 v, L-L or 2,400 v, L-N and an initial current of 400 amp for 10 seconds.

The value of such a resistor is:

$$\frac{2,400 \text{ v L-N}}{400 \text{ amp}} = 6 \text{ ohms}$$

Selection is made for a 51 G zero-sequence ground relay, connected to a 200/5 current transformer, zero-sequence type. The relay should be set at 0.5 (minimum setting).

$$\frac{400 \text{ amp}}{200/5} = 10 \text{ amps}$$

$$200/5 \times 0.5 \text{ min. tap} = 20. \text{ A min. pickup}$$

The relay range .5-2 amp will provide a satisfactory pick-up range of 20-80 amp. With the zero-sequence relay for ground-fault protection, only 20 amps of primary ground-fault current is required to pick-up the relay.

The fraction of the motor winding protected is:

$$\frac{400-20}{400} \times 100 \text{ percent} = 95 \text{ percent}$$

Thus, a fault located 5 percent of the winding turns away from the neutral will be detected, leaving only 5 percent of the winding unprotected.

The next section 6.5 will discuss application and calculation of grounding components for high-resistance grounding in low- and medium-voltage industrial power systems.

FIGURE 23 LINE-TO-GROUND FAULT CALCULATION AT FAULT POINT F_2

THE REACTANCE DIAGRAM OF THE POSITIVE, NEGATIVE AND ZERO SEQUENCE REACTANCES PER PHASE AT FAULT LOCATION F_2 IS:

$X_1 = 0.0644$ PER UNIT POSITIVE-SEQUENCE REACTANCE

$X_2 = 0.0644$ PER UNIT NEGATIVE-SEQUENCE REACTANCE

$X_0 = 0.08$ PER UNIT ZERO-SEQUENCE REACTANCE

THE GROUND FAULT PHASE-TO-NEUTRAL IS GIVEN BY THE SYMMETRICAL COMPONENTS FORMULA:

$$(1) \quad I_{L-G} = \frac{3 \times E_{L-G}}{X_1 + X_2 + X_0}$$

WHERE E_{L-G} IS IN VOLTS AND X_1, X_2 AND X_0 IN OHMS/PHASE

THE VALUES CALCULATED FOR X_1, X_2 AND X_0 WERE EXPRESSED IN PER-UNIT (p.u.) ON THE SELECTED BASE.

CONVERTING THEM IN OHMS BY THE FORMULA:

$$X_{Ohm} = \frac{X \text{ p.u.} \times KV^2 \times 1,000}{KVA \text{ BASE}}$$

$$X_1 = X_2 = \frac{0.0644 \times 4.16^2 \times 1,000}{10,000} = 0.1114 \text{ OHM}$$

$$X_0 = \frac{0.08 \times 4.16^2 \times 1,000}{10,000} = 0.1384 \text{ OHM}$$

SUBSTITUTING IN FORMULA (1)

$$I_{L-G} = \frac{3 \times \frac{4160 \text{ V}}{1.73}}{0.1114 + 0.1114 + 0.1384} = 19,972 \text{ AMP SYMMETRICAL}$$

THE GROUND-FAULT CURRENT IS TOO HIGH TO PROTECT THE MOTOR WINDINGS. A LOW-RESISTANCE NEUTRAL GROUNDING IS INDICATED TO REDUCE THE GROUND-FAULT CURRENT TO 400 AMP

Note: Total Z For A fault located at 5% winding turns away from Neutral is only 5% of the value found from $Z_1 + Z_2 + 3Z_n + Z_0$. Similarly voltage is 5% of E_a.

$$\therefore I_{LG} = \frac{5\%}{5\%} \times \frac{I_{LG}}{100}$$

$$I_{LG} = \frac{5\%}{5\%}\left(\frac{E_a}{Z_1 + Z_2 + Z_n + Z_0}\right)$$

In above example this will give $I_{LG} = 80.6$ Amp which is min. required to pick-up the relay

TABLE 5   SELECTION OF GROUNDING RESISTOR
For low-resistance grounding only
Type of relay

Equipment protected	Ground Residual	Overcurrent Ground-sensor	Differential
Wye-connected generators, motors and transformers	100 percent	400 amp	100 percent
Delta-connected generators, motors and feeders and	40 percent	200 amp	40 percent
tie-lines buses	100 percent ——	200 amp ——	—— 50 percent

6.5 Four Main Neutral Grounding Methods Available

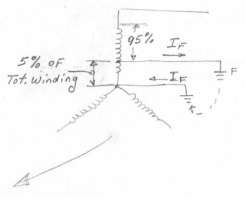

Fault @ 5% of the winding turns away from the neutral. ∴ 95% winding Z not in the fault I path & not included in total Z.

Section 6.1 discussed the basic factors influencing the engineer's selection of properly grounded or ungrounded neutral systems.

Section 6.2 presented the advantages and disadvantages of frequently-employed methods of system neutral grounding for low-voltage systems.

Section 6.3 dealt with recommended neutral grounding methods for medium-voltage 2.4- to 15-kv systems.

Section 6.4 covered neutral circuit arrangement, selection of system grounding point and symmetrical components calculation procedures. In part five, the author discusses application and calculation of grounding components for high-resistance grounding in low- and medium-voltage industrial power systems. Figures and tables are numbered consecutively.

Four main neutral grounding methods are available for the design engineer of an industrial power system. The system can be ungrounded, solidly grounded, low-resistance grounded or high-resistance grounded. A fifth method—reactance grounding—is seldom used in industrial power systems because of the severe transient overvoltages it can generate (as shown in part 3 of this series of articles).

Here are the advantages and disadvantages of the four main neutral grounding methods:

The *ungrounded system* allows continuation of operations at a ground fault occurrence on one phase. However, it has the disadvantage that if the

fault is not cleared, and another fault occurs in another phase, personnel may be subjected to dangerous overvoltages and also fire hazard becomes possible. Furthermore, the voltage spikes caused by switching surges, arcing faults, and transient conditions, can be of many times the magnitude of normal operating voltage, with the consequence of insulation breakdown.

The *solidly grounded system* limits system overvoltages and clears ground faults rapidly, but it has the disadvantage of interrupting operations immediately. Damage to the power might be high because of the high fault currents characteristic with solidly grounded systems.

Low resistance grounding is extensively used in medium-voltage systems because fault current is limited to a few hundred amperes, thus protecting rotating machinery from iron burning damage. The disadvantage is that this value of current is high enough to operate circuit protective devices. Faults must be cleared immediately as is the case also with solidly grounded systems.

High resistance grounding combines the advantages of the ungrounded system with those of the solidly grounded system. Indeed, the fault current is limited to a value allowing operations to continue until an orderly shutdown is possible and system overvoltages are kept to acceptable values. These two qualities make this method suitable for process industries where unscheduled outages have to be avoided and continuation of operation, even at a fault occurrence, is desired.

High resistance grounding is applied where neutral grounding is not acceptable because of a customer's preferences for ungrounded system

operating characteristics. This method is used mainly in process systems where continuity of operation at a ground-fault current occurrence is of great importance. High-resistance

High-resistance grounding limits transient voltages

grounding is also applied where there is an absence of adequate current transformers as the case may be in older systems or where the initial expense of installing the necessary grounding equipment is to be avoided.

Rather than operating an ungrounded system with the inherent disadvantage of dangerous transient overvoltages, high-resistance grounding can be applied.

High-resistance grounding limits the transient overvoltages resulting from line-to-ground faults to safe values, comparable to those encountered in lower-impedance grounding.

The steady-state fault current in high-resistance grounded systems is limited to less than one percent of the 3-phase fault current.

This small value of ground-fault current is not enough to energize the overcurrent protective devices, and consequently current transformers for purposes of ground-fault relaying are not considered. However, if the ground-fault current is permitted to flow for an extended period of time, the damages could exceed those of an ungrounded system by the creation of a deliberate ground circuit in the system neutral.

It is therefore important to remove the ground fault as soon as possible. There are ground-fault indicating and

181

locating equipment that detect and indicate the presence of a grounded circuit. Both ungrounded and high-resistance grounded systems are subject to the same problem of detecting the grounded circuit by ground-fault locating devices.

The operation of the ground-fault locating device is more efficient in the high-resistance grounded system (due to the flow of fault current) than in the ungrounded system.

The value of the resistance in a high-resistance grounding system has to be maximum equal, or smaller than the reactance of the charging current:
$R_o \le X_{co}$

The high-resistance grounding criteria is:
$$\frac{X_{co}}{R_o} \ge 1$$

Where R_o is the zero-sequence resistance and X_{co} the zero-sequence capacitive reactance. The same criteria also applies to the currents: $\dfrac{I_N}{I_c} \le 1$

Where I_N is the neutral ground-fault current and I_c is the 3-phase charging current.

Also: $\dfrac{\text{Kw in neutral resistor}}{\text{system 3-phase charging kva}}$
≥ 1

High resistance grounding for low-voltage industrial plant systems (480v), can be applied where there is no need for a solidly-grounded neutral to obtain 277v for lighting, and where continuity of operation must persist even with a fault developing in a feeder. Where production loss is to be avoided, and lighting is provided by existing 208/120 or 480-v systems, high-resistance grounding may be applied successfully on 480-v systems.

Figure 24 shows the diagram of a 480-v resistance grounded system with the neutral of the main transformer grounded through a resistor, ammeter and current relay.

A ground fault in any of the 3 phases causes current to flow from the fault-to-ground, through the current relay (for alarm circuit), through the ammeter, resistor and back to the transformer neutral. The role of the resistor is to limit the fault current; the current relay trips at current levels above 2.1 amp initiating an alarm, as shown in Figure 25.

If a ground fault develops on one phase, the ground ammeter indicates its existance and the audible alarm sounds. After the alarm is silenced, the ground must be located and removed as quickly as possible. This can be done by fault-detecting devices, usual-

FIGURE 24   DIAGRAM OF HIGH-RESISTANCE GROUNDED SYSTEM

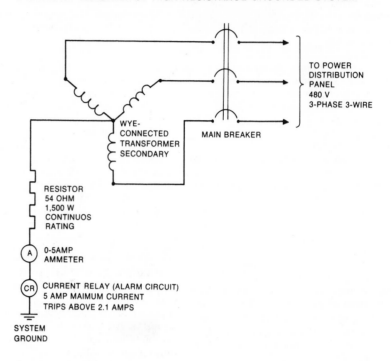

FIGURE 25   TEST AND GROUND-FAULT ALARM CIRCUIT

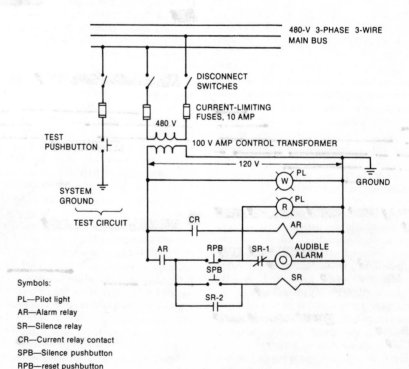

Symbols:

PL—Pilot light

AR—Alarm relay

SR—Silence relay

CR—Current relay contact

SPB—Silence pushbutton

RPB—reset pushbutton

RPB—reset pushbutton

Test circuit allows application of temporary ground to test alarm operation. Alarm circuit contact "CR" closes when current relay senses a ground fault. Operation of contact "CR" initiates audible and visual alarm.

ly clamp-on ammeters. The operating personnel are informed that a calculated risk is involved while searching for the fault, because if a second fault would occur in another phase, high damage might result.

The high resistance 480-v grounded system is treated as though the system were a 3-wire, 480-v ungrounded system with a neutral only at the power source. A neutral wire is not run with any feeder, but special care must be taken to assure that all conduits, cabinets, motor frames, etc. are positively bonded and/or grounded. The elimination of the neutral wire from the main feeder runs results in savings in conductors and conduits.

When a ground fault occurs in a resistance-grounded system, the voltage-to-ground of the two other conductors rises from 277 to 480 v which increases the possibility of a second ground fault. It is advisable to design the equipment to withstand 480 v to ground instead of 277 v.

On ungrounded low-voltage, Delta-connected systems, during ground faults, voltages can be as high as 10 to 20 times the system voltage which may cause serious breakdowns.

High-resistance grounding on low-voltage systems avoids such high overvoltages at fault occurrences, as the case is with ungrounded systems. These overvoltages occur mainly if the capacitance and the reactance of the faulted circuit are of such value as to create a resonant circuit. A neutral grounding, either solid or high-resistance, prevents such high-voltage resonant circuits with their damaging consequences.

Indeed, a high-resistance grounding has sufficient resistance in the ground circuit to dampen the oscillations generated by arcing ground conditions. The overvoltage is thus limited to about 250 percent of normal.

On the other hand, solid grounding of the neutral may be objectionable in industrial systems where an immediate machine outage and loss of production at a fault occurrence is unwanted. Resistance grounding avoids the need for special ground-sensing relays for each feeder and permits continuity of operation until the time is favorable for the removal of the ground fault. Alert and well-trained personnel are essential in plants using high-resistance grounding since locating the fault can take some time. For this reason the grounding resistor should be rated for extended duty.

High resistance grounding for medium voltage systems utilizes a neutral resistor with an ohmic value that approaches, but does not exceed, $X_{co}/3$, X_{co} being the zero-sequence capacitive reactance. The presence of such a resistor in the neutral introduces a resistive component of current to the ground fault which is equal to or slightly greater than the ungrounded system fault current. The result is a 45-deg maximum leading resistive-capacitive ground-fault current. The circuit is thus no longer capacitive as for grounded systems; it is, instead, a highly damped capacitive circuit which limits the possible self-generated transient overvoltages characteristic of the ungrounded systems during ground faults.

Indeed, the resistive current contributed by the neutral resistor adds 90 deg

Resistance grounding permits continuity of operation with a fault

to the capacitance current contributed by $X_{co}/3$.

The result is a total current close to one half or more than for the ungrounded system fault current. This reduced magnitude of current may be tolerated for some time before removal becomes necessary thus avoiding damage at fault point. This is the reason why resistance grounding is often used in process industries where continuation of service is very important until an alternate supply can be secured or fault points located and faults removed.

The tendency of fault escalation limits high ground resistance to about maximum 8 amp ground-fault for 2.4 kv and 4.16 kv. There are very few applications of high-resistance grounding for 13.8-kv. systems.

In new Wye systems, the cost of high-resistance grounding is quite modest. With a Wye-connected generator or transformer, there are two methods for connecting the grounding equipment (see Figures 26a and 26b). Figure 26a shows the simplest method involving a resistor approximately equal in ohms to the capacitive reactance-to-ground of the system and directly connected between the neutral point and ground. Usually a ground-fault relay type 51G provides the ground-fault protection and sounds an alarm. The other method uses a single-phase distribution transformer as shown in Figure 26b. The distribution transformer is usually rated line-to-line or line-to-neutral on the primary, and 240-or 120-v on the secon-

dary with a loading resistor connected across the secondary. The value of this resistor has the same equivalent value as the one selected in the first method, but with a reduced value by the square of the turns ratio of the transformer. At the occurrence of a ground fault, the current flows through the resistor and a voltage relay type 64 connected across the resistor. The voltage relay senses the voltage drop across the resistor and sounds an alarm. An overcurrent relay type 51G protects the distribution transformer for internal faults. The transformer and resistor must be selected for continuous duty; otherwise it would trip all sources of power to the bus. The first lowest cost will dictate the choice between these two methods which are applicable on low- on medium-voltage systems.

In case the system does not have an established neutral, two alternate arrangements can be used (see Figures 27a and 27b).

It is practical to connect either one of these two arrangements to the main bus of the system. The grounding transformers are connected through a circuit breaker to the main bus. The grounding transformer overcurrent relays type 51 trip the breaker in case of a fault in the grounding equipment. The Delta-connected current transformer relays will see only internal faults in the grounding transformer and not system ground faults.

The connection shown in Figure 27a has a zig-zag transformer providing a system neutral with a grounding resistor inserted between transformer neutral and ground. The grounding resistor is selected in the same way as that in Figure 26a. The grounding transformer should be large enough to continuously handle the ground-fault current.

A similar method of establishing a neutral point is shown in Figure 27b, but by means of a Wye-connected primary of a 3-phase or 3 single-phase transformers. The loading resistor is connected across the broken Delta-connected secondaries of the grounding transformers. A voltage relay type 64 also connected across the secondary transformer sounds an alarm when a ground fault produces a voltage drop across the resistor.

The ground fault seen by the grounding transformer winding and the system voltage rating will determine the required kva of the grounding transformer. The desired operation at a ground-fault occurrence will determine whether the selected kva rating is based on short time or continuous duty. As for the protective relaying for the grounding equipment, fault current magnitudes in high-resistance grounding are very small and relaying selectivity is not a consideration.

To calculate a high-resistance grounding, the total 3-phase system capacitive charging current (I_C) must be established. The line-to-ground capacitance associated with the system components determines the magnitude of the zero-phase sequence charging the value of current:

$$I_{CO} = \frac{I_C}{3}$$

necessary for determining the grounding equipment associated with high-resistance grounding for industrial power systems (see Figure 28).

The necessary total line-to-ground capacitances (C_O) of a system can be established by performing capacitance calculations for system components (Figures 29, 30). To determine the total line-to-ground capacitance, use the tables and curves which are available and provide typical charging currents of all power system components. The individual equipment (C_O) values in microfarads are added up for the entire system and a total value of (C_O) is thus obtained. After the (C_O) is determined, the system impedance capacitive component X_{CO} is calculated by the formula:

$$X_{CO} = \frac{10^6}{2\pi f c_O}$$

Where f = frequency.

This value is then introduced in the formula:

$$I_{CO} = \frac{V_{L-L}}{3X_{CO}}$$

Where V_{L-L} is the line-to-line voltage of the 3-phase system.

The value of zero-phase sequence charging current I_{CO} is thus obtained.

As an example, assume that the total charging capacitance of a 2,400-v, 3-phase system in microfarads per phase calculated by this method is: C_O = 5 microfarads/phase.

Then:

$$X_{CO} = \frac{10^6}{2 \times 3.14 \times 60 \times 5}$$

$$= -j531 \text{ ohms/phase}$$

and

$$I_{CO} = \frac{2,400 \text{ v}}{1.73 \times 531}$$

$$= 2.61 \text{ amp/phase}$$

The total system capacity charging current is: $I_C = 3 \times I_{CO} = 3 \times 2.61 = 7.83$ amp

Another possibility of determining the value of would be to use the manufacturer's constants of capacitances for system components. The best method would be to determine by test the magnitude of the zero-phase sequence

charging current (I_{CO}), this being the only accurate way. As I_{CO} represents the charging current per phase, $3 \times I_{CO}$ corresponds to the total line-to-ground charging current.

A simpler and practical method is to use Table 6 which provides approximate ranges within which the actual value of zero-sequence system charging current may be found.

If a system comprises an extensive amount of cables and motors, the upper limit of Table 6 should be used; if a system has a minimum amount of

cables and motors, the lower values of Table 6 will apply.

The 1971 edition of the National Electrical Code, Section 230-95, required tripping on ground fault for 480-v services rated 1,000 amp or more. This requirement was confusing when considering high-resistance grounding is to permit operations to be continued under ground-fault conditions. The 1975 National Electrical Code resolved this confusion by indicating that the "tripping" requirements apply only to solidly-grounded

FIGRE 26(a) SIMPLE METHOD OF HIGH-RESISTANCE SYSTEM GROUNDING (WHEN NEUTRAL EXISTS)

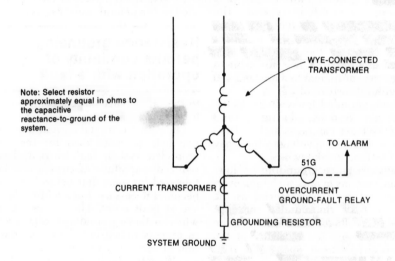

Note: Select resistor approximately equal in ohms to the capacitive reactance-to-ground of the system.

FIGRE 26(b) HIGH-RESISTANCE SYSTEM GROUNDING USING SINGLE-PHASE DISTRIBUTION TRANSFORMER

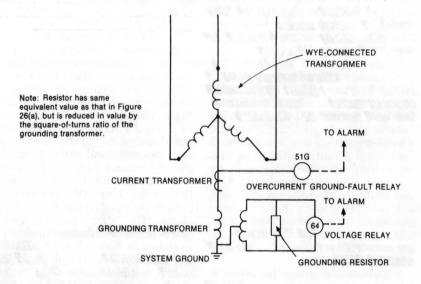

Note: Resistor has same equivalent value as that in Figure 26(a), but is reduced in value by the square-of-turns ratio of the grounding transformer.

TABLE 6 REPRESENTATIVE RANGE OF SYSTEM CHARGING CURRENT

System voltage	Charging current (3 x I) amp per 1,000 kva of system capacity*
460 v	0.1-2.0/1,000 kva
2,400 v	0.1-2.0/1,000 kva

These values do not include contribution from surge protective capacitors for rotating machinery.

systems. Section 230-95 of the 1978 National Electrical Code was significantly revised by the following exception:

"The provision of this section shall not apply to a service disconnecting means for a continuous industrial process where a non-orderly shutdown will introduce additional or increased hazard."

In other words, it was established that the provision of Section 230-95 (a) does not apply for 480-v systems that are high-resistance grounded. The reason for this change was to provide

FIGURE 27(a)   ZIG-ZAG TRANSFORMER PROVIDING SYSTEM NEUTRAL WITH GROUNDING RESISTOR

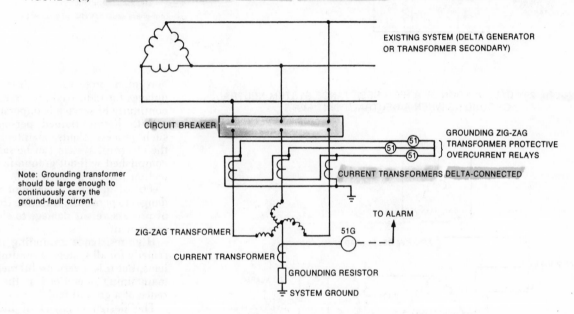

Note: Grounding transformer should be large enough to continuously carry the ground-fault current.

FIGURE 27(b)   HIGH-RESISTANCE GROUNDING WITH WYE-CONNECTED PRIMARY OF THREE, SINGLE-PHASE TRANSFORMERS

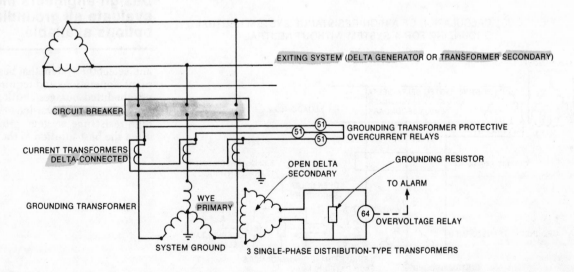

185

FIGURE 28 ZERO-SEQUENCE NETWORK SHOWING OPERATION OF NEUTRAL RESISTANCE WITH PHASE-TO-GROUND CAPACITANCE

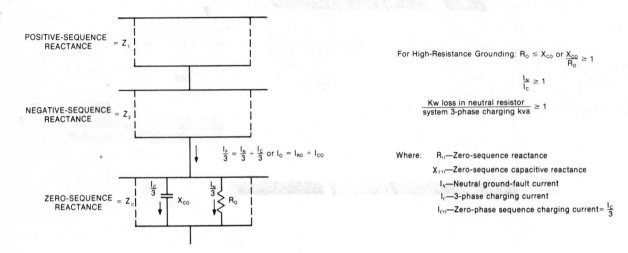

POSITIVE-SEQUENCE REACTANCE $= Z_1$

NEGATIVE-SEQUENCE REACTANCE $= Z_2$

$\frac{I_F}{3} = \frac{I_N}{3} + \frac{I_C}{3}$ or $I_0 = I_{RO} + I_{CO}$

ZERO-SEQUENCE REACTANCE $= Z_0$

$\frac{I_C}{3}$ X_{CO} $\frac{I_N}{3}$ R_O

For High-Resistance Grounding: $R_O \leq X_{CO}$ or $\frac{X_{CO}}{R_O} \geq 1$

$$\frac{I_N}{I_C} \geq 1$$

$$\frac{\text{Kw loss in neutral resistor}}{\text{system 3-phase charging kva}} \geq 1$$

Where: R_O—Zero-sequence reactance

X_{CO}—Zero-sequence capacitive reactance

I_N—Neutral ground-fault current

I_C—3-phase charging current

I_{CO}—Zero-phase sequence charging current$= \frac{I_C}{3}$

FIGURE 29 CALCULATION OF A HIGH-RESISTANCE SYSTEM NEUTRAL GROUNDING WHEN A NEUTRAL POINT ~~EISTS~~ *EXISTS*

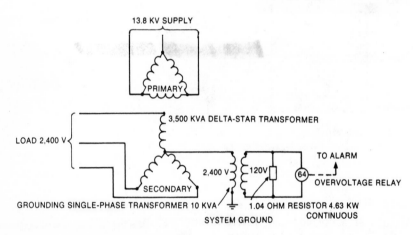

13.8 KV SUPPLY

PRIMARY

3,500 KVA DELTA-STAR TRANSFORMER

LOAD 2,400 V

SECONDARY

2,400 V   120V   (64)   TO ALARM   OVERVOLTAGE RELAY

GROUNDING SINGLE-PHASE TRANSFORMER 10 KVA

SYSTEM GROUND

1.04 OHM RESISTOR 4.63 KW CONTINUOUS

FIGURE 30 CALCULATION OF A HIGH-RESISTANCE SYSTEM NEUTRAL GROUNDING FOR A SYSTEM WITHOUT NEUTRAL

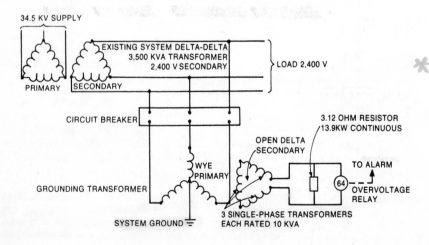

34.5 KV SUPPLY

PRIMARY   SECONDARY

EXISTING SYSTEM DELTA-DELTA 3,500 KVA TRANSFORMER 2,400 V SECONDARY

LOAD 2,400 V

CIRCUIT BREAKER

3.12 OHM RESISTOR 13.9KW CONTINUOUS

OPEN DELTA SECONDARY

TO ALARM

WYE PRIMARY

(64)   OVERVOLTAGE RELAY

GROUNDING TRANSFORMER

SYSTEM GROUND

3 SINGLE-PHASE TRANSFORMERS EACH RATED 10 KVA

maximum protection against service outages for industrial processes where continuity of service is imperative.

With highly trained personnel at such process plants, maintenance of the electrical system can be safely accomplished without ground-fault protection tripping devices. A special electrical design can account for any danger to personnel resulting from loss of process versus damage to electrical equipment.

High-resistance grounding is not a remedy for all system grounding problems, but it is a very useful method of maintaining operations at the occurrence of a ground fault.

The design engineer of industrial power distribution systems must evaluate all available grounding options

Design engineers must evaluate all grounding options available

and select the system that best suits the plant's operations and requirements. If unscheduled outages result in dangerous losses and hazardous conditions, high-resistance system grounding is often the best solution to the problem.

6.6 Generator Neutral Grounding Methods. Advantages and Disadvantages

Section 6.1 discussed basic factors influencing the engineer's selection of properly grounded or ungrounded neutral systems.

Section 6.2 presented the advantages and disadvantages of frequently employed methods of system neutral grounding for low-voltage systems.

Section 6.3 dealt with recommended neutral grounding methods for medium-voltage, 2.4- to 15-kv systems.

Section 6.4 covered neutral circuit arrangement, selection of system grounding point and symmetrical components calculation procedures.

Section 6.5 discussed the application of high-resistance grounding systems.

This section 6.6 explains the advantages and disadvantages of various methods available for generator neutral grounding. Figures and tables are numbered consecutively.

The advantages derived from neutral grounding of generators include:

- Limitation of mechanical stresses in generator windings under fault conditions external to the rotating machine.
- The need for selective relaying of line-to-ground faults, which implies a reasonably low impedance to ground.
- Limitation of damage at the fault point.
- Generator protection from lightning surges.

- Limitation of transient overvoltages.

Generator system grounding is obtained in two ways—by connecting the neutral point of the rotating machine to ground through some form of impedance, or by directly connecting to ground with no impedance intentionally inserted (solidly grounded).

Ungrounded operation of generators has the advantage of limiting the flow of line-to-ground fault currents (see Figure 31). Equally important, it has the disadvantage of allowing high overvoltage disturbances, and also makes it difficult to locate ground faults. This is why industry unanimously adopted some form of generator grounding.

The most important and frequently used neutral grounding methods are: neutral solidly grounding, neutral reactor grounding, neutral resistor grounding, and neutral distribution transformer with secondary resistor grounding. There are some other methods of generator neutral grounding, such as potential transformers and ground-fault neutralizers, but these are seldom applied in the United States.

Selecting the best method of grounding for a particular generator installation depends on the objective to be accomplished, and the electrical system components the engineer uses for grounding.

None of the grounding methods available can satisfy all of the requirements of grounding. The chosen method must be the best

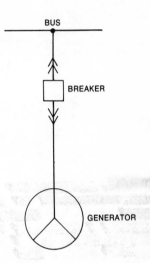

FIGURE 31 UNGROUNDED GENERATOR NEUTRAL

compromise between possibly conflicting advantages and disadvantages.

The various grounding methods differ in the magnitude of line-to-ground fault current each allows to flow. In general, high-fault current is associated with neutral reactor grounding. Intermediate values of fault current are associated with neutral resistors and grounding transformers, while low-fault current is associated with distribution transformer grounding with a secondary resistor.

Neutral grounding methods

Solidly grounding the generator neutral, results in the maximum fault current flow, and consequently, causes the maximum damage at fault point (see Figure 32). This method also results in the maximum stress in machine windings. With solid grounding, the ground-fault current through the generator winding will be greater than the 3-phase fault at the same

187

FIGURE 32 SOLID GROUNDED
GENERATOR NEUTRAL

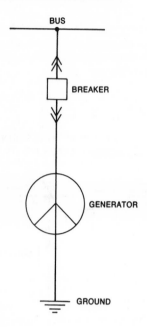

FIGURE 32 SOLID GROUNDED
GENERATOR NEUTRAL

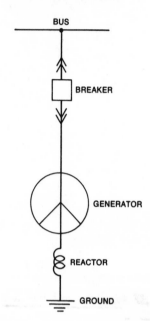

FIGURE 33 REACTOR GROUNDED
GENERATOR NEUTRAL

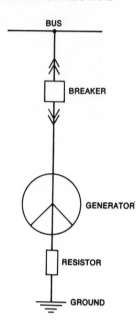

FIGURE 34 RESISTOR GROUNDED
GENERATOR NEUTRAL

location. Solid grounding is therefore not recommended for generators where the machine windings may be subjected to fault currents higher than the 3-phase fault currrents (as covered by ANSI Standards C-50).

The ground-fault current of a 3-phase system is: $I_F = \dfrac{3E_N}{X_1 + X_2 + X_0}$

Where: E_N = Line-to-neutral voltage
X_1 = Positive-sequence reactance (ohms/phase)
X_2 = Negative-sequence reactance (ohms/phase)
X_0 = Zero-sequence reactance (ohms/phase)

Because of the relatively low zero-sequence reactance in most synchronous machines, a solid line-to-ground fault at the machine terminals results in a winding current higher than the 3-phase fault current. And, if several machines are operated in parallel and only one machine is grounded, this effect is accentuated in the grounded machine.

Some neutral impedance must be used unless the user is willing to risk line-to-ground faults at, or close to, generator terminals.

For generators having reactance values such that the winding currents for line-to-ground faults at the generator terminals are limited to values equal to or less than 3-phase faults, the solid grounding method can be applied. In this particular case, the advantages and

disadvantages are the same as for reactor grounding.

Reactor grounding of the generator neutral (see Figure 33) has several advantages:

• It limits the line-to-ground voltage on the two unfaulted phases during line-to-ground fault.

• It allows the use of reduced lightning arresters if $\dfrac{X_0}{X_1}$ between 1 and 3.

• It limits transient overvoltages to safe value if $\dfrac{X_0}{X_1}$ is 10 or less.

• It allows for satisfactory differential relay operation for ground faults.

The disadvantages connected with this method are:

• Ground-fault currents may be relatively high (approximately 25 to 100 percent of 3-phase fault currents), with possible damage at fault point.

• Ground-fault currents for feeders rated at generator voltage, will have a wide range of magnitudes (as between faults near the bus and those remote from the bus).

• It is difficult to apply reactors suitable for both initial conditions as well as future system expansion.

The upper limit of reactance to be used is the value giving a maximum $\dfrac{X_0}{X_1}$ =10.

With values greater than this amount, serious transient overvoltages

may be generated. The lower limit of reactance $\dfrac{X_0}{X_1} = 1$ (considering the generator alone) is based on limiting the maximum generator winding ground-fault current to the 3-phase fault current.

Although neutral reactors can be applied for a ratio $\dfrac{X_0}{X_1} = 1$ through 10, the usual practice is to maintain an effective grounded system by keeping this ratio at 3 or less. This allows the use of a grounded neutral-type of lightning arrester. These arresters provide 25 percent lower protective level than is provided by ungrounded neutral arresters.

Reactor neutral grounding allows for better machine lightning protection. This method can be used where exposed overhead feeders from the bus generator would allow surges to arrive at the machine. Because high ground fault current is permitted this method can be applied to selective ground relaying of all generators and feeders tied to the same bus.

Neutral reactor grounding is necessary for 4-wire systems directly supplied by generator installations. This method prevents overvoltages during line-to-ground faults, which otherwise would damage the loads connected from the unfaulted phases to the neutral wire.

Neutral reactor grounding minimizes dynamic overvoltages, and is therefore used where the generator directly feeds cable networks. This is expecially true where there are considerable amounts of old cable with possible "weak spots."

The undesirable feature of neutral reactor grounding is that it can produce damages at the fault point. The disadvantage is the possibility of iron burning due to possible high ground-fault currents.

Because of these disadvantages, there is considerable disagreement among engineers concerning the application of the neutral reactor method.

For very large generators, the need to limit the magnitude of ground-fault current is the main reason for adopting the neutral resistor method, even though there are existing overhead feeders.

Neutral resistor grounding of generators is characterized by a more moderate value of line-to-ground fault— 100 to 2,000 amp (see Figure 34). This is obtained by selecting the resistor inserted between the generator neutral point and ground to be of a value equal to:
$$R_N = \frac{E_N}{I_F}$$
Where: E_N is the generator phase-to-neutral voltage in volts.
I_f is the desired ground-fault current in amp.
R_N is the resistor value in ohms.

Current through the neutral resistor can be limited to any value, but for large generators, selected current is usually from approximately 100 amp to about 1.5 times the normal rated generator current. A 100-amp current requires a 80-ohm resistor for a 13.8 kv generator, which is practical for this voltage class because of insulation requirements and conductor area. The other limit, 1.5 times normal rated current of the generator, is dictated by the loss in the resistor during single-phase-to-ground faults. If the current was several times the full load current, the loss in the resistor would be several times the normal full load of the generator, and resistor cost would be very high.

Since the value of the ground-fault current in resistor grounding is more moderate than with reactor grounding, the fault damage will generally be less than with a neutral reactor.

Neutral resistor grounding has the disadvantage of preventing the use of grounded neutral arresters. This would require a low ohmic value with extremely high losses in the resistor— with a corresponding large size and cost of same.

Grounded neutral arresters are not applicable with this grounding method, consequently, it is of no advantage to use a very low value of resistance. In general, the amount of current necessary for selective relaying determines the amount of resistance to be used.

Neutral resistor grounding considerably limits the line-to-ground fault current magnitude. This permits a selective relaying of ground faults and, at the same time, prevents serious transient overvoltages.

The disadvantage of this method is the occurence of higher dynamic overvoltages on the unfaulted phases which prevents the use of grounded neutral arresters.

The neutral resistor grounding method is used where there are no direct lightning exposures, but where sufficient current is required for selective relaying. Neutral resistor grounding can be applied to an installation with several generators but without exposed overhead feeders bussed at generator voltage, or for generators connected directly to Delta windings of step-up transformers. It can also be applied where power is transmitted at generator voltage and stepped down through transformers connected Delta on the generator's output side. In these cases, the resistor limits the ground-fault current to almost a constant value for a fault anywhere on the feeders.

The *distribution transformer with secondary resistor grounding method* is in effect, a very high-resistance ground, where the ground-fault currents are limited to 5-10 amps (see Figure 35).

This reduces the possibility of fault damage at ground-fault point. High-speed relaying and field or neutral breakers are not required to de-energize the generator before damage occurs. The generator should be tripped at the occurrence of a ground fault, since the possibility of another ground fault at another phase may result in a high fault current with greater damage.

This method of generator neutral grounding is used extensively for "unit-generators" supplying Delta windings of step-up transformers. This is because a ground fault at generator voltage is isolated from the high-voltage system, and a ground fault on the high-voltage system is not affected

FIGURE 35 DISTRIBUTION TRANSFORMER WITH
SECONDARY RESISTOR GROUNDING

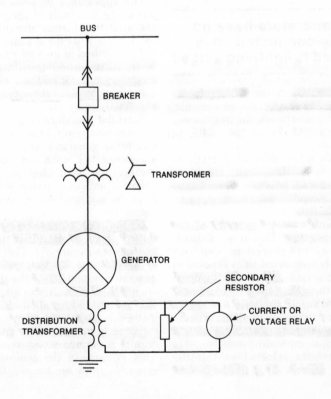

by the method used in generator grounding.

The main advantage of the distribution transformer with secondary resistor combination is that the resistor used in the secondary of the transformer is of low ohmic value and sturdy construction, as compared to the high-ohm, low-current resistor, used directly in the generator neutral.

Effective resistance in the neutral generator circuit of the resistor across the transformer secondary is stepped up with the square of turns ratio of the distribution transformer. Relaying of the generator for ground fault is obtained by a current or a voltage relay on the neutral transformer's secondary. The time setting of this relay is coordinated with other protective devices.

Transformer and resistor size is related to the capacitive current-to-ground at a ground-fault occurrence. The capacitor to ground must be determined for the generator, transformer, cables, terminal surge capacitors, etc. The objective when calculating resistor and neutral transformer sizes is to make the transformer current equal to the capacitive current. This will avoid high transient voltages and will suppress harmonics, making possible a low setting for the ground relay.

The distribution transformer for any generator will seldom exceed 50 kva, and is usually of a liquid filled or air-insulated type construction with an

Unit-generators have no directly-connected lines exposed to lightning surges

insulation class of the same value as that of the generator. As an example, for 13.8 kv generators, the transformer must be a 13.8 kv to 480-, 240-, or 120-v unit.

As with other grounding methods discussed, no dangerous transient overvoltages are possible, provided the grounding equipment ratings are correctly selected.

Lightning arresters must be of the ungrounded type. This is not a disadvantage in "unit-generators" that have no directly-connected lines exposed to lightning surges. On the high-voltage side of the transformer, an arrester should be used to limit the surges originating in the high-voltage system.

The *ground-fault neutralizer* method of generator grounding consists of a neutral reactor selected so that the charging current in a line-to-ground

fault is neutralized by an inductive reactive component of current contributed by the ground-fault neutralizer (see Figure 36). The net current in the fault is thus reduced to a minimum, and kept in phase with the fault voltage. Transitory ground faults are automatically extinguished with a ground-fault neutralizer grounded system.

The ground-fault neutralizer method limits mechanical stresses in generator windings, as well as transient overvoltages and damage at fault point. In spite of the advantages of this method, there are also disadvantages. For example, very sensitive and selective directional ground relays cannot detect a faulted feeder from a group of feeders operating at generator voltage. Because of this disadvantage, this method is not frequently employed in the U.S.; however, it is in use on a number of generator systems in Europe.

Potential transformer grounding of generators is a very high reactive type of grounding similar to an ungrounded system. The line-to-ground-fault current is very low, making this type of grounding suitable for limiting damage at fault point.

Potential transformer grounding is seldom used due to its tendency to facilitate high transient overvoltages that result from switching at generator voltage, or from line-to-ground faults that generate arcing grounds.

The appearance of a voltage at the secondary terminals of the grounding potential transformer usually sounds an alarm or trips the machine.

This method of grounding is similar to the distribution transformer with secondary resistor method, although it does not have resistance damping characteristics.

Potential transformer grounding of the generator neutral may be used only when the generator and transformer are connected with no intervening breaker (no switching at generator voltage), and only when it has been carefully analyzed that resonances will not occur.

Grounding transformers are installed solely to establish the system neutral (see Figure 37). They are used to provide the neutral ground on a generator system when the generators are not Wye-connected or are not available for grounding all the time. This method is also used where only one machine is tied to a bus, and feeders require a permanent system ground. This is because the removal of the generator from service would also re-

FIGURE 36 GROUND-FAULT NEUTRALIZER GROUNDING

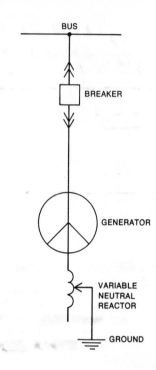

move the only existing ground point of the generator. The same applies with several machines on the same bus, where all of the generators might at some times be shut down.

To provide a permanent system ground in such cases, a grounding transformer—either zig-zag or Wye-Delta—is installed at generator bus. For a short time current rating, the zig-zag transformer is more frequently used because of its lower cost.

Despite the fact that the application of a grounding transformer on the bus, together with distribution transformer grounding of the generator does not allow the use of grounded neutral arresters, this method of grounding has several advantages:

• The ground current for feeder relaying does not change greatly when the generator is "on" or "off" the bus.

• If a line-to-ground fault occurs during normal operation, the fault current can be reduced rapidly to a very low value by tripping the generator main breaker.

• Line-to-ground faults of the machine, before closing on the bus, are provided with very low fault-current flow.

A one-minute current rating is usually used for the grounding transformer size and impedance, assuring also the

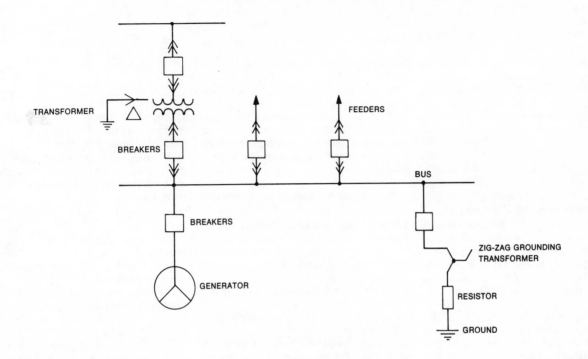

desired current for relaying purposes. To prevent high transient overvoltages, the fault current should not be limited below 25 percent of the 3-phase fault $\left(\dfrac{X_0}{X_1} = 10\right)$.

If 4-wire feeders are connected to the output bus, a ratio $\dfrac{X_0}{X_1} = 3$ or less is provided to prevent hi-potting line-to-neutral connected loads during ground faults. If less than 25 percent of the 3-phase fault is desired, a resistor should be inserted in the neutral of the grounding bank.

Summary

To limit winding stresses in grounded generators, some neutral impedance is required in almost all cases.

The need for selective ground relaying including several machines and feeders bused at generator voltage, requires a fairly low impedance-to-ground. In addition, there is the necessity of suppressing transient overvoltages caused by arcing ground faults or switching disturbances, as well as the need to minimize destructive damages at fault point.

These requirements can be met by either a neutral resistor, reactor, distribution transformer with secondary resistor grounding, or by a grounding

transformer connected to generator bus.

Medium-voltage generators are usually neutral resistance grounded because of the benefits of restricting ground-fault currents to low values (approximately 5 percent of 3-phase fault currents).

Low-voltage generators are usually neutral reactance grounded, with ground fault limited to a maximum 100 percent of the 3-phase fault, thus facilitating selective operation of direct-acting trips on low-voltage breakers.

Where overhead feeders connected to the generator bus may expose the generator to lightning surges, neutral reactor grounding is preferred. Reactors should be selected to give a ratio $\dfrac{X_0}{X_1}$ = between 1 and 3. This allows the use of the grounded-neutral type of lightning arresters.

On large generators, the limiting of damaging high ground-fault currents is very important. In such cases, the use of neutral resistor grounding is preferable.

For generating systems feeding cable networks, neutral reactors are preferred, provided the main objective is to keep dynamic overvoltages on the cables at low values. If, on the other hand, the cable fault current is to be

kept at low value, the neutral resistor method of grounding is recommended.

In cases where several machines are bused at generator voltage and no feeders are connected to this bus, the generator neutral resistor method is preferred.

For "generator-transformer" unit installations, the preferred method of grounding is by neutral distribution transformer with secondary resistor (see Figure 39).

Single generator stations, having feeders at generator voltage, require a grounding transformer bank of the Zig-Zag of Wye-Delta type, connected to the main bus. The same method is used to obtain a ground point if the system is fed by a Delta transformer or a Delta machine winding.

In selecting the preferred grounding method, the design engineer must consider all aspects of his particular application, and select the best compromise between the advantages and disadvantages inherent in each method that best suits his requirements.

6.7 Selection and Calculation of Equipment Ratings for Generator Neutral Reactance and Low-Resistance Grounding

Section 6.6 discussed the various available methods of generator neutral grounding, as well as their advantages and disadvantages. This section 6.7, shows how to select and calculate the equipment ratings for the generator neutral reactance grounding methods.

The necessity for grounding the generator neutral through some form of an impedance is explained by the following advantages:

• Limitations of excessive stresses in the machine windings at the occurance of a ground fault.

• Suppression of transient overvoltages caused by arcing faults or switching disturbances.

• Possibility of selective ground fault relaying.

• Allowing the application of reduced rated lightning arresters.

• Limitation to acceptable values of the magnitude of ground-fault current at the point of fault.

For these reasons, the most frequently employed methods of neutral generator grounding are by means of: 1. Neutral reactor; 2. Neutral resistor (low resistance grounding); 3. Distribution transformer with secondary resistor (high resistance grounding); 4. Grounding transformer connected to generator bus.

Reactance grounding is usually employed for low voltage generators. The ground fault is limited to maximum 100 percent of the value of a three-phase fault. This also makes possible the selective operation of direct acting trips on low voltage breakers.

The reactance grounding method permits the use of neutral arresters making this method preferred where lightning exposure is severe. The reactor method of grounding is suitable for 4-wire systems.

This method is also employed for generators feeding cables on which dynamic overvoltages must be kept at low values.

In general by keeping $\frac{X_0}{X_1}$ between 1 and 3, application of reduced rated lightning arresters is made possible.

If $\frac{X_0}{X_1}$ does not exceed 10, transient overvoltages are limited to safe values.

The ratio $\frac{X_0}{X_1} = 10$, corresponds to a limitation ground fault current to minimum 25 percent of the three-phase fault current.

Acceptable resistor cost and size is limited by highest fault current

Selection and calculation

The selection and calculation of grounding equipment rating is based on the limitation of the line-to-ground fault to a value no greater than the three-phase fault at the generator terminals.

To specify the reactor for such an application, data must be obtained from the generator name-plate or from the manufacturer. Furthermore, the characteristic data of the electric circuit must be known.

The maximum single-phase to ground short-circuit current is dictated by the positive subtransient (X''_d), negative (X_2) and zero sequence (X_0) reactances of the generator and reactor, and the positive (X_{1s}), negative (X_{2s}), and zero sequence (X_{0s}) reactances of the rest of the grounded or ungrounded system sources.

Since the maximum reactor current lasts only a few cycles, it should be used to design the reactor for mechanical strength. The current value for the reactor heating is determined from the transient reactance of the generator X'_d and the system, using the internal voltage behind transient reactance.

A single line-to-ground fault for a generator with neutral reactance grounding can be calculated by the formula:

(Formula 1) $I_G = \dfrac{3E_{L-N}}{X_1 + X_2 + X_0 + 3X_N}$

The resistance is usually neglected where:

X_1 = Positive sequence reactance of generator (ohms)

X_2 = Negative sequence reactance of generator (ohms)

X_0 = Zero sequence reactance of generator (ohms)

X_N = Reactance of reactor (ohms)

E_{L-N} = Line to neutral voltage (volts)

I_G = Ground-fault current (amperes)

The reactor is rated to carry the fault current for a limited time, which in industrial systems with relays protecting the grounding equipment is usually 10 sec to maximum 60 sec. The reactor's insulation class is determined by the line to neutral voltage of the circuit and the voltage rating, and is calculated by multiplying the rated current by the impedance of the reactor.

The rated current of the grounding reactor is the RMS symmetrical neutral current in amps that the reactor must carry for its rated time (10 sec to one minute) without exceeding the standard temperature limits.

Momentary duty calculations

For the momentary duty calculations of the reactor, the positive sequence reactance (X_1) is considered to be equal to the machine subtransient reactance (X''_d); for the thermal rating, the transient value of the machine reactance is applied.

To calculate the required reactance of the reactor in the neutral of the machine, the main condition is to limit the fault current in the generator winding to the three-phase fault current.

The line-to-ground fault is expressed by:

(Formula 1) $I_G = \dfrac{3E_{L-N}}{X_1 + X_2 + X_0 + 3X_N}$

The three-phase fault current is expressed by the formula:

(Formula 2) $I_{3phase} = \dfrac{E_{L-N}}{X_1}$

To fulfill the condition that the ground fault current is limited to the three-phase fault, Formula 1 must be equal with Formula 2:

(Formula 1-Formula 2)

$$\frac{E}{X_1} = \frac{3E_{L-N}}{X_1 + X_2 + X_0 + 3X_N}$$

Usually for industrial generators X_2 is assumed to be equal to X_1.

Consequently the equality is reduced to

$$\frac{E_{L-N}}{X_1} = \frac{3E_{L-N}}{2X_1 + X_0 + 3X_N}$$

or $2X_1 + X_0 + 3X_N - 3X$; resolving for X_N
(Formula 3)

$$X_N = \frac{X_1 - X_0}{3}$$

expresses the reactance of a neutral generator reactor in ohms, and should be equal to the positive sequence minus the zero sequence reactances of the generator in ohms per phase, all divided by 3.

The following example calculation shows how generator neutral grounding reactors can be calculated, based on the limitation of the machine winding ground fault current to the maximum three-phase fault. Assume a system as shown in Figure 38.

Determine the reactance of the machine grounding reactor by Formula 3 where X_1 is taken as the subtransient reactance of the generator, $X''_d = 12$ and X_0 as the zero sequence of the reactor $X_0 = 6$.

Using Formula 4,

(Formula 4)

$$X_{ohms} = \frac{X\% \times \overline{kv^2} \times 10}{Base\ kva}$$

in ohms, and selecting the generator 1,250 kva as base.

The positive and zero sequence reactances of the generator are:
(Formula 4)

$$X_1 = \frac{12 \times \overline{0.48^2} \times 10}{1250\ kva} = \underset{0.0221}{\cancel{0.221}}\ ohms$$

(Formula 4)

$$X_0 = \frac{6 \times \overline{0.48^2} \times 10}{1250\ kva} = 0.011\ ohms$$

When introducing in 3, Formula 3:

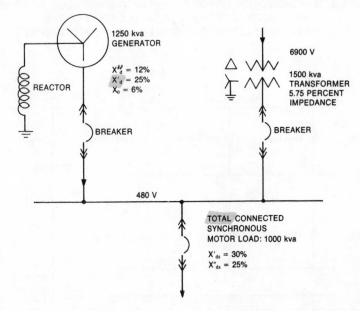

FIGURE 38 REACTANCE GROUNDED GENERATOR AND SOLIDLY GROUNDED TRANSFORMER IN A 480 V INDUSTRIAL POWER SYSTEM

1250 kva GENERATOR
$X''_d = 12\%$
$X'_d = 25\%$
$X_0 = 6\%$

REACTOR

BREAKER

480 V

6900 V

1500 kva TRANSFORMER 5.75 PERCENT IMPEDANCE

BREAKER

TOTAL CONNECTED SYNCHRONOUS MOTOR LOAD: 1000 kva
$X'_{ds} = 30\%$
$X''_{ds} = 25\%$

$$X_N = \frac{X_1 - X_0}{3} = \frac{0.221 - 0.011}{3}$$

$$= 0.07\ ohms$$

The reactance of the neutral reactor is 0.07 ohms.

To calculate the *current rating* of the reactor, the total ground fault current must be determined by Formula 1.

The positive sequence reactance of the system X_1 is obtained by using the transient reactance $X'_{ds} = 25$ percent of the synchronous machine; the negative sequence reactance of the system X_2 is considered equal to the subtransient reactance of the synchronous machine $X''_{ds} = 12$ percent.

The positive negative and zero reactances of the system are:
(Formula 4)

$$X_1 = \frac{25 \times \overline{0.48^2} \times 10}{12500\ kva} = 0.046\ ohms$$

$$X_2 = \frac{12 \times \overline{0.48^2} \times 10}{12500\ kva} = 0.221\ ohms$$

$$X_0 = \frac{6 \times \overline{0.48^2} \times 10}{12500\ kva} = 0.011\ ohms$$

The positive, negative and zero sequence reactances of the transformer are:

$$X_1 = X_2 = X_0 = \frac{5.75 \times \overline{0.48^2} \times 10}{1500\ kva}$$
$$\simeq 0.0088\ ohms$$

The positive and negative sequence reactances of the connected load are:
(Formula 4)

$$X_1 = \frac{30 \times \overline{0.48^2} \times 10}{1000\ kva} = 0.0691\ ohms$$

$$X_2 = \frac{25 \times \overline{0.48^2} \times 10}{1000\ kva} = 0.0576\ ohms$$

Figure 39 shows the positive, negative and zero sequence network impedances required to calculate the total system ground-fault current. Introducing the combined total reactances in formula 1, the total is:

$$I_G = \frac{3 \times \frac{480\text{ V}}{\sqrt{3}}}{0.0067 + 0.0074 + 0.0085}$$
$$\cong 37,000 \text{ amp}$$

The equivalent circuit (Figure 39) shows that this total ground fault current will divide through the path to ground in inverse proportion to the impedance in the path.

The ground fault through the reactor is:

$$I_{G_R} = \frac{0.0085}{0.0221} \times I_G = \frac{0.0085}{0.221} \times 37,000$$
$$\cong 1,420 \text{ amp}$$

The ground-fault current through the transformer solid grounding is:

$$I_{G_T} = \frac{0.0085}{0.0088} \times I_G = \frac{0.0085}{0.0088} \times 37,000$$
$$\cong 35,580 \text{ amp}$$

Reactor ratings

The reactor must be rated at least for 1,500 amps. Either a 10 sec or 1 minute reactor may be used. The IEEE application guide for the grounding of synchronous generator systems recommends 1 minute rating if there are exposed feeders at generator voltage; otherwise a 10 sec rating is recommended. The more conservative 1 minute rating is usually preferred because system expansion may later result in higher ground-fault currents than expected.

For the generator of the sample calculation the grounding reactor in the neutral of the 480V generator must be capable to carry 1,500 amps for one minute and must have a reactance of 0.07 ohms.

The reactor OHMIC value is depended on the grounded generator alone, whereas the reactor current-time rating depends upon the system reactances as well as the grounded generator reactances.

Resistance grounding uses a low value of resistance, and is generally applied for Wye connected generators in medium voltage systems with no direct lightning exposure. If lightning

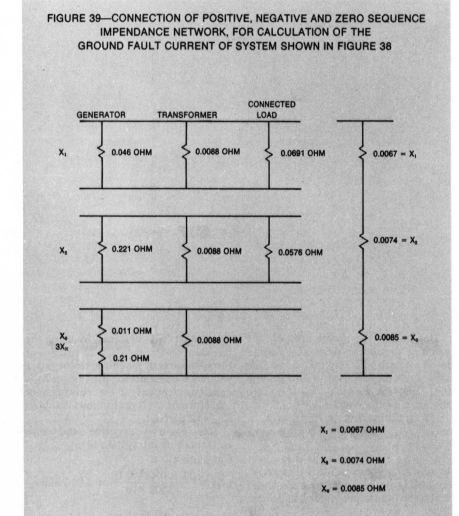

FIGURE 39—CONNECTION OF POSITIVE, NEGATIVE AND ZERO SEQUENCE IMPENDANCE NETWORK, FOR CALCULATION OF THE GROUND FAULT CURRENT OF SYSTEM SHOWN IN FIGURE 38

$X_1 = 0.0067$ OHM

$X_2 = 0.0074$ OHM

$X_0 = 0.0085$ OHM

TABLE 6   SELECTION OF GROUNDING RESISTOR
(Values shown are minimum recommended ground-fault current values in percent of rated relay current - transformers)

EQUIPMENT TO PROTECT	TYPE OF RELAY	
	GROUND OVER-CURRENT PERCENT	DIFFER-ENTIAL PERCENT
WYE CONNECTED GENERATORS, MOTORS, AND TRANSFORMERS	100	100
DELTA CONNECTED GENERATORS, MOTORS, AND TRANSFORMERS	40	40
FEEDERS AND LINES	100	—

TABLE 7   TYPICAL MINIMUM VALUES OF RESISTOR RATINGS
(Approx. 5% of 3-phase current)

SYSTEM 3-PHASE VOLTAGE	SHORT-CIRCUIT MVA	RESISTOR AMPERE RATING
13,800	1,000	2,000
	500	1,000
	250	500
	150	300
6,900	500	2,000
	250	1,000
	150	600
	100	400
4,160	250	2,000
	150	1,000
	100	800
	50	400
2,400	150	2,000
	100	1,200
	50	600
	25	300

arresters are required they must be of the ungrounded neutral type. In the range of 2.4 - 13kv, limited ground-fault current is desirable to reduce the line-to-ground fault, to permit selective relaying, and to prevent high transient overvoltages.

A moderate value of line-to-ground fault in the order of 100-2000 amp is characteristic for most generator neutral resistors. Consequently, fault damage values with neutral resistors is less than would occur using neutral reactors. Cast-grid resistors have an economic upper limit of resistance based on minimum 100 amp. For a 13.8 kv generator, about 80 ohm resistor are obtained by selecting the fault current to 100 amp.

For more than 80 ohm at 13.8 kv the cross-section and insulation requirements would make the resistor uneconomical.

Acceptable resistor cost and size is limited by the highest fault current allowed to flow. For practical applications, the ohms required for a neutral resistor is obtained by selecting the maximum desired ground-fault current and dividing the generator phase-to-neutral voltage by the selected fault current. Usually the generator reactance can be omitted. The formula is

$$\frac{E_N}{I_{GF}} = R_{ohms}$$

where:

E_N = Phase to neutral voltage of gnerator in volts.

I_{GF} = Maximum desired ground-fault current in amps.

R_{OHMS} = Resistance of grounding resistor in ohms.

The current through the neutral resistor is usually limited between 100 amps and maximum 1.5 times the normal rated generator current. The upper limit of 1.5 times of normal rated current is imposed by the loss in the resistor during ground faults. If the current would be more than 1.5 times the normal rated generator current, a lower ohm resistor would be used, with a loss of several times the normal full load of the machine, resulting in a very high resistor cost.

The practical and economical value of resistance is between a high value of 80 ohms and a low value permitting a fault current flow of approximately 1.5 times the full load of generator current.

In calculating the neutral resistor required, the current necessary for a satisfactory relaying must be established and the resistor calculated to satisfy this requirement.

For example, a generator with a radial feeder directly connected to the generator bus, must have the neutral resistance calculated to give satisfactory relaying for a fault that would occur at the far end of the feeder.

Minimum ground fault

The minimum ground fault required is determined by the ratings of current transformers and the type of relays in the circuit. The magnitude of ground-fault current must be sufficient to operate all relays. If the current is made high enough to operate the relays in the larger circuits, it also will be adequate for the smaller circuits. The selection of the ground fault currents necessary for a satisfactory operation

of various relays expressed in terms of the relay current transformer rating is shown in Table 6.

Minimum values of resistor ratings in amps can also be estimated as being approximately equal to 5 percent of three-phase fault current value. Table 7 shows how to select minimum values of resistor amp rating for different medium-voltages, based on three phase short-circuit in mva, with the following observations:

• Larger resistor amp rating may be required if there are C.T's in the circuit whose primary current ratings are larger than the figures in column 3.

• If several resistors are used on a system, the maximum total ground fault current will be approximately equal to the sum of the resistor ratings.

• For satisfactory relay coordination purposes, the resistor amp rating should be selected between 400 and 2,000 amp and in compliance with a thermal rating of maximum 750 deg C temperature rise up through one minute duty, in conformance with IEEE standard 32-1972: "Neutral Grounding Devices Requirements".

The resistor ohms, current rating and time rating must be specified when ordering. For example, a neutral resistor for a 13.8 kv generator to allow 500 amp line-to-ground fault current is specified as follows:

One indoor grounding resistor, cast-grid type for neutral connection in a 13.8 kv generator, capable of carrying 500 amp for 1 minute, and having a resistance of:

$$\frac{13,800/\sqrt{3}}{500} \cong 16 \text{ ohms}$$

6.8 Selection and Calculation of Neutral Grounding Equipment for Generators Grounded by Distribution Transformers with Secondary Resistors

The previous section 6.7 showed how to select and calculate the neutral grounding equipment for generators grounded by the reactance and low resistance methods. This final section 6.8 discusses the selection and calculation of generator neutral grounding equipment for generators grounded by distribution transformers with secondary resistors. This method is, in fact, high resistance grounding. Also discussed are grounding transformers connected to generator bus for delta-connected generators or systems.

The main objective for grounding generator neutrals is to assure protection to the machine and to other equipment in the system. From the standpoint of the generator winding's mechanical strength, the grounding of the generator neutral must be through an impedance sufficient to limit the ground fault current to the three-phase short circuit current value.

The distribution transformer with secondary resistor method of grounding limits fault currents to values as low as 5-15 amp. This method of grounding considerably reduces the possibility of fault damage at the ground fault point. In addition, high speed relaying and field or neutral breakers are not necessary for deenergizing the generator before damage occurs. However, it is advisable to trip the generator at the occurence of the first ground fault to avoid damage with a possible second ground fault. Furthermore, this grounding method uses a resistor of low ohmic value and

TABLE 8	CAPACITANCE IN MICROFARADS/1000 FT FOR POWER CABLE IN INDUSTRIAL PLANTS			
SIZE AWG OR MCM	CAPITANCE IN MICROFARADS/1,000 ft SHIELDED POWER CABLES			
	5 KV	15 KV	23 KV	34.5 KV
8	0.0607	—	—	—
6	0.0709	—	—	—
4	0.0836	—	—	—
2	0.0993	0.0401	—	—
1/0	0.1202	0.0524	0.0388	—
2/0	0.1321	0.0507	0.0441	0.0319
4/0	0.1600	0.0715	0.0546	0.0358
250	0.1598	0.0776	0.0588	0.0460
350	0.1846	0.0844	0.0634	0.0496
500	0.215	0.0920	0.0685	0.0532
750	0.241	0.0981	0.0743	0.0573
1,000	0.274	0.1118	0.0789	0.0617

TABLE 9	CAPACITANCE OF SURGE SUPPRESSION CAPICITORS IN MICROFARADS.		
VOLTAGE	CAPACITANCE	IN	MFD
480 V			1.0
2,400 V			0.5
4,160 V			0.5
13,800 V			0.25

sturdy construction as compared with the high-ohm, low-current resistor method of generator neutral grounding.

The generator relaying for ground fault detection is obtained by a voltage relay connected in parallel on the secondary side of the neutral transformer. The relay is set to coordinate with other ground fault protective devices in the system.

The size of the grounding transformer as well as of the resistor is relayed to the capacitive charging current to ground at a ground-fault occurence. The capacitive charging current to

ground can be determined by summing up the various components of circuit capacitance for all the electrical system such as: generators, transformers, cables, terminal surge capacitors, busway, etc. Zero-sequence capacitance per phase values for the principal circuit components are shown in Figure 40 and Tables VIII and IX.

When calculating neutral transformer and resistor sizes, the main objective should be to make the transformer current equal to the capacitive charging current of all the electrical system. This avoids high transient overvol-

196

tages, suppresses harmonics and makes possible low settings for ground relays.

The distribution grounding transformer is a means of making possible a low ohmic value of resistor and having an effect as of a high resistance in the generator neutral.

A distribution transformer seldom exceeds 50 kva, and is of liquid-filled or air-insulated type construction with an insulation class of the same value as that of the generator. This method of generator neutral grounding is extensively used and is a standard grounding method for "unit-connected" generators; that is, generators directly connected to a step-up transformer.

With the distribution transformer and secondary resistor grounding system, lightning arresters must be of the ungrounded type. This is not a disadvantage in "unit-connected" generators since they do not usually have directly connected lines exposed to lightning surges. On the high voltage side of the transformer, lightning arresters must be used to limit the surges originating in the high voltage system.

The following example calculation shows the procedure to follow for calculating the ratings of a distribution transformer and its secondary resistor. Figure 41 shows a 11.5 kv - 75,000 kva, 1,800 - rpm, 60 - Hz turbo-generator provided with surge-protective capacitors. The zero sequence capacitance per phase (C_0) for the circuit components are:

Generator	0.320 mfd
Generator surge capacitor	0.250 mfd
Generator leads	0.060 mfd
Power transformer	0.004 mfd
Total C_0 =	0.634 mfd/phase

See Fig. 40 and Tables VIII & IX

for C_0 values typical for transformers.

The capacitive charging current, I_{oc}, in amp per phase is expressed by Formula 5:

$$I_{oc} = \frac{V_{L-L}}{\sqrt{3} \times X_{co}}$$

Where X_{co} : $X_{co} = \frac{10^6}{2\pi f C_0}$

X_{co} = Capacitive reactance in ohms/phase

π = 3.14

f = Frequency = 60 Hz

C_0 = Total charging capacitance in microfarad per phase (mf/phase)

Introducing the value of C_0 = 0.634 mfd/phase in Formula 5:

$$I_{oc} = \frac{11,500}{1.73 \times \dfrac{10^6}{2 \times 3.14 \times 60 \times 0.634}}$$

$$= \frac{11,500 \times 2 \times 3.14 \times 60 \times 0.634}{1.73 \times 10^6}$$

FIGURE 40   CAPACITANCE TO GROUND OF TURBINE-GENERATOR WINDINGS FOR 13.2 KV MACHINES IN MICROFARADS PER PHASE.
(FOR OTHER VOLTAGES MULTIPLY BY FACTOR K IN INSERT)

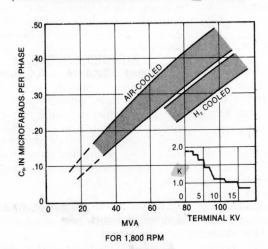

FOR 1,800 RPM

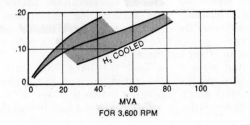

FOR 3,600 RPM

FIGURE 41   GENERATOR GROUNDING THROUGH DISTRIBUTION TRANSFORMER WITH SECONDARY RESISTOR

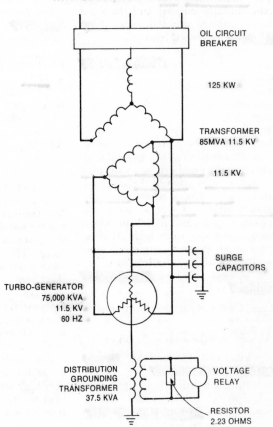

197

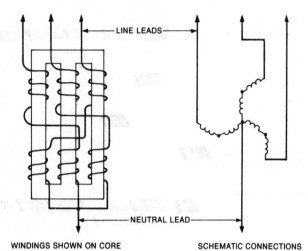

WINDINGS SHOWN ON CORE   SCHEMATIC CONNECTIONS

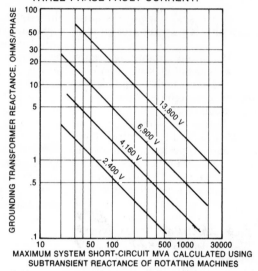

MAXIMUM SYSTEM SHORT-CIRCUIT MVA CALCULATED USING
SUBTRANSIENT REACTANCE OF ROTATING MACHINES

= 1.58 amp per phase

The total capacitive fault current is three times the zero sequence capacitive current. Total capacitive fault current = 3 x 1.58 amp = 4.74 amp.

The standard practice is to apply a resistor with an energy loss equal or slightly exceeding the capacitive kva during fault conditions.

The transformer kva, is the product of the primary current and the rated primary voltage divided by an overload factor as shown below:

Time	Overload Factor
1 minute	4.7
5 minutes	2.8
30 minutes	1.8
1 hour	1.6
2 hours	1.4

In order to avoid excessive magnetizing inrush current at a ground fault occurence, the rated primary voltage of the transformer should be approximately $1\frac{1}{2}$ times the generator line-to-neutral voltage. If automatic tripping is required, it should follow after a reasonable time-delay. However, for small systems, a ground relay sounding an alarm is satisfactory.

For our example, the capacitive kva developed is:

$$\frac{KV_{L-L}}{1.73} \text{ x total capacitive fault current}$$

$$= \frac{11.5 \text{ kv}}{1.73} \times 4.74 \text{ amp} = 31.5 \text{ kva}$$

31.5 kva should be the energy dissipated by the resistor.

Selecting a distribution transformer of 11,500 v primary and 460 v secondary, the open-circuit secondary voltage is: $\frac{460 \text{ v}}{1.73} = 265 \text{ v}$

The current rating of the resistor is:

$$\frac{31,500 \text{ w}}{265 \text{ v}} = 119 \text{ amp}$$

The resistance of the resistor is:

$$\frac{265 \text{ volts}}{119 \text{ amp}} = 2.23 \text{ ohms}$$

The kva duty on the transformer is:
11.5 kv x 4.74 amp = 54.4 kva

For a transformer with a one-hour duty cycle, the transformer must be rated for:

$$\frac{54.5 \text{ kva}}{1.6 \text{ (Factor from time table for 1 hour)}} = 34 \text{ kva}$$

A standard 37.5-kva transformer may be selected for this application. If the duty cycle would be selected for 5 minutes, a transformer rating of $\frac{54.6 \text{ kva}}{2.8} = 19.5$ kva would suffice. A standard rating of 25 kva would be selected.

In general, it is preferable to be on the conservative side for the transformer rating selection to avoid having its reactance become an important factor. The resistors should be selected on a continuous duty basis because their size and cost are not significant factors.

Usually oil-immersed or air-cooled transformers are preferred. The relay on the transformer secondary may be of the current or voltage type.

The method employed is in effect a generator neutral grounding with a very high resistance. Instead of a bulky high-voltage resistor, a step-down transformer with a low voltage resistor is employed. The distribution transformer with secondary resistor method of grounding is ideally suited for avoiding high transient overvoltages from switching or arcing, reducing harmonic voltages, and making possible lower settings of ground fault relays. It is the main method for "unit-connected" generators.

Grounding Transformers are used in existing delta-connected systems or in systems where neutrals may not be available or for delta-connected generators. In such systems, the grounding transformers are used to obtain the neutral. Grounding transformers are of the zig-zag, wye-delta, or T-connected type. The most commonly used type is the three-phase zig-zag transformer with no secondary winding, connected internally as shown in Figure 42. For more operational details and connections of the grounding transformer at different system voltages, see section 6.2.

The electrical specifications for a grounding transformer must include the following data:

Voltage—line-to-line system voltage.
Current— maximum neutral current.
For a solidly grounded system the current is determined by the grounding transformer and system impedances. For a resistance grounded system, the current is determined by the neutral resistor.

Time is usually determined to carry the rated current for a short time, ranging between 10 and 60 seconds.

Reactance is a function of the initial

Dist. xFMR. chosen has a turns ratio = $\alpha = \frac{11.5 \, KV_{LL}}{0.46 \, KV} = 25$

V applied on primary during fault = $\frac{11.5 \, KV_{LL}}{\sqrt{3}} = 6.6395$

on secondary of this dist xFMR. $v = \frac{6.6395}{25} = 265 \, V.$

symmetrical three-phase short circuit kva of the system.

The reactance of the grounding transformer to limit the ground-fault curent to 25 percent of three-phase current is shown in Figure 43. To limit transient overvoltages, the ratio $\frac{X_0}{X_1}$ should be equal to or less than 10.

To be able to use neutral type lightning arresters, $\frac{X_0}{X_1}$ should be equal to or less than 3.

For a system with a grounding transformer, X_0 is the principal factor in the above conditions. X_1, the positive sequence reactance, is the reactance of the system to initial symmetrical rms three-phase short-circuit currents. X_1 must be based on the subtransient reactance of rotating machines. Consequently the reactance of the grounding transformer is a function of the initial symmetrical three-phase short circuit in kva of the system.

The formula for the transformer reactance, X_{GT}, in an ungrounded system for any $\frac{X_0}{X_1}$ ratio is given by Formula 6:

$$X_{GT} = \frac{\frac{X_0}{X_1} \times \overline{kv}^2 \times 1,000}{\text{System symmetrical 3-phase short circuit in kva}}$$

To limit transient overvoltages,

$$\frac{X_0}{X_1} = 10$$

Introducing in formula 6:

$$X_{GT} = \frac{10,000 \times \overline{kv}^2}{\text{System symmetrical 3-phase short circuit in kva}}$$

The typical value of grounding transformer reactances shown in Figure 43 are based on this formula.

When the grounding transformer is solidly grounded, and grounded neutral type lightning arresters are applied, Formula 6 becomes:
Formula 7:

$$X_{GT} = \frac{3,000 \times \overline{kv}^2}{\text{System symmetrical 3-phase short circuit in kva}}$$

$\frac{X_0}{X_1} = 3$: condition for using 3-phase grounded neutral lightning arresters.

When the grounding transformer is low resistance grounded, the condition

$$\frac{X_0}{X_1} = 10 \text{ applies.}$$

For systems of 600 v or lower, it is desirable to permit the flow of ground fault currents greater than 25 percent of the initial symmetrical rms three-phase short-circuit currents to assure positive tripping of protective devices. In such systems, the grounding transformer is usually solidly connected to ground.

For medium voltage systems, the grounding transformer is usually resistance connected to ground to permit limitation of ground fault current, thus avoiding motor winding and/or iron burning and to allow sensitive selective tripping of ground fault relays.

The following numerical example shows how to calculate, select, and specify a grounding zig-zag transformer with ground resistor for a medium voltage system.

Figure 44 shows a delta system which requires a ground neutral point by means of an outdoor grounding transformer and resistor. The system is 2.4 kv, delta connected; the system's initial three-phase symmetrical short circuit is 150,000 kva. The maximum ground fault current allowed to flow through the resistor is 2,000 amp which is approximately five percent of the three-phase fault (see Table VII of section 6.7). Using Formula 6:

$$X_{GT} = \frac{\frac{X_0}{X_1} \times \overline{kv}^2 \times 1,000}{\overline{\text{System initial symmetrical 3-phase short circuit kva}}}$$

and $\frac{X_0}{X_1} = 10$ which limits transient overvoltages to acceptable values:

$$X_{GT} = \frac{10 \times \overline{2.4kv}^2 \times 1,000}{150,000 \text{ kva}}$$

$$= 0.38 \text{ ohms per phase reactance}$$

Through each phase of the zig-zag transformer, the maximum flow of ground fault current is 666 amp. A total flow of 2,000 amp from neutral to ground through the grounding resistor is allowed without exceeding transformer temperature rise of 257 F for a period of 10 seconds. The grounding resistor ohms:

$$\frac{\frac{2,400 \text{ v}}{\sqrt{3}}}{2,000 \text{ A}} = \text{approx. 0.7 ohms}$$

The specification for the zig-zag transformer and resistor should contain the following information.

1. One outdoor neutral grounding resistor, corrosion-resistant steel, for connection in the neutral of a 2,400-

FIGURE 44 GROUNDING ZIG-ZAG TRANSFORMER AND RESISTOR GROUND-FAULT PROTECTION

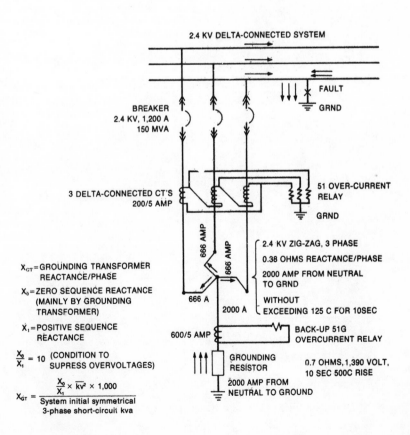

volt, 3-phase, 60 –Hz circuit. The resistor shall be rated for an applied $\frac{2,400 \text{ v}}{\sqrt{3}} = 1,390$ volts and an initial current of 2,000 amp. The resistor shall withstand operation at the rated voltage for 10 seconds without exceeding a temperature rise of 932 F.

2. One grounding transformer, three-phase, oil-immersed, self-cooled, zig-zag type, for use on 2,400 volt, three-phase, 60-Hz circuit. The transformer shall be designed to introduce no more than 0.38 ohms reactance per phase between each line terminal and neutral point. It shall carry 666 amp from each line terminal to neutral and 2,000 amp through the neutral lead to ground for a period of 10 seconds without exceeding a temperature rise of 257 F.

3. The breaker for the grounding transformer shall be rated 2.4-kv, 1,200-amp, 150-mva interrupting capacity.

4. The current transformers for the grounding transformer line may be rated about ¼ of the phase current or 200/5 amp. Three over-current phase relays will provide protection for phase faults in the grounding transformer.

5. For the neutral circuit, the donut (zero sequence) current transformer should be rated 600/5 amp and insulated for use on a 2,400—volt circuit. This back-up relay should be of the time-overcurrent type and set to wait for all other system ground relaying to first remove ground faults.

The degree of sensitivity for the ground fault relaying equipment using the combination of a donut current transformer and 51G relay covers all but one and a half percent of the winding of the protected motor near its neutral. For example, if we let 1,000 amp flow on a full line-to-ground fault, this puts $\frac{2,400 \text{ v}}{\sqrt{3}} = 1,390$ v

on the neutral resistor which is:

$$\frac{1,390 \text{ v}}{1,000 \text{ A}} = 1.39 \text{ ohms}$$

If the fault is one and a half percent of the way out from the neutral, the voltage across the neutral resistor is one and a half percent of full voltage on the line which is:

$$\frac{1.5}{100} \times \frac{2,400 \text{ v}}{1.73} = 20.8 \text{ v}$$

$$I = \frac{E}{R} = \frac{20.8 \text{ v}}{1.39 \text{ w}} = 15 \text{ amp}$$

The donut current transformer and 51G relay combination will pick-up on a 12-15 amp fault and, therefore, will see this one and a half percent of the winding out from the neutral.

7

Electrical Energy Savings in Industrial Plants

General considerations

Energy conservation is important and essential for a sound economical policy. The energy crisis has brought about dramatic increases in power costs.

During 1973 and 1974 electric power rates increased an average of 60 percent. Recent predictions estimate that power costs will increase at a rate of 12-15 percent a year during the next five years. A more optimistic forecast is 7 percent per year for the next 15 years.

To obviate in part these increases, a sound policy of energy conservation and waste prevention is absolutely necessary.

Energy independence will not be achieved without the development of new and existing resources and without the enforcement of sound energy conservation and power management programs.

It is, therefore, appropriate that more and more attention should be given to various means of energy savings and elimination of energy waste.

This article discusses means of saving electric energy in industrial power systems by:
- Power factor improvement
- High efficiency motors
- High intensity discharge (HID) lamp lighting
- Electric load management
- Static adjustable frequency drive systems

Also discussed are: costly energy bill reductions, order of magnitude in energy savings and payback for the necessary equipment to achieve these savings.

Power factor improvement

Power factor is the ratio of actual power being used in a circuit expressed in watts or kilowatts (w or kw) to the power which is apparently drawn from the line expressed in volt-amperes or kilovolt-amperes (va, kva). The power factor ratio is of great importance in ac circuits. A low power factor means poor electrical efficiency that is a costly proposition because the actual power consumption is less than the volt-ampere product. The electric circuit sees the volt-amperes but the load uses only watts. If the volt ampere value exceeds the watts consumption, extra current is drawn from the power lines causing the volt-amperes to rise to much above the real watts necessary.

The simplest and most economical way to improve the power factor is by capacitors. Capacitors supply the necessary reactive magnetizing current to motors, thus removing the reactive current supplied by the power supply company lines. The consequences are unloading the cables, releasing electrical system capacity (kva) of transformers, reducing system losses, and reducing power bills where low power-factor penalty rates are enforced. In addition, by improving the power factor, voltage levels are increased, resulting in improved motor efficiencies, improved lamp illumination and reduced losses in transformers and generators.

To illustrate the reduced demand cost by means of power factor improvement, assume a power factor improvement from 0.75 to 0.9. An economy in demand charge of $0.5/kw/ month can be obtained. The required capacitor for such a power factor improvement is 0.4 kvar per kilowatt, which at a price of $10 per kilovar, amounts to $4.

The cost of capacitors is thus amortized in eight months. After eight months the energy required will continuously cost less by $0.5/kw/month, which at an average price of $2/kw/ month represents a 25 percent savings in energy bills.

High efficiency motors

A motor's efficiency rating shows how well it converts electrical energy into mechanical energy. The larger the rating the more efficiently the motor uses energy. It is the ratio of watts out, over watts in; the difference being the motor losses made up of electrical losses, plus friction, plus windage.

Since electric power rate charges are based on total power usage, it is important to use motors with the highest efficiency possible. This way, kilowatt-hour and demand charges are kept to a minimum.

More than 75 percent of industrial users' electric bills are related to the cost of running electric motors.

With the forecast energy shortage and continuous increases in energy rates of 12 percent for each of the next five years, this becomes a problem.

High efficiency motors solve part of this problem by reducing electrical losses in the motor. The core losses are reduced by redesigning the construction of the motor. Resistance losses are reduced by the increase in copper size windings. Eddy currents and hysteresis core losses are reduced by means of special lamination steel processing, thus reducing the wasted energy required to produce the magnetic flux.

Core losses are reduced by the addition of more steel to the stator and rotor and by specially processed rotor laminations. A cooler operation is the consequence of all these improvements.

The kva saved is

$$KVA = \frac{746 \times HP \times 10^{-3}}{1.73}$$
$$\times \left(\frac{1}{EFF_1 \times PF} - \frac{1}{EFF_2 \times PF} \right)$$

EFF_1 = improved efficiency
EFF_2 = industry average efficiency
PF = power factor

Energy dollars saved per year = kw saved x cost/kwh x hours running per year. As an example assuming an operation of 16 hours/day for 5 days/wk and for a period of 52 wks/year, with an energy cost of $0.04/kwh and for 2, 10, 50, and 100 hp motors (see Table 1).

HID lamps

Usually called HID (high-intensity-discharge) lamps, light is produced in an arc tube by current passing through a vapor at relatively high pressure, compared with low pressure in fluorescent lamps. The HID family includes: mercury-vapor, metal-halide and high-pressure sodium lamps that contain sodium and mercury.

The HID lamps are popular for indoor and outdoor use since they are: low in operating cost per footcandle, have high efficiency, and long life expectancy thereby minimizing relamping costs.

High pressure sodium lamps are the most widely used lamp *outdoors* because of their high efficiency, good optical controls, small size and warm uniform golden-white color.

For *indoor* use in industrial buildings, HPS lamps are used because of their high efficiency that makes them more economical than other light sources.

In the national interest, to avoid wasteful use of electric power, HPS lamps have following advantages:

• They are the most efficient since the power saving can be as high as 40 percent while at the same time the light output is increased 23 percent.

• They help maintain a high power factor thus avoiding extra charges imposed by electric companies.

• The improvement in color rendition of HPS lamps makes them suitable for most indoor and outdoor ap-

plications. HPS lamps have long life expectancy and their relamping costs are lower than with any other lamps.

If lighting level in an area is higher than the recommended level, instead of turning lamps off, the use of reduced wattage fluorescent lamps can lower the cost of power by helping maintain adequate power factor thus reducing energy expenditure as shown in Table 2.

Annual operating cost savings, system cost, payback period, and return on investment of HPS lamps over mercury lamps is shown in cost comparison work-sheet example Table 3.

Table 4 shows the cost analysis of an equal illumination level for a new 10,000 ft, high-bay industrial area.

The cost analysis in Table 4 indicates that an equal illumination level produced by 400 w HID lamps require 108 mercury, 61 metal-halide or 40 HPS lamp luminaires.

The energy cost for the HPS system is lower than that for either of the other two systems.

The HPS system uses about $1,083 less in electricity annually than the metal-halide system and $5,520 less than a 1,000-w incandescent system.

An industrial plant switching from incandescent to HPS lighting, would recover the HPS system's initial cost in about two years. Furthermore, as energy costs are continuously increasing, the payback period gets shorter, return of investment is increasing and energy cost savings become more significant. Table 5 shows the performance potentials of mercury-vapor, metal-halide and HPS lamps.

Electric load management

Electrical energy management involves energy conservation and control of power demand. The function of the devices controlling power demand is to turn loads on and off, based on the time of day, or to control loads based on input signals. It all boils down to

reducing the total peak kw hours of electrical energy consumed by the plant.

Utilities charge for large demands to avoid excessive demand peaks that require costly system equipment committment. This demand charge can be reduced by limiting simultaneous operation of devices, especially in large energy consuming loads. It can be achieved by a control system which measures the demand continuously and switches off selected loads at certain moments to avoid peak demands.

By smoothing the demand peaks, a programmable energy demand controller can reduce demand from 10 to 40 percent. These demand controller computers have paid for themselves in less than one year's time.

Some 5,000 kw is about the minimum demand that is practical to control with a complex *programmable computer energy controller* and unless there is at least 20 percent of the load which can be controlled, there is no point in investing in a demand controller. Using a typical return-on-investment program and taking in account the investment tax credit depreciation allowance based on a standard of 8 years depreciation for electronic equipment and a 15 percent return on investment, a savings of $500/month justifies a $30,000 investment. Experience has proven in applying power demand process control computers, 15 percent reduction in power cost has been realized in less than one year by timing electrical loads to prevent simultaneous occurrences that would raise demand peak level beyond the maximum economic demand.

The basic functions of an energy management system are:

• Demand control to maintain peak demand (kw or kva) registered during any billing period below a preset level.

• Energy conservation, to reduce

TABLE 1 ENERGY SAVINGS EACH YEAR

Motor	Efficiency	Premium Motor Additional Cost	Saving in Energy	Pay-out Period
2 hp	77.8 − 72.4 = 5.4	284 − 216 = 68	0.143 kw x $0.04/kwh x 4160 Hrs/Yr. = $23.79	2 Yr. 10 Mth
10 hp	86.6 − 83.7 = 2.9	530 − 398 = 132	0.299 kw x Ditto = $49.75	2 Yr. 8 Mth
50 hp	89.7 − 88.9 = 0.8	1994 − 1828 = 166	0.374 kw x Ditto = $62.23	2 Yr. 8 Mth
100 hp	91.0 − 90.3 = 0.7	4568 − 4286 = 282	0.636 kw x Ditto = $105.83	2 Yr. 8 Mth

energy consumption of loads when plant activity is at medium or low level.

• Time of day scheduling to reduce energy consumption by turning loads on and off at specified times.

• Management information to allow fine turning of the system and accumulation of reference information for past performances and future uses.

Microprocessor load programmers are manufactured in different sizes corresponding to the number of loads programmed. Their prices vary with the number of load control circuits and according to different manufacturers. Their costs vary from approximately $1,200 for 6-load control circuits to $30,000 for 70-load control circuits. Five different duty cycle programs can be available for any load. Photocell inputs coordinate controls for external lighting. Temperature input overrides duty cycle programs to insure comfort at all times. Individual loads can be by-passed at user's option. Quartz crystal clock provides program accuracies within seconds per month. Battery back-up automatically retains memory and runs clock up to 14 days so that programs cannot be lost in the event of prolonged power failure. Data stored in memory, either as calculated information or program data, can be quickly called up for display by the operator. Record printers are available which provide digital printout of date, time, and demand, automatically at the end of each demand interval.

Static adjustable frequency drive systems

A static-adjustable-frequency drive system utilizes solid state components to convert standard fixed frequencies, and fixed voltage power sources into variable frequency and variable voltage outputs to drive standard ac motors at controllable variable speeds.

The principle of speed control for adjustable frequency drives is based on the fundamental formula:

$$N = \frac{120f}{P}$$

N = Synchronous speed (RPM)
f = frequency (CPS) (Hz)
P = No. of poles

The number of poles is set by design and manufacturer. The formula shows that by varying the frequency the speed varies proportionally.

Adjustable frequency drive systems have an inverter interposed between the plant power supply and motor. The inverter converts the fixed power supply to an adjustable frequency output to obtain the desired motor speed.

The speed is infinitely adjustable by means of a potentiometer varying the frequency.

A static adjustable frequency drive consists of (see accompanying figure):
1) Rectifier Section (Rectifies ac to dc);
2) Inverter Section (Converts dc to ac);
3) Oscillator Section (Determines the frequency at which the silicon con-

TABLE 2—PERFORMANCE AND ECONOMIC COMPARISON OF CONVENTIONAL AND REDUCED WATTAGE FLUORESCENT LAMPS

Lamp	Power Consumption (lamp watts)	Rated Initial Output (lumens)	Rated Average Life (hours)	Power Cost Saving* (dollars)
Incandescent, Extended Service				
Conventional	60	740	2500	
Reduced Wattage Fluorescent	54	645	2500	0.45
Conventional	100	1480	2500	
Reduced Wattage Fluorescent	90	1230	2500	0.75
Conventional	150	2350	2500	
Reduced Wattage Fluorescent	135	1990	2500	1.14
Incandescent, Industrial Service				
Conventional	60	670	3500	
Reduced Wattage Fluorescent	54	590	3500	0.63
Conventional	100	1280	3500	
Reduced Wattage Fluorescent	90	1090	3500	1.05
Conventional	150	2150	3500	
Reduced Wattage Fluorescent	135	1790	3500	1.59
Fluorescent, 48-Inch Rapid-Start Cool White				
Conventional	40	3150	20,000+	
Reduced Wattage Fluorescent	34	2800	20,000	3.60
Fluorescent, 48-Inch Rapid-Start Warm White				
Conventional	40	3200	20,000+	
Reduced Wattage Fluorescent	34	2900	20,000	3.60
Fluorescent, 96-Inch Cool White				
Conventional	75	6300	12,000	
Reduced Wattage Fluorescent	60	5220	12,000	3.60
Fluorescent, 96-Inch Warm White				
Conventional	75	6400	12,000	
Reduced Wattage Fluorescent	60	5220	12,000	3.60
Mercury-Vapor, Clear				
Conventional	400	21,000	24,000+	
Reduced Wattage Fluorescent	300	14,000	16,000	48.00
Mercury-Vapor, Deluxe White/				
Conventional	400	23,000	24,000+	
Reduced Wattage Fluorescent	300	15,700	16,000+	48.00

*Approximate saving from use of Reduced Wattage Fluorescent lamps in place of conventional lamps. Based on rated average life of Reduced Wattage Fluorescent lamps and on power cost of $0.03 per kilowatthour.
+Phosphor coated.
Courtesy "Westinghouse Engineer"

TABLE 3 COST COMPARISON WORKSHEET EXAMPLE

			Present	*Proposed*
A.	Lamp Type	(A)	H36GW-1000/DX	C400
B.	Number of Luminaires	(B)	100	100
C.	Maintained Lumens	(C)	44,700	45,000
D.	Net Price of Lamp (at 50 percent Discount)	(D)	$ 15.75	$ 30
E.	Rated Lamp Life (From Specification Guide, S400)	(E)	24,000	20,000
F.	Wattage Per Luminaire (Including Ballast Wattage)	(F)	1,080	480
G.	Installed Cost Per Luminaire (Fixture, Lamp, Labor, & Hardware Cost)	(G)	$ —	$ 182
H.	Annual Cost of Replacement Parts (i.e., Ballast, etc.)	(H)	$ —	$ —
I.	Estimated Labor Cost to Replace One (1) Lamp	(I)	$ 5	$ 5
J.	Estimated Cleaning Cost Per Luminaire	(J)	$ 1	$ 1
K.	Cleaning Per Year	(K)	1	1
L.	Estimated Annual Replacements: For H36: 1 × 100 × 4000 ÷ 24,000 = 16,666 = 17 lamps. For C400: 1 × 100 × 4000 ÷ 20,000 = 20 lamps	(L)	17	20
M.	Annual Cost of Replacement Lamps: (Assume 50% Discount) For H36: 17 lamps × $15.75 per lamp net = $268 For C400: 20 lamps × $30.00 per lamp net = $600	(M)	$ 268	$ 600
N.	Labor Cost for Lamp Replacements: For H36: $5 per lamp × 17 lamps = $85 For C400: $5 per lamp × 20 lamps = $100	(N)	$ 85	$ 100
O.	Annual Cleaning Cost No. luminaires × cleaning cost per luminaire × cleaning per year.	(O)	$ 100	$ 100
P.	Total Annual Maintenance Cost: For H36: 0 + $268 + $85 + $100 = $453 For C400: 0 + $600 + $100 + $100 = $800	(P)	$ 453	$ 800
Q.	Annual Energy Cost For H36: 100 × 1080 × 4000 × 0.03 ÷ 1000 = $12,960 For C400: 100 × 480 × 4000 × 0.03 ÷ 1000 = $5,760	(Q)	$ 12,960	$ 5,760
R.	Total Annual Operating Costs: For H36: $453 + $12,960 = $13,413 For C400: $800 + $5,760 = $6,560 Note the large proportion of energy cost to total annual operating cost and the savings with more efficient lamps	(R)	$ 13,413	$ 6,560
S.	Annual Operating Cost Savings: $13,413 − $6,560	(S)	$ 6,853	
T.	Proposed System Cost: $182 × 100	(T)	$ 18,200	
U.	Payback Period: Proposed system cost annual savings Note: The cost of capital has been excluded from this calculation but can be added to the proposed system cost.	(U)	2.7 years	
V.	Return on Investment (ROI): Annual savings proposed system cost. (ROI is a term used in financial decision making)	(V)	38%	

STATIC ADJUSTABLE FREQUENCY DRIVE

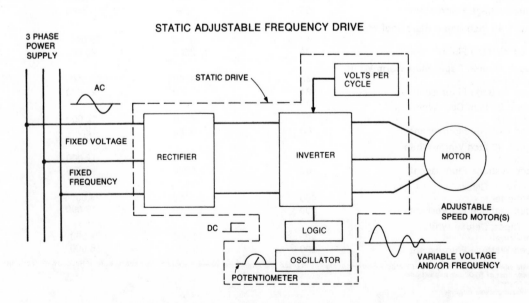

TABLE 4 COST ANALYSIS FOR LIGHTING A 10,000-SQ FT INDUSTRIAL AREA

	400-w high pressure sodium	400-w metal halide	400-w mercury	Two-lamp 800 ma fluorescent	1,000-w incandescent
Number of luminaires	40	61	108	114	65
Total input watts, kw (including ballast wattage)	19	28.06	48.06	28.5	65
Total initial cost (including luminaire lamp, wiring, installation costs)	$11,248	$12,171	$18,845	$14,077	$12,503
Annual owning cost (estimated as 15 percent of luminaire, wiring, installation costs)	$1,506	$1,684	$2,705	$2,043	$1,823
Annual lamp replacement cost	$242	$379	$135	$121	$611
Annual maintenance cost	$24	$73	$54	$182	$780
Annual energy cost*	$2,280	$3,367	$5,767	$3,420	$7,800
Total annual operating cost	$2,546	$3,819	$5,956	$3,723	$9,191
Total annual cost for system	$4,052	$5,503	$6,661	$5,767	$11,044

*Based on 4,000 hr annual operation and 3 cents/kwh.

Courtesy General Electric Co.

trolled rectifier operates); 4) Logic Section (Determines the sequence at which S.C.R. operates); 5) Volts/Cycle Regulator Section (Adjusts the power output maintaining automatically same ratio output of voltage to frequency at all speeds).

The advantages of using static adjustable frequency drives can be obtained mainly in pump drive systems, namely:

• *High efficiency* throughout the entire pump operating speeds resulting in *reduced operating costs due to energy savings.*

• Simplified motor selection since no special winding or frame sizing is required.

• No preventive maintenance required since the inverter ensures maximum on the line time and consequently *high-reliability.*

• Motor protected by the current limiting property of electronic devices.

Conclusion

Cost reduction is the heart of an energy conservation plan based on energy management. With energy becoming more scarce and costly the energy problem is not going to go away unless cooperation of employees and management seek out all kinds of ways to save energy and eliminate waste in energy consumption.

TABLE 5 PERFORMANCE POTENTIALS OF MERCURY-VAPOR, METAL-HALIDE AND HPS LAMPS

	Lamp and wattage		Initial Lumens	Average mean lumen over life	Average rated life, hr*
Mercury	50		1,575	1,260	16,000
	75		2,800	2,250	16,000
	100		4,200	3,530	24,000+
	175		8,600	7,650	24,000+
	250		12,000	10,400	24,000+
	400		22,500	19,100	24,000+
	700		42,000	33,600	24,000+
	1,000		63,000	47,500	24,000+
Metal halide	175		14,000	10,800	7,500
	400		34,000†	27,200	10,000
	1,000	(clear	110,000	88,000	10,000
		coated	105,000	83,000	10,000
High-pressure sodium	70	(diffuse	5,400	4,860	12,000
	70	coated	5,800	5,220	20,000
	100	(diffuse	8,800	7,920	20,000
	100	coated)	9,500	8,550	20,000
	150		15,000	13,500	24,000
	150		16,000	14,400	24,000
	250		25,500	23,200	24,000
	250/S		30,000	27,300	24,000
	400	(diffuse	47,500	42,750	24,000
	400	coated)	50,000	45,000	24,000
	1,000		140,000	127,400	24,000

*Based on operation for an average of 10 hours per start

†Vertical burning

Courtesy General Electric Co.

Index